THE ENGLISH TRADITION: FICTION

THE ENGLISH TRADITION: FICTION

THE ENGLISH TRADITION: NONFICTION

THE ENGLISH TRADITION: POETRY

THE ENGLISH TRADITION: DRAMA

THE ENGLISH TRADITION: FICTION

Marjorie Wescott Barrows
Formerly, General Editor
Macmillan Literary Heritage

Robert P. Bletter
Director, Teachers College Press
New York City

Donald G. Kobler
Chairman, English Department
Housatonic Valley Regional High School
Falls River, Connecticut

Bertrand Evans
Professor Emeritus of English
University of California
Berkeley, California

James E. Frey
Associate Professor of English
California State University
Fresno, California

Matthew Dolkey
Professor of English
Kean College of New Jersey
Union, New Jersey

Nelda B. Kubat
English Coordinator
Lansing High School
Ludlowville, New York

James G. Magill
Formerly, Chairman, English Department
Lincoln High School
Manitowoc, Wisconsin

A revision of *The Early Years of English Literature, Spenser to Goldsmith, Romantic and Victorian Writers,* and *Modern English Prose and Poetry,* previously published by Macmillan Publishing Co., Inc.

MACMILLAN PUBLISHING CO., INC. New York
COLLIER MACMILLAN PUBLISHERS London

ACKNOWLEDGMENTS

For permission to reprint copyright material in this book, grateful acknowledgment is made to the following:

J. M. Dent & Sons, Ltd.: For "The Secret Sharer" from *Twixt Land and Sea* by Joseph Conrad. Reprinted by permission of the publishers and the trustees of the Joseph Conrad Estate.

Doubleday & Company, Inc.: For "The Verger" by W. Somerset Maugham. Copyright 1929 by W. Somerset Maugham from *Cosmopolitans*, by W. Somerset Maugham. Reprinted by permission of Doubleday & Company, Inc.

Alfred A. Knopf, Inc.: For "On Saturday Afternoon" from *The Loneliness of the Long Distance Runner* by Alan Sillitoe. Copyright © 1959 by Alan Sillitoe. Reprinted by permission of Alfred A. Knopf, Inc.

Macmillan & Co. Ltd.: For "Three Strangers" from *Wessex Tales*. Reprinted by permission of the Publishers.

The New American Library of World Literature, Inc.: For excerpts from *Le Morte d'Arthur* by Sir Thomas Malory, translated by Keith Baines, copyright © 1962 by Keith Baines, published by arrangement with The New American Library of World Literature, Inc., New York.

Harold Ober Associates: For "Miss Pinkerton's Apocalypse" from *The Go-Away Bird and Other Stories* by Muriel Spark. Copyright © 1958 by Muriel Spark. Reprinted by permisson of Harold Ober Associates, Inc.

Laurence Pollinger Limited: For "The End of the Party" from *Twenty-One Stories* by Graham Greene. Reprinted by permission of the Publishers.

Random House, Inc.: For "The Wind Blows" by Katherine Mansfield from *The Short Stories of Katherine Mansfield* and "The Celestial Omnibus" from *The Collected Tales* of E. M. Forster. Reprinted by permission of the Publishers.

Sidgwick & Jackson, Ltd.: For "The Celestial Omnibus" by E. M. Forster from *The Collected Short Stories of E. M. Forster*. Reprinted by permission of the Publisher.

The Society of Authors: For "The Wind Blows" by Katherine Mansfield from *The Short Stories of Katherine Mansfield*. Reprinted by permission of the Publishers.

Cover design by William S. Shields

Macmillan Publishing Co., Inc.
866 Third Avenue, New York, New York 10022
Collier-Macmillan Canada, Ltd.

Printed in the United States of America

Contents

The Short Story in England 281

INTRODUCTION

Before the eighteenth century, Englishmen recorded most narratives either as poetry or as drama. Narrative poems were especially loved during the centuries when stories were told or sung to an audience. Both ballads and long epics such as *Beowulf* arose from the popularity of narrative poetry. Somewhat later, drama grew more popular among commoners; people found they preferred to watch the narrative acted out before their eyes.

Since the eighteenth century, however, the most popular English narratives have been written in the form of prose fiction. This change of taste can be explained partially by the type of narrative poem and drama produced in the period: in trying for elegance and wit, the best poets and playwrights demanded a great deal of sophistication from their audiences.

Partially, however, the change in taste to prose fiction can be traced to the growing number of literate commoners, and the greater availability (and cheapness) of printed matter. Untrained for works that demanded intellectual effort, the commoners and workers still wanted entertaining material to read in their leisure. Thus the prose tale, which demanded neither an appreciation of poetic technique nor an ability to visualize dramatic action, was in greater and greater demand. Soon, however, the writers of prose narratives began to place more stringent artistic demands on themselves and to strive for greater quality in their work. Another literary and artistic form had developed.

From the eighteenth century to the present, prose fiction has remained the most popular form of narration. Though newer forms of narrative such as cinema may eventually supersede fiction in popularity, as an art form fiction appears to be indestructible—quite capable of retaining a large share of the public's attention. It is undeniably true that England has produced more than her share of superb fiction in the past. To understand the English mind, one must understand the art forms in which that mind has best expressed itself.

This book begins by presenting the student with a small sample of the work produced by three giants of modern English literature—James Joyce, D. H. Lawrence, and Joseph Conrad. Each has been of crucial importance in shaping modern fiction, not only that of England and America, but also that of the entire Western world. Though the styles in which each chose to write appear quite different, all bear witness to the modern concern with the craftsmanship and construction of a tale, with the hidden impulses and motives of the human personality, and with the struggles and crises one must face in order to learn what it means to be human. Because Joyce, Lawrence, and Conrad are among the greatest prose writers in the English language, they are an excellent trio with which to start a study of English fiction. One cannot assess anything with complete skill unless he knows what possibilities for excellence exist.

Conversely, one never knows how far an art form has travelled until he knows where it started. Section Two of this text presents the significant beginnings—several of the first narratives from which modern prose fiction grew. Section Three includes samples from some of the great eighteenth- and nineteenth-century novels which remain high points in the history of English literature. And last, the book presents a sampling of twentieth-century short stories, the form in which recent writers have done some of their most exciting experimentation. In this section, "the tale's the thing"; therefore, headnotes about the individual writers and their work as a whole have been omitted. It is hoped that such a book as this one will give the student a small taste of the great feast of English fiction which awaits him if he wishes to enjoy it.

THE ENGLISH TRADITION: FICTION

MODERN PERSPECTIVES

The principal focus of modern fiction is on man, but, very particularly, on man as he exists within himself, including the fears, impulses, and inner conflicts that motivate him. In modern fiction, man is seldom in harmony with his environment; rather, he is alienated from it. He is alienated from his fellow men and, more crucially, from himself.

Certainly the theories of Freud and the psychologists who came after him did much to foster a climate that enabled the psychological literature of the twentieth century to flourish. Freud's exploration of the unconsious and his use of free association to uncover the unconscious motivations of man were employed in literature by James Joyce, among others.

JAMES JOYCE sought to give his readers "a fluid succession of presents" (that is, a succession of "nows"). In his struggle to present the thoughts, dreams, and desires of his characters directly, with no intervening author to explain them, he made use of the stream-of-consciousness technique. This technique attempts to reveal, through a flow of words, the mind of a character in its meanders, reflections, and inconsistencies, as it is affected by all those external forces that play upon it.

All of Joyce's stories and novels may be illuminated by an understanding of what he called epiphanies—moments of spiritual insight. Joyce implied that such moments may be experienced by anyone who is sensitive to them. Through so simple a thing as a sudden snatch of conversation, a trivial incident, or a momentary gesture, one may gain a sudden revelation into the mystery of life. Some critics interpret *Dubliners* (the volume of short stories from which "Eveline" is taken) as a collection of epiphanies, the meaning of each usually conveyed by a single sentence or phrase near the end of the story. This phrase suddenly illuminates everything that has happened previously, including the descriptive details, the thoughts of the characters, and the symbols in the story.

D. H. LAWRENCE wrote that "the business of art is to reveal the relation between man and his circumambient[1] universe at the living moment . . . the Now." He wanted to reveal the "true and vivid relationships in all their flow and change." Lawrence sought to examine the conflict that exists between civilization and its values and the unconscious part of man, which was for him the true realm of reality. Lawrence put his faith in instinct and intuition, in the "blood" as he sometimes called it. Here is how he expressed it in a letter:

> My great religion is a belief in the blood, the flesh, as being wiser than the intellect. We can go wrong in our minds. But what our blood feels and believes and says is always true.

This idea is reflected in "The Rocking-Horse Winner." The mother, caught up in the desire for the material wealth, ease, and security that civilization encourages, is tormented by fear. Her confusion and fear are passed on to her son, who hears them pulsating throughout their house. The boy goes down into the depths of his imagination to find "luck" for his mother. He desperately rides his rocking-horse to get the information he needs to help her, and in so doing, is destroyed.

Another bold experimenter in prose fiction at the beginning of the twentieth century was JOSEPH CONRAD. As an artist, he tried to render the truth of life, and to do this he abandoned the plot of conventional fiction because he felt

[1]*circumambient:* surrounding

that its artificiality obscured the truth. The imagination, he maintained, should be used "to describe human hearts and not to create events that are, properly speaking, accidents only." Certainly in "The Secret Sharer" Conrad searches the human heart and reveals his deep understanding of the duality of man and his search for identity.

The fact that many of his novels and stories deal with the sea does not make Conrad simply a writer of sea stories. He himself pointed out that his material was the psychological problems of human beings who happened to be on ships. For him the sea was a laboratory where he could investigate the nature of man and the motives that make him act as he does. In "The Secret Sharer," the sea is the "laboratory" where the young captain must test himself and his worth.

Joyce, Lawrence, and Conrad are without doubt three of the most important figures in modern English fiction. The insights and techniques that they brought to their highly individual writing serve to provide considerable information about the form that English fiction was to take in the twentieth century.

James Joyce

In a letter to his publisher, Joyce wrote that in *Dubliners* his aim was "to write a chapter of the moral history of my country, and I chose Dublin for the scene because that city seemed to me the centre of paralysis." *Dubliners* is a collection of fifteen stories, in which, because of a paralysis of will, the characters are unable to act effectively in dealing with their frustrations. The emphasis in these stories is more on what the characters think and feel than on what they do. An understanding of their surroundings and of their relationships with others is presented in a kind of slow-motion picture of daily routines and reactions to ordinary events.

During most of his life, Joyce lived and worked outside Ireland, but what he chose to write about was Ireland, and especially Dublin. His purpose, as he said, was not only to give his countrymen "one good look at themselves" in a "nicely polished looking-glass," but also to give all men such a look. The human condition which Joyce pictured is not confined to Irishmen nor to Dublin.

Eveline

She sat at the window watching the evening invade the avenue. Her head was leaned against the window curtains and in her nostrils was the odour of dusty cretonne.[1] She was tired.

Few people passed. The man out of the last house passed on his way home; she heard his footsteps clacking along the concrete pavement and afterwards crunching on the cinder path before the new red houses. One time there used to be a field there in which they used to play every evening with other people's children. Then a man from Belfast bought the field and built houses in it—not like their little brown houses but bright brick houses with shining roofs. The children of the

[1]*cretonne:* heavy, patterned cloth

avenue used to play together in that field—the Devines, the Waters, the Dunns, little Keogh the cripple, she and her brothers and sisters. Ernest, however, never played: he was too grown up. Her father used often to hunt them in out of the field with his blackthorn stick; but usually little Keogh used to keep *nix* and call out when he saw her father coming. Still they seemed to have been rather happy then. Her father was not so bad then; and besides, her mother was alive. That was a long time ago; she and her brothers and sisters were all grown up; her mother was dead. Tizzie Dunn was dead, too, and the Waters had gone back to England. Everything changes. Now she was going to go away like the others, to leave her home.

Home! She looked round the room, reviewing all its familiar objects which she had dusted once a week for so many years, wondering where on earth all the dust came from. Perhaps she would never see again those familiar objects from which she had never dreamed of being divided. And yet during all those years she had never found out the name of the priest whose yellowing photograph hung on the wall above the broken harmonium[2] beside the coloured print of the promises made to Blessed Margaret Mary Alacoque. He had been a school friend of her father. Whenever he showed the photograph to a visitor her father used to pass it with a casual word:

"He is in Melbourne now."

She had consented to go away, to leave her home. Was that wise? She tried to weigh each side of the question. In her home anyway she had shelter and food; she had those whom she had known all her life about her. Of course she had to work hard, both in the house and at business. What would they say of her in the Stores when they found out that she had run away with a fellow? Say she was a fool, perhaps; and her place would be filled up by advertisement. Miss Gavan would be glad. She had always had an edge on her, especially whenever there were people listening.

"Miss Hill, don't you see these ladies are waiting?"

"Look lively, Miss Hill, please."

[2]*harmonium:* small organ

She would not cry many tears at leaving the Stores.

But in her new home, in a distant unknown country, it would not be like that. Then she would be married—she, Eveline. People would treat her with respect then. She would not be treated as her mother had been. Even now, though she was over nineteen, she sometimes felt herself in danger of her father's violence. She knew it was that that had given her the palpitations. When they were growing up he had never gone for her, like he used to go for Harry and Ernest, because she was a girl; but latterly he had begun to threaten her and say what he would do to her only for her dead mother's sake. And now she had nobody to protect her. Ernest was dead and Harry, who was in the church decorating business, was nearly always down somewhere in the country. Besides, the invariable squabble for money on Saturday nights had begun to weary her unspeakably. She always gave her entire wages—seven shillings—and Harry always sent up what he could but the trouble was to get any money from her father. He said she used to squander the money, that she had no head, that he wasn't going to give her his hard-earned money to throw about the streets, and much more, for he was usually fairly bad on Saturday night. In the end he would give her the money and ask her had she any intention of buying Sunday's dinner. Then she had to rush out as quickly as she could and do her marketing, holding her black leather purse tightly in her hand as she elbowed her way through the crowds and returning home late under her load of provisions. She had hard work to keep the house together and to see that the two young children who had been left to her charge went to school regularly and got their meals regularly. It was hard work—a hard life— but now that she was about to leave it she did not find it a wholly undesirable life.

She was about to explore another life with Frank. Frank was very kind, manly, open-hearted. She was to go away with him by the night-boat to be his wife and to live with him in Buenos Aires where he had a home waiting for her. How well she remembered the first time she had seen him; he was lodging in a house on the main road where she used to visit. It seemed a few weeks ago. He was standing at the gate, his peaked cap pushed back on his head and his hair tumbled forward over a face of bronze. Then they had come to know each other. He used to meet her outside the Stores every evening and see her home. He took her to see *The Bohemian Girl* and she felt elated as she sat in an unaccustomed part of the theatre with him. He was awfully fond of music and sang a little. People knew that they were courting and, when he sang about the lass that loves a sailor, she always felt pleasantly confused. He used to call her Poppens out of fun. First of all it had been an excitement for her to have a fellow and then she had begun to like him. He had tales of distant countries. He had started as a deck boy at a pound a month on a ship of the Allan Line going out to Canada. He told her the names of the ships he had been on and the names of the different services. He had sailed through the Straits of Magellan and he told her stories of the terrible Patagonians. He had fallen on his feet in Buenos Aires, he said, and had come over to the old country just for a holiday. Of course, her father had found out the affair and had forbidden her to have anything to say to him.

"I know these sailor chaps," he said.

One day he had quarrelled with Frank and after that she had to meet her lover secretly.

The evening deepened in the avenue. The white of two letters in her lap grew indistinct. One was to Harry; the other was to her father. Ernest had been her favourite but she liked Harry too. Her father was becoming old lately, she noticed; he would miss her. Sometimes he could be very nice. Not long before, when she had been laid up for a day, he had read her out a ghost story and made toast for her at the fire. Another day, when their mother was alive, they had all gone for a picnic to the Hill of Howth. She remembered her father putting on her mother's bonnet to make the children laugh.

Her time was running out but she continued to sit by the window, leaning her head against the window curtain, inhaling the odour of dusty cretonne. Down far in the avenue she could hear a street organ playing. She knew the air. Strange that it should come that very night to remind her of the promise to her mother, her promise to keep the home together as long as she could. She remembered the last night of her mother's illness; she was again in the close dark room at the other side of the hall and outside she heard a melancholy air of Italy. The organplayer had been ordered to go away and given sixpence. She remembered her father strutting back into the sickroom saying:

"Damned Italians! coming over here!"

As she mused the pitiful vision of her mother's life laid its spell on the very quick of her being—that life of commonplace sacrifices closing in final craziness. She trembled as she heard again her mother's voice saying constantly with foolish insistence:

"Derevaun Seraun! Derevaun Seraun!"[3]

She stood up in a sudden impulse of terror. Escape! She must escape! Frank would save her. He would give her life, perhaps love, too. But she wanted to live. Why should she be unhappy? She had a right to happiness. Frank would take her in his arms, fold her in his arms. He would save her.

She stood among the swaying crowd in the station at the North Wall. He held her hand and she knew that he was speaking to her, saying something about the passage over and over again. The station was full of soldiers with brown baggages. Through the wide doors of the sheds she caught a glimpse of the black mass of the boat, lying in beside the quay wall, with illumined portholes. She answered nothing. She felt her cheek pale and cold and, out of a maze of distress, she prayed to God to direct her, to show her what was her duty. The boat blew a long mournful whistle into the mist. If she went, tomorrow she would be on the sea with Frank, steaming towards Buenos Aires. Their passage had been booked. Could she still draw back after all he had done for her? Her distress awoke a nausea in her body and she kept moving her lips in silent fervent prayer.

A bell clanged upon her heart. She felt him seize her hand:

"Come!"

All the seas of the world tumbled about her heart. He was

[3]*Derevaun Seraun!* The meaning of this puzzling exclamation is not positively known. One suggestion is that it is corrupt Gaelic for "The end of pleasure is pain."

drawing her into them: he would drown her. She gripped with both hands at the iron railing.

"Come!"

No! No! No! It was impossible. Her hands clutched the iron in frenzy. Amid the seas she sent a cry of anguish.

"Eveline! Evvy!"

He rushed beyond the barrier and called to her to follow. He was shouted at to go on but he still called to her. She set her white face to him, passive, like a helpless animal. Her eyes gave him no sign of love or farewell or recognition.

FOR DISCUSSION

1. Do you consider Eveline's final decision wise or foolish? Study the ways in which the author prepares you for her decision. When does she make up her mind? What are the compelling motives in her decision?
2. As Eveline thinks about her life, trying to decide whether she is wise to leave with Frank, the reader learns about her life at home and at business. Which of the circumstances of this life are most important in making her decide to leave with Frank? On what does she base her belief that her life was not "wholly undesirable"? What advantages might her new life have over her old one?
3. Compare Eveline's relationship with her father and with her mother. What contrasts are suggested between Frank and Eveline's father? As Eveline is thinking about her decision, what reminds her particularly of her mother? From what you learn of her mother's life, would you say her mother was happy and satisfied? What, in Eveline's reminiscence, gives her that "sudden impulse of terror"?
4. Joyce described his style in *Dubliners* as one of "scrupulous meanness"; that is, it is deliberately and carefully barren and stingy of details. Why is such a style well suited to Eveline's story? Note, however, that the details he does include are highly significant, for example the references to dust. What aspect of dust is emphasized? What do these references suggest about Eveline's view of her life?

5. Note the contrast between the dustiness of Eveline's home atmosphere and the sea, her potential means of escape. What impression is made on Eveline by Frank's sea tales? The sea, however, is not only a means of escape. What aspect of the sea is suggested by the final mention of it in the story? What effect is created by the image of Eveline standing at an iron railing, "passive, like a helpless animal"?

FOR COMPOSITION

1. In a short composition, analyze the descriptions of sounds in the story and show how sounds figured in Eveline's reminiscence.
2. Using the specific details and the descriptions of scenes Eveline remembers in this story, reconstruct in an essay what Dublin life must have been like at the beginning of the twentieth century. How much can you guess about the economic level of the average Dubliner, about his daily routine, his occupations, and his attitudes? Back up all your assumptions with phrases from the story.
3. What limitations does Joyce place on his story by telling it strictly through the thoughts of one uneducated Irish girl? What special effects does this narrative method make possible? Write a theme in which these questions are discussed.

D. H. Lawrence

Some people put as much faith in hunches as in facts; women, for example, are sometimes thought to have unusual powers of intuition, a kind of inner knowledge not based on reasoning. Lawrence had more faith in intuitive behavior than in the powers of reason and logic. He particularly admired various primitive peoples whom he studied in his wide travels throughout the world. He believed that these primitive people, who relied on their hunches and intuitions, enjoyed a more satisfying life than men in Western society, who have used their powers of reason to create a mechanized, industrial society. He also felt that Western society places a distorted emphasis on money and success.

In his short stories and novels, D. H. Lawrence frequently pictured characters who have unusual powers of intuition, who live by their hunches. Some of these stories and novels resemble fantasies because Lawrence considered the "unreal" more appropriate than the "real" as a method of dealing with such an intangible idea as the power of intuition.

The Rocking-Horse Winner

There was a woman who was beautiful, who started with all the advantages, yet she had no luck. She married for love, and the love turned to dust. She had bonny[1] children, yet she felt they had been thrust upon her, and she could not love them. They looked at her coldly, as if they were finding fault with her. And hurriedly she felt she must cover up some fault in herself. Yet what it was that she must cover up she never knew. Nevertheless, when her children were present, she always felt the centre of her heart go hard. This troubled her, and in her manner she was all the more gentle and anxious for her children, as if she loved them very much. Only she herself knew that at the centre of her heart was a

[1]*bonny:* handsome

hard little place that could not feel love, no, not for anybody. Everybody else said of her: "She is such a good mother. She adores her children." Only she herself, and her children themselves, knew it was not so. They read it in each other's eyes.

There were a boy and two little girls. They lived in a pleasant house, with a garden, and they had discreet servants, and felt themselves superior to anyone in the neighbourhood.

Although they lived in style, they felt always an anxiety in the house. There was never enough money. The mother had a small income, and the father had a small income, but not nearly enough for the social position which they had to keep up. The father went in to town to some office. But though he had good prospects, these prospects never materialized. There was always the grinding sense of the shortage of money, though the style was always kept up.

At last the mother said: "I will see if *I* can't make something." But she did not know where to begin. She racked her brains, and tried this thing and the other, but could not find anything successful. The failure made deep lines come into her face. Her children were growing up, they would have to go to school. There must be more money, there must be more money. The father, who was always very handsome and expensive in his tastes, seemed as if he never *would* be able to do anything worth doing. And the mother, who had a great belief in herself, did not succeed any better, and her tastes were just as expensive.

And so the house came to be haunted by the unspoken phrase: *There must be more money! There must be more money!* The children could hear it all the time, though nobody said it aloud. They heard it at Christmas, when the expensive and splendid toys filled the nursery. Behind the shining modern rocking-horse, behind the smart[2] doll's-house, a voice would start whispering: "There *must* be more money! There *must* be more money! There *must* be more money!" And the children would stop playing, to listen for a moment. They would look into each other's eyes, to see if they had all

[2]*smart:* stylish

heard. And each one saw in the eyes of the other two that they too had heard. "There *must* be more money! There *must* be more money!"

It came whispering from the springs of the still-swaying rocking-horse, and even the horse, bending his wooden, champing head, heard it. The big doll, sitting so pink and smirking in her new pram, could hear it quite plainly, and seemed to be smirking all the more self-consciously because of it. The foolish puppy, too, that took the place of the teddy-bear, he was looking so extraordinarily foolish for no other reason but that he heard the secret whisper all over the house: "There *must* be more money!"

Yet nobody ever said it aloud. The whisper was everywhere, and therefore no one spoke it. Just as no one ever says: "We are breathing!" in spite of the fact that breath is coming and going all the time.

"Mother," said the boy Paul one day, "why don't we keep a car of our own? Why do we always use uncle's, or else a taxi?"

"Because we're the poor members of the family," said the mother.

"But why *are* we, mother?"

"Well—I suppose," she said slowly and bitterly, "it's because your father has no luck."

The boy was silent for some time.

"Is luck money, mother?" he asked, rather timidly.

"No, Paul. Not quite. It's what causes you to have money."

"Oh!" said Paul vaguely. "I thought when Uncle Oscar said *filthy lucker*, it meant money."

"*Filthy lucre* does mean money," said the mother. "But it's lucre, not luck."

"Oh!" said the boy. "Then what *is* luck, mother?"

"It's what causes you to have money. If you're lucky you have money. That's why it's better to be born lucky than rich. If you're rich, you may lose your money. But if you're lucky, you will always get more money."

"Oh! Will you? And is father not lucky?"

"Very unlucky, I should say," she said bitterly.

The boy watched her with unsure eyes.

The uncle was delighted to find that his small nephew was posted with all the racing news. Bassett, the young gardener, who had been wounded in the left foot in the war and had got his present job through Oscar Cresswell, whose batman[3] he had been, was a perfect blade[4] of the "turf." He lived in the racing events, and the small boy lived with him.

Oscar Cresswell got it all from Bassett.

"Master Paul comes and asks me, so I can't do more than tell him, sir," said Bassett, his face terribly serious, as if he were speaking of religious matters.

"And does he ever put anything on a horse he fancies?"

"Well—I don't want to give him away—he's a young sport, a fine sport, sir. Would you mind asking him himself? He sort of takes a pleasure in it, and perhaps he'd feel I was giving him away, sir, if you don't mind."

Bassett was serious as a church.

The uncle went back to his nephew, and took him off for a ride in the car.

"Say, Paul, old man, do you ever put anything on a horse?" the uncle asked.

The boy watched the handsome man closely.

"Why, do you think I oughtn't to?" he parried.

"Not a bit of it! I thought perhaps you might give me a tip for the Lincoln."

The car sped on into the country, going down to Uncle Oscar's place in Hampshire.

"Honour bright?" said the nephew.

"Honour bright, son!" said the uncle.

"Well, then, Daffodil."

"Daffodil! I doubt it, sonny. What about Mirza?"

"I only know the winner," said the boy. "That's Daffodil."

"Daffodil, eh?"

There was a pause. Daffodil was an obscure horse comparatively.

"Uncle!"

"Yes, son?"

[3]*batman:* army officer's servant
[4]*blade:* dashing young man

"You won't let it go any further, will you? I promised Bassett."

"Bassett be damned, old man! What's he got to do with it?"

"We're partners. We've been partners from the first. Uncle, he lent me my first five shillings, which I lost. I promised him, honour bright, it was only between me and him; only you gave me that ten-shilling note I started winning with, so I thought you were lucky. You won't let it go any further, will you?"

The boy gazed at his uncle from those big, hot, blue eyes, set rather close together. The uncle stirred and laughed uneasily.

"Right you are, son! I'll keep your tip private. Daffodil, eh? How much are you putting on him?"

"All except twenty pounds," said the boy. "I keep that in reserve."

The uncle thought it a good joke.

"You keep twenty pounds in reserve, do you, you young romancer? What are you betting, then?"

"I'm betting three hundred," said the boy gravely. "But it's between you and me, Uncle Oscar! Honour bright?"

The uncle burst into a roar of laughter.

"It's between you and me all right, you young Nat Gould," he said, laughingly. "But where's your three hundred?"

"Bassett keeps it for me. We're partners."

"You are, are you! And what is Bassett putting on Daffodil?"

"He won't go quite as high as I do, I expect. Perhaps he'll go a hundred and fifty."

"What, pennies?" laughed the uncle.

"Pounds," said the child, with a surprised look at his uncle. "Bassett keeps a bigger reserve than I do."

Between wonder and amusement Uncle Oscar was silent. He pursued the matter no further, but he determined to take his nephew with him to the Lincoln races.

"Now, son," he said, "I'm putting twenty on Mirza, and I'll put five for you on any horse you fancy. What's your pick?"

"Daffodil, uncle."

"No, not the fiver on Daffodil!"

"I should if it was my own fiver," said the child.

"Good! Good! Right you are! A fiver for me and a fiver for you on Daffodil."

The child had never been to a race-meeting before, and his eyes were blue fire. He pursed his mouth tight, and watched. A Frenchman just in front had put his money on Lancelot. Wild with excitement, he flayed his arms up and down, yelling *"Lancelot! Lancelot!"* in his French accent.

Daffodil came in first, Lancelot second, Mirza third. The child, flushed and with eyes blazing, was curiously serene. His uncle brought him four five-pound notes, four to one.

"What am I to do with these?" he cried, waving them before the boy's eyes.

"I suppose we'll talk to Bassett," said the boy. "I expect I have fifteen hundred now; and twenty in reserve; and this twenty."

His uncle studied him for some moments.

"Look here, son!" he said. "You're not serious about Bassett and that fifteen hundred, are you?"

"Yes, I am. But it's between you and me, uncle. Honour bright!"

"Honour bright all right, son! But I must talk to Bassett."

"If you'd like to be a partner, uncle, with Bassett and me, we could all be partners. Only, you'd have to promise, honour bright, uncle, not to let it go beyond us three. Bassett and I are lucky, and you must be lucky, because it was your ten shillings I started winning with. . . ."

Uncle Oscar took both Bassett and Paul into Richmond Park for an afternoon, and there they talked.

"It's like this, you see, sir," Bassett said. "Master Paul would get me talking about racing events, spinning yarns, you know, sir. And he was always keen on knowing if I'd made or if I'd lost. It's about a year since, now, that I put five shillings on Blush of Dawn for him—and we lost. Then the luck turned, with that ten shillings he had from you, that we put on Singhalese. And since that time, it's been pretty steady, all things considering. What do you say, Master Paul?"

"We're all right when we're sure," said Paul. "It's when we're not quite sure that we go down."

"Oh, but we're careful then," said Bassett.

"But when are you *sure?*" smiled Uncle Oscar.

"It's Master Paul, sir," said Bassett, in a secret, religious voice. "It's as if he had it from heaven. Like Daffodil, now, for the Lincoln. That was as sure as eggs."

"Did you put anything on Daffodil?" asked Oscar Cresswell.

"Yes, sir. I made my bit."

"And my nephew?"

Bassett was obstinately silent, looking at Paul.

"I made twelve hundred, didn't I, Bassett? I told uncle I was putting three hundred on Daffodil."

"That's right," said Bassett, nodding.

"But where's the money?" asked the uncle.

"I keep it safe locked up, sir. Master Paul he can have it any minute he likes to ask for it."

"What, fifteen hundred pounds?"

"And twenty! And *forty*, that is, with the twenty he made on the course."

"It's amazing!" said the uncle.

"If Master Paul offers you to be partners, sir, I would, if I were you; if you'll excuse me," said Bassett.

Oscar Cresswell thought about it.

"I'll see the money," he said.

They drove home again, and sure enough, Bassett came round to the garden-house with fifteen hundred pounds in notes. The twenty pounds reserve was left with Joe Glee, in the Turf Commission deposit.

"You see, it's all right, uncle, when I'm *sure!* Then we go strong, for all we're worth. Don't we, Bassett?"

"We do that, Master Paul."

"And when are you sure?" said the uncle, laughing.

"Oh, well, sometimes I'm *absolutely* sure, like about Daffodil," said the boy; "and sometimes I have an idea; and sometimes I haven't even an idea, have I, Bassett? Then we're careful, because we mostly go down."

"You do, do you! And when you're sure, like about Daffodil, what makes you sure, sonny?"

"Oh, well, I don't know," said the boy uneasily. "I'm sure, you know, uncle; that's all."

"It's as if he had it from heaven, sir," Bassett reiterated.

"I should say so!" said the uncle.

But he became a partner. And when the Leger was coming on, Paul was "sure" about Lively Spark, which was a quite inconsiderable horse. The boy insisted on putting a thousand on the horse, Basset went for five hundred, and Oscar Cresswell two hundred. Lively Spark came in first, and the betting had been ten to one against him. Paul had made ten thousand.

"You see," he said, "I was absolutely sure of him."

Even Oscar Cresswell had cleared two thousand.

"Look here, son," he said, "this sort of thing makes me nervous."

"It needn't, uncle! Perhaps I shan't be sure again for a long time."

"But what are you going to do with your money?" asked the uncle.

"Of course," said the boy, "I started it for mother. She said she had no luck, because father is unlucky, so I thought if *I* was lucky, it might stop whispering."

"What might stop whispering?"

"Our house. I *hate* our house for whispering."

"What does it whisper?"

"Why—why"—the boy fidgeted—"why, I don't know. But it's always short of money, you know, uncle."

"I know it, son, I know it."

"You know people send mother writs, don't you, uncle?"

"I'm afraid I do," said the uncle.

"And then the house whispers, like people laughing at you behind your back. It's awful, that is! I thought if I was lucky . . ."

"You might stop it," added the uncle.

The boy watched him with big blue eyes, that had an uncanny cold fire in them, and he said never a word.

"Well, then!" said the uncle. "What are we doing?"

"I shouldn't like mother to know I was lucky," said the boy.

"Why not, son?"

"She'd stop me."

"I don't think she would."

"Oh!"—and the boy writhed in an odd way—"I *don't* want her to know, uncle."

"All right, son! We'll manage it without her knowing."

They managed it very easily. Paul, at the other's suggestion, handed over five thousand pounds to his uncle, who deposited it with the family lawyer, who was then to inform Paul's mother that a relative had put five thousand pounds into his hands, which sum was to be paid out a thousand pounds at a time, on the mother's birthday, for the next five years.

"So she'll have a birthday present of a thousand pounds for five successive years," said Uncle Oscar. "I hope it won't make it all the harder for her later."

Paul's mother had her birthday in November. The house had been "whispering" worse than ever lately, and, even in spite of his luck, Paul could not bear up against it. He was very anxious to see the effect of the birthday letter, telling his mother about the thousand pounds.

When there were no visitors, Paul now took his meals with his parents, as he was beyond the nursery control. His mother went into town nearly every day. She had discovered that she had an odd knack of sketching furs and dress materials, so she worked secretly in the studio of a friend who was the chief "artist" for the leading drapers. She drew the figures of ladies in furs and ladies in silk and sequins for the newspaper advertisements. This young woman artist earned several thousand pounds a year, but Paul's mother only made several hundreds, and she was again dissatisfied. She so wanted to be first in something, and she did not succeed, even in making sketches for drapery advertisements.

She was down to breakfast on the morning of her birthday. Paul watched her face as she read her letters. He knew the lawyer's letter. As his mother read it, her face hardened and became more expressionless. Then a cold, determined look came on her mouth. She hid the letter under the pile of others, and said not a word about it.

"Didn't you have anything nice in the post for your birthday, mother?" said Paul.

"Quite moderately nice," she said, her voice cold and absent.

She went away to town without saying more.

But in the afternoon Uncle Oscar appeared. He said Paul's mother had had a long interview with the lawyer, asking if the whole five thousand could not be advanced at once, as she was in debt.

"What do you think, uncle?" said the boy.

"I leave it to you, son."

"Oh, let her have it, then! We can get some more with the other," said the boy.

"A bird in the hand is worth two in the bush, laddie!" said Uncle Oscar.

"But I'm sure to *know* for the Grand National; or the Lincolnshire; or else the Derby. I'm sure to know for *one* of them," said Paul.

So Uncle Oscar signed the agreement, and Paul's mother touched the whole five thousand. Then something very curious happened. The voices in the house suddenly went mad, like a chorus of frogs on a spring evening. There were certain new furnishings, and Paul had a tutor. He was *really* going to Eton, his father's school, in the following autumn. There were flowers in the winter, and a blossoming of the luxury Paul's mother had been used to. And yet the voices in the house, behind the sprays of mimosa and almond blossom, and from under the piles of iridescent cushions, simply trilled and screamed in a sort of ecstasy: "There *must* be more money! Oh-h-h; there *must* be more money. Oh, now, now-w! Now-w-w—there *must* be more money!—more than ever! More than ever!"

It frightened Paul terribly. He studied away at his Latin and Greek with his tutors. But his intense hours were spent with Bassett. The Grand National had gone by: he had not "known," and had lost a hundred pounds. Summer was at hand. He was in agony for the Lincoln. But even for the Lincoln he didn't "know," and he lost fifty pounds. He became wild-eyed and strange, as if something were going to explode in him.

"Let it alone, son! Don't you bother about it!" urged Uncle Oscar. But it was as if the boy couldn't really hear what his uncle was saying.

"I've got to know for the Derby! I've got to know for the

Derby!" the child reiterated, his big blue eyes blazing with a sort of madness.

His mother noticed how overwrought he was.

"You'd better go to the seaside. Wouldn't you like to go now to the seaside, instead of waiting? I think you'd better," she said, looking down at him anxiously, her heart curiously heavy because of him.

But the child lifted his uncanny blue eyes.

"I couldn't possibly go before the Derby, mother!" he said. "I couldn't possibly."

"Why not?" she said, her voice becoming heavy when she was opposed. "Why not? You can still go from the seaside to see the Derby with your Uncle Oscar, if that's what you wish. No need for you to wait here. Besides, I think you care too much about these races. It's a bad sign. My family has been a gambling family, and you won't know till you grow up how much damage it has done. But it has done damage. I shall have to send Bassett away, and ask Uncle Oscar not to talk racing to you, unless you promise to be reasonable about it; go away to the seaside and forget it. You're all nerves!"

"I'll do what you like, mother, so long as you don't send me away till after the Derby," the boy said.

"Send you away from where? Just from this house?"

"Yes," he said, gazing at her.

"Why, you curious child, what makes you care about this house so much, suddenly? I never knew you loved it."

He gazed at her without speaking. He had a secret within a secret, something he had not divulged, even to Bassett or to his Uncle Oscar.

But his mother, after standing undecided and a little bit sullen for some moments, said:

"Very well, then! Don't go to the seaside till after the Derby, if you don't wish it. But promise me you won't let your nerves go to pieces. Promise you won't think so much about horse-racing and *events*, as you call them!"

"Oh, no," said the boy casually. "I won't think much about them, mother. You needn't worry. I wouldn't worry, mother, if I were you."

"If you were me and I were you," said his mother, "I wonder what we *should* do!"

"But you know you needn't worry, mother, don't you?" the boy repeated.

"I should be awfully glad to know it," she said wearily.

"Oh, well, you *can*, you know. I mean, you *ought* to know you needn't worry," he insisted.

"Ought I? Then I'll see about it," she said.

Paul's secret of secrets was his wooden horse, that which had no name. Since he was emancipated from a nurse and a nursery-governess, he had had his rocking-horse removed to his own bedroom at the top of the house.

"Surely, you're too big for a rocking-horse!" his mother had remonstrated.

"Well, you see, mother, till I can have a *real* horse, I like to have *some* sort of animal about," had been his quaint answer.

"Do you feel he keeps you company?" she laughed.

"Oh, yes! He's very good, he always keeps me company, when I'm there," said Paul.

So the horse, rather shabby, stood in an arrested prance in the boy's bedroom.

The Derby was drawing near, and the boy grew more and more tense. He hardly heard what was spoken to him, he was very frail, and his eyes were really uncanny. His mother had sudden strange seizures of uneasiness about him. Sometimes, for half-an-hour, she would feel a sudden anxiety about him that was almost anguish. She wanted to rush to him at once, and know he was safe.

Two nights before the Derby, she was at a big party in town, when one of her rushes of anxiety about her boy, her first-born, gripped her heart till she could hardly speak. She fought with the feeling, might and main, for she believed in commonsense. But it was too strong. She had to leave the dance and go downstairs to telephone to the country. The children's nursery-governess was terribly surprised and startled at being rung up in the night.

"Are the children all right, Miss Wilmot?"

"Oh, yes, they are quite all right."

"Master Paul? Is he all right?"

"He went to bed as right as a trivet. Shall I run up and look at him?"

"No," said Paul's mother reluctantly. "No! Don't trouble. It's all right. Don't sit up. We shall be home fairly soon." She did not want her son's privacy intruded upon.

"Very good," said the governess.

It was about one o'clock when Paul's mother and father drove up to their house. All was still. Paul's mother went to her room and slipped off her white fur cloak. She had told her maid not to wait up for her. She heard her husband downstairs, mixing a whisky-and-soda.

And then, because of the strange anxiety at her heart, she stole upstairs to her son's room. Noiselessly she went along the upper corridor. Was there a faint noise? What was it?

She stood, with arrested muscles, outside his door, listening. There was a strange, heavy, and yet not loud noise. Her heart stood still. It was a soundless noise, yet rushing and powerful. Something huge, in violent, hushed motion. What was it? What in God's name was it? She ought to know. She felt that she knew the noise. She knew what it was.

Yet she could not place it. She couldn't say what it was. And on and on it went, like a madness.

Softly, frozen with anxiety and fear, she turned the door-handle.

The room was dark. Yet in the space near the window, she heard and saw something plunging to and fro. She gazed in fear and amazement.

Then suddenly she switched on the light, and saw her son, in his green pyjamas, madly surging on the rocking-horse. The blaze of light suddenly lit him up, as he urged the wooden horse, and lit her up, as she stood, blonde, in her dress of pale green and crystal, in the doorway.

"Paul!" she cried. "Whatever are you doing?"

"It's Malabar!" he screamed, in a powerful strange voice. "It's Malabar!"

His eyes blazed at her for one strange and senseless second, as he ceased urging his wooden horse. Then he fell with a crash to the ground, and she, all her tormented motherhood flooding upon her, rushed to gather him up.

But he was unconscious, and unconscious he remained,

with some brain-fever. He talked and tossed, and his mother sat stonily by his side.

"Malabar! It's Malabar! Bassett, Bassett, I *know!* It's Malabar!"

So the child cried, trying to get up and urge the rocking-horse that gave him his inspiration.

"What does he mean by Malabar?" asked the heartfrozen mother.

"I don't know," said the father stonily.

"What does he mean by Malabar?" she asked her brother Oscar.

"It's one of the horses running for the Derby," was the answer.

And, in spite of himself, Oscar Cresswell spoke to Bassett, and himself put a thousand on Malabar: at fourteen to one.

The third day of the illness was critical; they were waiting for a change. The boy, with his rather long, curly hair, was tossing ceaselessly on the pillow. He neither slept nor regained consciousness, and his eyes were like blue stones. His mother sat, feeling her heart had gone, turned actually into a stone.

In the evening, Oscar Cresswell did not come, but Bassett sent a message, saying could he come up for one moment, just one moment? Paul's mother was very angry at the intrusion, but on second thought she agreed. The boy was the same. Perhaps Bassett might bring him to consciousness.

The gardener, a shortish fellow with a little brown moustache, and sharp little brown eyes, tiptoed into the room, touched his imaginary cap to Paul's mother, and stole to the bedside, staring with glittering, smallish eyes, at the tossing, dying child.

"Master Paul!" he whispered. "Master Paul! Malabar came in first all right, a clean win. I did as you told me. You've made over seventy thousand pounds, you have; you've got over eighty thousand. Malabar came in all right, Master Paul."

"Malabar! Malabar! Did I say Malabar, mother? Did I say Malabar? Do you think I'm lucky, mother? I knew Malabar, didn't I? Over eighty thousand pounds! I call that lucky, don't you, mother? Over eighty thousand pounds! I knew, didn't I know I knew? Malabar came in all right. If I ride my horse till I'm sure, then I tell you, Bassett, you can go as high as you like. Did you go for all you were worth, Bassett?"

"I went for a thousand on it, Master Paul."

"I never told you, mother, that if I can ride my horse, and *get there*, then I'm absolutely sure—oh, absolutely! Mother, did I ever tell you? I *am* lucky!"

"No, you never did," said the mother.

But the boy died in the night.

And even as he lay dead, his mother heard her brother's voice saying to her: "My God, Hester, you're eighty-odd thousand to the good, and a poor devil of a son to the bad. But, poor devil, poor devil, he's best gone out of a life where he rides his rocking-horse to find a winner."

FOR DISCUSSION

1. Who is responsible for the tragedy? Could it have been avoided?
2. How does Paul look and act when he is riding his horse? What does this foreshadow? What is the effect on him when he doesn't "know"? How much does the boy understand of what is happening to him and to his mother?
3. What is your interpretation of the voices in the house? How does the whispering change after the mother receives the money from Paul's anonymous gift? Why is Paul frightened? Why, even though frightened, does he persist in his riding? What does the mother's response to the gift of money reveal about her character?
4. According to what definition of luck is Paul's mother unlucky? Study all the passages in the story in which there is a discussion of luck: first of Paul with his mother, then with Uncle Oscar. Is Paul right in thinking his mother would stop his gambling on the horses if she knew?
5. What is Paul's secret within a secret? Why does he keep it from everyone? Would the outcome of the story have been different if someone else had found out?
6. Explain the mother's reaction to the son's illness. How do you

interpret the uncle's final remark? What commentary does the author intend to bring out by this remark?

FOR COMPOSITION

1. An important moment in this story, the beginning of the rising action, is the discussion between Paul and his mother about the meaning of luck. After studying this conversation, write a discussion of the mother's view of luck and of its influence on her attitudes toward her life and family.
2. There was a good deal of emphasis in the story on the sense of anxiety about money, partly expressed in the whispering voices which Paul constantly heard. Re-examine the story for the references to the voices, and then write a discussion of the way the anxiety, even when not voiced, affected the children.

Joseph Conrad

Conrad stated as his major theme, "the solidarity in mysterious origin, in toil, in joy, in hope, in uncertain fate, which binds men to each other and all mankind to the visible world. My task which I am trying to achieve," he said, "is, by the power of the written word, to make you hear, to make you feel . . . , before all, to make you *see*." His masterful descriptions, not only of the sea itself but also of the situations it creates, achieve an unusual intensity and tension. The essential loneliness of each man is a recurrent theme in many of his stories and novels. Man is not an alien solely by himself; he shares being an alien with every other man.

Many of Conrad's stories end tragically; nearly all convey a sense of the tragic. The problems which concerned him most were serious moral problems—problems of guilt, justice, and moral obligation, and of conflict between action and contemplation.

The Secret Sharer

I

On my right hand there were lines of fishing stakes resembling a mysterious system of half-submerged bamboo fences, incomprehensible in its division of the domain of tropical fishes, and crazy of aspect as if abandoned forever by some nomad tribe of fishermen now gone to the other end of the ocean; for there was no sign of human habitation as far as the eye could reach. To the left a group of barren islets, suggesting ruins of stone walls, towers, and blockhouses, had its foundations set in a blue sea that itself looked solid, so still and stable did it lie below my feet; even the track of light from the westering sun shone smoothly, without that animated glitter which tells of an imperceptible ripple. And when I turned my head to take a parting glance at the tug which had just left us anchored outside the bar, I saw the straight line of the flat shore joined to the stable sea, edge to edge, with a perfect and unmarked closeness, in one leveled floor half brown, half blue under the enormous dome of the sky. Corresponding in their insignificance to the islets of the sea, two small clumps of trees, one on each side of the only fault in the impeccable joint, marked the mouth of the river Meinam we had just left on the first preparatory stage of our homeward journey; and, far back on the inland level, a larger and loftier mass, the grove surrounding the great Paknam pagoda, was the only thing on which the eye could rest from the vain task of exploring the monotonous sweep of the horizon. Here and there gleams as of a few scattered pieces of silver marked the windings of the great river; and on the nearest of them, just within the bar, the tug steaming right into the land became lost to my sight, hull and funnel and masts, as though the impassive earth had swallowed her up without an effort, without a tremor. My eye followed the light cloud of her smoke, now here, now there, above the plain, according to the devious curves of the stream, but always fainter and farther away, till I lost it at last behind the miter-shaped hill of the great pagoda. And then I was left alone with my ship, anchored at the head of the Gulf of Siam.

She floated at the starting point of a long journey, very still in an immense stillness, the shadows of her spars flung far to the eastward by the setting sun. At that moment I was alone on her decks. There was not a sound in her—and around us nothing moved, nothing lived, not a canoe on the water, not a bird in the air, not a cloud in the sky. In this breathless pause at the threshold of a long passage we seemed to be measuring our fitness for a long and arduous enterprise, the appointed task of both our existences to be carried out, far from all human eyes, with only sky and sea for spectators and for judges.

There must have been some glare in the air to interfere with one's sight, because it was only just before the sun left us that my roaming eyes made out beyond the highest ridge of the principal islet of the group something which did away with the solemnity of perfect solitude. The tide of darkness flowed on swiftly; and with tropical suddenness a swarm of stars came out above the shadowy earth, while I lingered yet, my hand resting lightly on my ship's rail as if on the shoulder of a trusted friend. But, with all that multitude of celestial bodies staring down at one, the comfort of quiet communion with her was gone for good. And there were also disturbing sounds by this time—voices, footsteps forward; the steward flitted along the main deck, a busily ministering spirit; a hand bell tinkled urgently under the poop deck. . . .

I found my two officers waiting for me near the supper table, in the lighted cuddy.[1] We sat down at once, and as I helped the chief mate, I said:

"Are you aware that there is a ship anchored inside the islands? I saw her mastheads above the ridge as the sun went down."

He raised sharply his simple face, overcharged by a terrible growth of whisker, and emitted his usual ejaculation: "Bless my soul, sir! You don't say so!"

My second mate was a round-cheeked, silent young man, grave beyond his years, I thought; but as our eyes happened to meet I detected a slight quiver on his lips. I looked down at once. It was not my part to encourage sneering on board my ship. It must be said, too, that I knew very little of my officers. In consequence of certain events of no particular significance, except to myself, I had been appointed to the command only a fortnight before. Neither did I know much of the hands[2] forward. All these people had been together for eighteen months or so, and my position was that of the only stranger on board. I mention this because it has some bearing on what is to follow. But what I felt most was my being a stranger to the ship; and if all the truth must be told, I was somewhat of a stranger to myself. The youngest man on board (barring the second mate), and untried as yet by a position of the fullest responsibility, I was willing to take the adequacy of the others for granted. They had simply to be equal to their tasks; but I wondered how far I should turn out faith-

[1]*cuddy:* ship's kitchen
[2]*hands:* common seamen

ful to that ideal conception of one's own personality every man sets up for himself secretly.

Meantime the chief mate, with an almost visible effect of collaboration[3] on the part of his round eyes and frightful whiskers, was trying to evolve a theory of the anchored ship. His dominant trait was to take all things into earnest consideration. He was of a painstaking turn of mind. As he used to say, he "liked to account to himself" for practically everything that came in his way, down to a miserable scorpion he had found in his cabin a week before. The why and the wherefore of that scorpion—how it got on board and came to select his room rather than the pantry (which was a dark place and more what a scorpion would be partial to), and how on earth it managed to drown itself in the inkwell of his writing desk—had exercised him infinitely. The ship within the islands was much more easily accounted for; and just as we were about to rise from table he made his pronouncement. She was, he doubted not, a ship from home lately arrived. Probably she drew too much water to cross the bar except at the top of spring tides. Therefore she went into that natural harbor to wait for a few days in preference to remaining in an open roadstead.

"That's so," confirmed the second mate, suddenly, in his slightly hoarse voice. "She draws over twenty feet. She's the Liverpool ship *Sephora* with a cargo of coal. Hundred and twenty-three days from Cardiff."

We looked at him in surprise.

"The tugboat skipper told me when he came on board for your letters, sir," explained the young man. "He expects to take her up the river the day after tomorrow."

After thus overwhelming us with the extent of his information he slipped out of the cabin. The mate observed regretfully that he "could not account for that young fellow's whims." What prevented him telling us all about it at once, he wanted to know.

I detained him as he was making a move. For the last two

[3]*collaboration:* working together

days the crew had had plenty of hard work, and the night before they had very little sleep. I felt painfully that I—a stranger—was doing something unusual when I directed him to let all hands turn in without setting an anchor watch. I proposed to keep on deck myself till one o'clock or thereabouts. I would get the second mate to relieve me at that hour.

"He will turn out the cook and the steward at four," I concluded, "and then give you a call. Of course at the slightest sign of any sort of wind we'll have the hands up and make a start at once."

He concealed his astonishment. "Very well, sir." Outside the cuddy he put his head in the second mate's door to inform him of my unheard-of caprice to take a five hours' anchor watch on myself. I heard the other raise his voice incredulously—"What? The Captain himself?" Then a few more murmurs, a door closed, then another. A few moments later I went on deck.

My strangeness, which had made me sleepless, had prompted that unconventional arrangement, as if I had expected in those solitary hours of the night to get on terms with the ship of which I knew nothing, manned by men of whom I knew very little more. Fast alongside a wharf, littered like any ship in port with a tangle of unrelated shore people, I had hardly seen her yet properly. Now, as she lay cleared for sea, the stretch of her main deck seemed to me very fine under the stars. Very fine, very roomy for her size, and very inviting. I descended the poop and paced the waist, my mind picturing to myself the coming passage through the Malay Archipelago, down the Indian Ocean, and up the Atlantic. All its phases were familiar enough to me, every characteristic, all the alternatives which were likely to face me on the high seas—everything! . . . except the novel responsibility of command. But I took heart from the reasonable thought that the ship was like other ships, the men like other men, and that the sea was not likely to keep any special surprises expressly for my discomfiture.

Arrived at that comforting conclusion, I bethought myself of a cigar and went below to get it. All was still down there. Everybody at the after end of the ship was sleeping profoundly. I came out again on the quarter-deck, agreeably at ease in my sleeping suit on that warm breathless night, barefooted, a glowing cigar in my teeth, and, going forward, I was met by the profound silence of the fore end of the ship. Only as I passed the door of the forecastle I heard a deep, quiet, trustful sigh of some sleeper inside. And suddenly I rejoiced in the great security of the sea as compared with the unrest of the land, in my choice of that untempted life presenting no disquieting problems, invested with an elementary moral beauty by the absolute straightforwardness of its appeal and by the singleness of its purpose.

The riding light in the forerigging burned with a clear, untroubled, as if symbolic, flame, confident and bright in the mysterious shades of the night. Passing on my way aft along the other side of the ship, I observed that the rope side-ladder, put over, no doubt, for the master of the tug when he came to fetch away our letters, had not been hauled in as it should have been. I became annoyed at this, for exactitude in small matters is the very soul of discipline. Then I reflected that I had myself peremptorily[4] dismissed my officers from duty, and by my own act had prevented the anchor watch being formally set and things properly attended to. I asked myself whether it was wise ever to interfere with the established routine of duties even from the kindest of motives. My action might have made me appear eccentric. Goodness only knew how that absurdly whiskered mate would "account" for my conduct, and what the whole ship thought of that informality of their new captain. I was vexed with myself.

Not from compunction[5] certainly, but, as it were mechanically, I proceeded to get the ladder in myself. Now a side-ladder of that sort is a light affair and comes in easily, yet my vigorous tug, which should have brought it flying on board, merely recoiled upon my body in a totally unexpected jerk. What the devil! . . . I was so astounded by the immovableness of that ladder that I remained stock-still, trying to account

[4]*peremptorily:* dictatorially
[5]*compunction:* feeling of guilt

for it to myself like that imbecile mate of mine. In the end, of course, I put my head over the rail.

The side of the ship made an opaque belt of shadow on the darkling glassy shimmer of the sea. But I saw at once something elongated and pale floating very close to the ladder. Before I could form a guess a faint flash of phosphorescent light, which seemed to issue suddenly from the naked body of a man, flickered in the sleeping water with the elusive, silent play of summer lightning in a night sky. With a gasp I saw revealed to my stare a pair of feet, the long legs, a broad livid back immersed right up to the neck in a greenish cadaverous[6] glow. One hand, awash, clutched the bottom rung of the ladder. He was complete but for the head. A headless corpse! The cigar dropped out of my gaping mouth with a tiny plop and a short hiss quite audible in the absolute stillness of all things under heaven. At that I suppose he raised up his face, a dimly pale oval in the shadow of the ship's side. But even then I could only barely make out down there the shape of his black-haired head. However, it was enough for the horrid, frost-bound sensation which had gripped me about the chest to pass off. The moment of vain exclamations was past, too. I only climbed on the spare spar and leaned over the rail as far as I could, to bring my eyes nearer to that mystery floating alongside.

As he hung by the ladder, like a resting swimmer, the sea-lightning played about his limbs at every stir; and he appeared in it ghastly, silvery, fishlike. He remained as mute as a fish too. He made no motion to get out of the water, either. It was inconceivable that he should not attempt to come on board, and strangely troubling to suspect that perhaps he did not want to. And my first words were prompted by just that troubled incertitude.

"What's the matter?" I asked in my ordinary tone, speaking down to the face upturned exactly under mine.

"Cramp," it answered, no louder. Then slightly anxious, "I say, no need to call anyone."

"I was not going to," I said.

[6]*cadaverous:* pale or death-like

"Are you alone on deck?"

"Yes."

I had somehow the impression that he was on the point of letting go the ladder to swim away beyond my ken—mysterious as he came. But, for the moment, this being appearing as if he had risen from the bottom of the sea (it was certainly the nearest land to the ship) wanted only to know the time. I told him. And he, down there, tentatively:

"I suppose your captain's turned in?"

"I am sure he isn't," I said.

He seemed to struggle with himself, for I heard something like the low, bitter murmur of doubt. "What's the good?" His next words came out with a hesitating effort.

"Look here, my man. Could you call him out quietly?"

I thought the time had come to declare myself.

"*I* am the captain."

I heard a "By Jove!" whispered at the level of the water. The phosphorescence flashed in the swirl of the water all about his limbs, his other hand seized the ladder.

"My name's Leggatt."

The voice was calm and resolute. A good voice. The self-possession of that man had somehow induced a corresponding state in myself. It was very quietly that I remarked:

"You must be a good swimmer."

"Yes. I've been in the water practically since nine o'clock. The question for me now is whether I am to let go this ladder and go on swimming till I sink from exhaustion or—to come on board here."

I felt this was no mere formula of desperate speech, but a real alternative in the view of a strong soul. I should have gathered from this that he was young; indeed, it is only the young who are ever confronted by such clear issues. But at the time it was pure intuition on my part. A mysterious communication was established already between us two—in the face of that silent, darkened tropical sea. I was young, too; young enough to make no comment. The man in the water began suddenly to climb up the ladder, and I hastened away from the rail to fetch some clothes.

Before entering the cabin I stood still, listening in the

lobby at the foot of the stairs. A faint snore came through the closed door of the chief mate's room. The second mate's door was on the hook, but the darkness in there was absolutely soundless. He, too, was young and could sleep like a stone. Remained the steward, but he was not likely to wake up before he was called. I got a sleeping suit out of my room and, coming back on deck, saw the naked man from the sea sitting on the main hatch, glimmering white in the darkness, his elbows on his knees and his head in his hands. In a moment he had concealed his damp body in a sleeping suit of the same gray-stripe pattern as the one I was wearing and followed me like my double on the poop. Together we moved right aft, barefoot, silent.

"What is it? I asked in a deadened voice, taking the lighted lamp out of the binnacle,[7] and raising it to his face.

"An ugly business."

He had rather regular features; a good mouth; light eyes under somewhat heavy, dark eyebrows; a smooth, square forehead; no growth on his cheeks; a small, brown mustache, and a well-shaped round chin. His expression was concentrated, meditative, under the inspecting light of the lamp I held up to his face; such as a man thinking hard in solitude might wear. My sleeping suit was just right for his size. A well-knit young fellow of twenty-five at most. He caught his lower lip with the edge of white, even teeth.

"Yes," I said, replacing the lamp in the binnacle. The warm, heavy tropical night closed upon his head again.

"There's a ship over there," he murmured.

"Yes, I know. The *Sephora*. Did you know of us?"

"Hadn't the slightest idea. I am the mate of her—" He paused and corrected himself. "I should say I *was*."

"Aha! Something wrong?"

"Yes. Very wrong indeed. I've killed a man."

"What do you mean? Just now?"

"No, on the passage. Weeks ago. Thirty-nine south. When I say a man—"

"Fit of temper," I suggested, confidently.

[7]*binnacle:* case holding the ship's compass and lamp

The shadowy, dark head, like mine, seemed to nod imperceptibly above the ghostly gray of my sleeping suit. It was, in the night, as though I had been faced by my own reflection in the depths of a somber and immense mirror.

"A pretty thing to have to own up to for a Conway[8] boy," murmured my double, distinctly.

"You're a Conway boy?"

"I am," he said, as if startled. Then, slowly . . . "Perhaps you too—"

It was so; but being a couple of years older I had left before he joined. After a quick interchange of dates a silence fell; and I thought suddenly of my absurd mate with his terrific whiskers and the "Bless my soul—you don't say so" type of intellect. My double gave me an inkling of his thoughts by saying: "My father's a parson in Norfolk. Do you see me before a judge and jury on that charge? For myself I can't see the necessity. There are fellows that an angel from heaven—And I am not that. He was one of those creatures that are just simmering all the time with a silly sort of wickedness. Miserable devils that have no business to live at all. He wouldn't do his duty and wouldn't let anybody else do theirs. But what's the good of talking! You know well enough the sort of ill-conditioned snarling cur—"

He appealed to me as if our experience had been identical as our clothes. And I knew well enough the pestiferous[9] danger of such a character where there are no means of legal repression. And I knew well enough also that my double there was no homicidal ruffian. I did not think of asking him for details, and he told me the story roughly in brusque, disconnected sentences. I needed no more. I saw it all going on as though I were myself inside that other sleeping suit.

"It happened while we were setting a reefed[10] foresail, at dusk. Reefed foresail! You understand the sort of weather. The only sail we had left to keep the ship running; so you may guess what it had been like for days. Anxious sort of job,

[8]*Conway:* cadet ship used to train boys for the British merchant marine
[9]*pestiferous:* harmfully contagious
[10]*reefed:* tied down

that. He gave me some of his cursed insolence at the sheet.[11] I tell you I was overdone with this terrific weather that seemed to have no end to it. Terrific, I tell you—and a deep ship. I believe the fellow was half-crazy with funk.[12] It was no time for gentlemanly reproof, so I turned round and felled him like an ox. He up and at me. We closed just as an awful sea made for the ship. All hands saw it coming and took to the rigging, but I had him by the throat, and went on shaking him like a rat, the men above us yelling, 'Look out! Look out!' Then a crash as if the sky had fallen on my head. They say that for over ten minutes hardly anything was to be seen of the ship—just the three masts and a bit of the forecastle head and of the poop all awash driving along in a smother of foam. It was a miracle that they found us, jammed together behind the forebitts. It's clear that I meant business, because I was holding him by the throat still when they picked us up. He was black in the face. It was too much for them. It seems they rushed us aft together, gripped as we were, screaming, 'Murder!' like a lot of lunatics, and broke into the cuddy. And the ship running for her life, touch and go all the time, any minute her last in a sea fit to turn your hair gray only a-looking at it. I understand that the skipper, too, started raving like the rest of them. The man had been deprived of sleep for more than a week, and to have this sprung on him at the height of a furious gale nearly drove him out of his mind. I wonder they didn't fling me overboard after getting the carcass of their precious shipmate out of my fingers. They had rather a job to separate us, I've been told. A sufficiently fierce story to make an old judge and a respectable jury sit up a bit. The first thing I heard when I came to myself was the maddening howling of that endless gale, and on that the voice of the old man. He was hanging on to my bunk, staring into my face out of his sou'wester.

"'Mr. Leggatt, you have killed a man. You can act no longer as chief mate of this ship.'"

His care to subdue his voice made it sound monotonous.

[11]*sheet:* rope attached to a sail
[12]*funk:* panic

He rested a hand on the end of the skylight to steady himself with, and all that time did not stir a limb, so far as I could see. "Nice little tale for a quiet tea party," he concluded in the same tone.

One of my hands, too, rested on the end of the skylight; neither did I stir a limb, so far as I knew. We stood less than a foot from each other. It occurred to me that if old "Bless my soul—you don't say so" were to put his head up the companion and catch sight of us, he would think he was seeing double, or imagine himself come upon a scene of weird witchcraft; the strange captain having a quiet confabulation by the wheel with his own gray ghost. I became very much concerned to prevent anything of the sort. I heard the other's soothing undertone.

"My father's a parson in Norfolk," it said. Evidently he had forgotten he had told me this important fact before. Truly a nice little tale.

"You had better slip down into my stateroom now," I said, moving off stealthily. My double followed my movements; our bare feet made no sound; I let him in, closed the door with care, and, after giving a call to the second mate, returned on deck for my relief.

"Not much sign of any wind yet," I remarked when he approached.

"No, sir. Not much," he assented, sleepily, in his hoarse voice, with just enough deference, no more, and barely suppressing a yawn.

"Well, that's all you have to look out for. You have got your orders."

"Yes, sir."

I paced a turn or two on the poop and saw him take up his position face forward with his elbow in the ratlines of the mizzen-rigging before I went below. The mate's faint snoring was still going on peacefully. The cuddy lamp was burning over the table on which stood a vase with flowers, a polite attention from the ship's provision merchant—the last flowers we should see for the next three months at the very least. Two bunches of bananas hung from the beam symmetrically, one on each side of the rudder-casing. Everything was as before in the ship—except that two of her captain's sleeping suits were simultaneously in use, one motionless in the cuddy, the other keeping very still in the captain's stateroom.

It must be explained here that my cabin had the form of the capital letter L, the door being within the angle and opening into the short part of the letter. A couch was to the left, the bed-place to the right; my writing desk and the chronometer's[13] table faced the door. But anyone opening it, unless he stepped right inside, had no view of what I call the long (or vertical) part of the letter. It contained some lockers surmounted by a bookcase; and a few clothes, a thick jacket or two, caps, oilskin coat, and such-like, hung on hooks. There was at the bottom of that part a door opening into my bathroom, which could be entered also directly from the saloon. But that way was never used.

The mysterious arrival had discovered the advantage of this particular shape. Entering my room, lighted strongly by a big bulkhead lamp swung on gimbals above my writing desk, I did not see him anywhere till he stepped out quietly from behind the coats hung in the recessed part.

"I heard somebody moving about, and went in there at once," he whispered.

I, too, spoke under my breath.

"Nobody is likely to come in here without knocking and getting permission."

He nodded. His face was thin and the sunburn faded, as though he had been ill. And no wonder. He had been, I heard presently, kept under arrest in his cabin for nearly seven weeks. But there was nothing sickly in his eyes or in his expression. He was not a bit like me, really; yet, as we stood leaning over my bedplace, whispering side by side, with our dark heads together and our backs to the door, anybody bold enough to open it stealthily would have been treated to the uncanny sight of a double captain busy talking in whispers with his other self.

"But all this doesn't tell me how you came to hang on to our side-ladder," I inquired, in the hardly audible murmurs

[13]*chronometer:* timepiece

we used, after he had told me something more of the proceedings on board the *Sephora* once the bad weather was over.

"When we sighted Java Head I had had time to think all those matters out several times over. I had six weeks of doing nothing else, and with only an hour or so every evening for a tramp on the quarter-deck."

He whispered, his arms folded on the side of my bed-place, staring through the open port. And I could imagine perfectly the manner of this thinking out—a stubborn if not a steadfast operation; something of which I should have been perfectly incapable.

"I reckoned it would be dark before we closed with the land," he continued, so low that I had to strain my hearing, near as we were to each other, shoulder touching shoulder almost. "So I asked to speak to the old man. He always seemed very sick when he came to see me—as if he could not look me in the face. You know, that foresail saved the ship. She was too deep to have run long under bare poles. And it was I that managed to set it for him. Anyway, he came. When I had him in my cabin—he stood by the door looking at me as if I had the halter around my neck already—I asked him right away to leave my cabin door unlocked at night while the ship was going through Sunda Straits. There would be the Java coast within two or three miles, off Angier Point. I wanted nothing more. I've had a prize for swimming my second year in the Conway."

"I can't believe it," I breathed out.

"God only knows why they locked me in every night. To see some of their faces you'd have thought they were afraid I'd go about at night strangling people. Am I a murdering brute? Do I look it? By Jove! If I had been, he wouldn't have trusted himself like that into my room. You'll say I might have chucked him aside and bolted out, there and then—it was dark already. Well, no. And for the same reason I wouldn't think of trying to smash the door. There would have been a rush to stop me at the noise, and I did not mean to get into a confounded scrimmage. Somebody else might have got killed—for I would not have broken out only to get chucked back, and I did not want any more of that work. He refused, looking more sick than ever. He was afraid of the men, and also of the old second mate of his who had been sailing with him for years—a gray-headed old humbug; and his steward, too, had been with him devil knows how long—seventeen years or more—a dogmatic sort of loafer who hated me like poison, just because I was the chief mate. No chief mate ever made more than one voyage in the *Sephora*, you know. Those two old chaps ran the ship. Devil only knows what the skipper wasn't afraid of (all his nerve went to pieces altogether in that hellish spell of bad weather we had)—of what the law would do to him—of his wife, perhaps. Oh yes! she's on board. Though I don't think she would have meddled. She would have been only too glad to have me out of the ship in any way. The 'brand of Cain'[14] business, don't you see. That's all right. I was ready enough to go off wandering on the face of the earth—and that was price enough to pay for an Abel of that sort. Anyhow, he wouldn't listen to me. 'This thing must take its course. I represent the law here.' He was shaking like a leaf. 'So you won't?' 'No!' 'Then I hope you will be able to sleep on that,' I said, and turned my back on him. 'I wonder that *you* can,' cries he, and locks the door.

"Well, after that, I couldn't. Not very well. That was three weeks ago. We have had a slow passage through the Java Sea; drifted about Carimata for ten days. When we anchored here they thought, I suppose, it was all right. The nearest land (and that's five miles) is the ship's destination; the consul would soon set about catching me; and there would have been no object in bolting to these islets there. I don't suppose there's a drop of water on them. I don't know how it was, but tonight that steward, after bringing me my supper, went out to let me eat it, and left the door unlocked. And I ate it—all there was, too. After I had finished I strolled out on the quarter-deck. I don't know that I meant to do anything. A breath of fresh air was all I wanted, I believe. Then a sudden

[14]*Cain:* son of Adam and Eve, who murdered his brother Abel and was exiled from his father's home; a mark supposedly identifies Cain's fellow murderers.

temptation came over me. I kicked off my slippers and was in the water before I had made up my mind fairly. Somebody heard the splash and they raised an awful hullabaloo. 'He's gone! Lower the boats! He's committed suicide! No, he's swimming.' Certainly I was swimming. It's not so easy for a swimmer like me to commit suicide by drowning. I landed on the nearest islet before the boat left the ship's side. I heard them pulling about in the dark, hailing, and so on, but after a bit they gave up. Everything quieted down and the anchorage became as still as death. I sat down on a stone and began to think. I felt certain they would start searching for me at daylight. There was no place to hide on those stony things—and if there had been, what would have been the good? But now I was clear of that ship, I was not going back. So after a while I took off all my clothes, tied them up in a bundle with a stone inside, and dropped them in the deep water on the outer side of that islet. That was suicide enough for me. Let them think what they liked, but I didn't mean to drown myself. I meant to swim till I sank—but that's not the same thing. I struck out for another of these little islands, and it was from that one that I first saw your riding light. Something to swim for. I went on easily, and on the way I came upon a flat rock a foot or two above water. In the daytime, I dare say, you might make it out with a glass from your poop. I scrambled up on it and rested myself for a bit. Then I made another start. That last spell must have been over a mile."

His whisper was getting fainter and fainter, and all the time he stared straight out through the porthole, in which there was not even a star to be seen. I had not interrupted him. There was something that made comment impossible in his narrative, or perhaps in himself; a sort of feeling, a quality, which I can't find a name for. And when he ceased, all I found was a futile whisper: "So you swam for our light?"

"Yes—straight for it. It was something to swim for. I couldn't see any stars low down because the coast was in the way, and I couldn't see the land, either. The water was like glass. One might have been swimming in a confounded thousand-feet deep cistern with no place for scrambling out anywhere; but what I didn't like was the notion of swimming round and round like a crazed bullock before I gave out; and as I didn't mean to go back . . . No. Do you see me being hauled back, stark naked, off one of these little islands by the scruff of the neck and fighting like a wild beast? Somebody would have got killed for certain, and I did not want any of that. So I went on. Then your ladder—"

"Why didn't you hail the ship?" I asked, a little louder.

He touched my shoulder lightly. Lazy footsteps came right over our heads and stopped. The second mate had crossed from the other side of the poop and might have been hanging over the rail, for all we knew.

"He couldn't hear us talking—could he?" My double breathed into my ear, anxiously.

His anxiety was an answer, a sufficient answer, to the question I had put to him. An answer containing all the difficulty of that situation. I closed the porthole quietly, to make sure. A louder word might have been overheard.

"Who's that?" he whispered then.

"My second mate. But I don't know much more of the fellow than you do."

And I told him a little about myself. I had been appointed to take charge while I least expected anything of the sort, not quite a fortnight ago. I didn't know either the ship or the people. Hadn't had the time in port to look about me or size anybody up. And as to the crew, all they knew was that I was appointed to take the ship home. For the rest, I was almost as much of a stranger on board as himself, I said. And at the moment I felt it most acutely. I felt that it would take very little to make me a suspect person in the eyes of the ship's company.

He had turned about meantime; and we, the two strangers in the ship, faced each other in identical attitudes.

"Your ladder—" he murmured, after a silence. "Who'd have thought of finding a ladder hanging over at night in a ship anchored out here! I felt just then a very unpleasant faintness. After the life I've been leading for nine weeks, anybody would have got out of condition. I wasn't capable of swimming round as far as your rudder chains. And, lo and behold! there was a ladder to get hold of. After I gripped it

I said to myself, 'What's the good?' When I saw a man's head looking over I thought I would swim away presently and leave him shouting—in whatever language it was. I didn't mind being looked at. I—I liked it. And then you speaking to me so quietly—as if you had expected me—made me hold on a little longer. It had been a confounded lonely time—I don't mean while swimming. I was glad to talk a little to somebody that didn't belong to the *Sephora.* As to asking for the captain, that was a mere impulse. It could have been no use, with all the ship knowing about me and the other people pretty certain to be round here in the morning. I don't know—I wanted to be seen, to talk to somebody, before I went on. I don't know what I would have said. . . . 'Fine night, isn't it?' or something of the sort."

"Do you think they will be round here presently?" I asked with some incredulity.

"Quite likely," he said, faintly.

He looked extremely haggard all of a sudden. His head rolled on his shoulders.

"H'm. We shall see then. Meantime get into that bed," I whispered. "Want help? There."

It was a rather high bed-place with a set of drawers underneath. This amazing swimmer really needed the lift I gave him by seizing his leg. He tumbled in, rolled over on his back, and flung one arm across his eyes. And then, with his face nearly hidden, he must have looked exactly as I used to look in that bed. I gazed upon my other self for a while before drawing across carefully the two green serge curtains, which ran on a brass rod. I thought for a moment of pinning them together for greater safety, but I sat down on the couch, and once there I felt unwilling to rise and hunt for a pin. I would do it in a moment. I was extremely tired, in a peculiarly intimate way, by the strain of stealthiness, by the effort of whispering and the general secrecy of this excitement. It was three o'clock by now and I had been on my feet since nine, but I was not sleepy; I could not have gone to sleep. I sat there, fagged out, looking at the curtains, trying to clear my mind of the confused sensation of being in two places at once, greatly bothered by an exasperating knocking in my head. It was a relief to discover suddenly that it was not in my head at all, but on the outside of the door. Before I could collect myself, the words "Come in" were out of my mouth, and the steward entered with a tray, bringing in my morning coffee. I had slept, after all, and I was so frightened that I shouted. "This way! I am here, Steward," as though he had been miles away. He put down the tray on the table next the couch and only then said, very quietly, "I can see you are here, sir." I felt him give me a keen look, but I dared not meet his eyes just then. He must have wondered why I had drawn the curtains of my bed before going to sleep on the couch. He went out, hooking the door open as usual.

I heard the crew washing decks above me. I knew I would have been told at once if there had been any wind. Calm, I thought, and I was doubly vexed. Indeed, I felt dual more than ever. The steward reappeared suddenly in the doorway. I jumped up from the couch so quickly that he gave a start.

"What do you want here?"

"Close your port, sir—they are washing decks."

"It is closed," I said, reddening.

"Very well, sir." But he did not move from the doorway and returned my stare in an extraordinary, equivocal[15] manner for a time. Then his eyes wavered, all his expression changed, and in a voice unusually gentle, almost coaxingly:

"May I come in to take the empty cup away, sir?"

"Of course!" I turned my back on him while he popped in and out. Then I unhooked and closed the door and even pushed the bolt. This sort of thing could not go on very long. The cabin was as hot as an oven, too. I took a peep at my double, and discovered that he had not moved, his arm was still over his eyes; but his chest heaved; his hair was wet; his chin glistened with perspiration. I reached over him and opened the port.

"I must show myself on deck," I reflected.

Of course, theoretically, I could do what I liked, with no one to say nay to me within the whole circle of the horizon; but to lock my cabin door and take the key away I did not

[15] *equivocal:* uncertain or doubtful

dare. Directly I put my head out of the companion I saw the group of my two officers, the second mate barefooted, the chief mate in long India-rubber boots, near the break of the poop, and the steward half way down the poop ladder talking to them eagerly. He happened to catch sight of me and dived, the second ran down on the main deck shouting some order or other, and the chief mate came to meet me, touching his cap.

There was a sort of curiosity in his eye that I did not like. I don't know whether the steward had told them that I was "queer" only, or downright drunk, but I know the man meant to have a good look at me. I watched him coming with a smile which, as he got into point-blank range, took effect and froze his very whiskers. I did not give him time to open his lips.

"Square the yards by lifts and braces[16] before the hands go to breakfast."

It was the first particular order I had given on board that ship; and I stayed on deck to see it executed, too. I had felt the need of asserting myself without loss of time. That sneering young cub got taken down a peg or two on that occasion, and I also seized the opportunity of having a good look at the face of every foremast man as they filed past me to go to the after braces. At breakfast time, eating nothing myself, I presided with such frigid dignity that the two mates were only too glad to escape from the cabin as soon as decency permitted; and all the time the dual working of my mind distracted me almost to the point of insanity. I was constantly watching myself, my secret self, as dependent on my actions as my own personality, sleeping in that bed behind that door which faced me as I sat at the head of the table. It was very much like being mad, only it was worse because one was aware of it.

I had to shake him for a solid minute, but when at last he opened his eyes it was in the full possession of his senses, with an inquiring look.

"All's well so far," I whispered. "Now you must vanish into the bathroom."

[16]*Square . . . braces:* Set the ship's masts in order to sail directly before the wind.

He did so, as noiseless as a ghost, and then I rang for the steward, and facing him boldly, directed him to tidy up my stateroom while I was having my bath—"and be quick about it." As my tone admitted of no excuses, he said, "Yes, sir," and ran off to fetch his dustpan and brushes. I took a bath and did most of my dressing, splashing, and whistling softly for the steward's edification, while the secret sharer of my life stood drawn up bolt upright in that little space, his face looking very sunken in daylight, his eyelids lowered under the stern, dark line of his eyebrows drawn together by a slight frown.

When I left him to go back to my room the steward was finishing dusting. I sent for the mate and engaged him in some insignificant conversation. It was, as it were, trifling with the terrific character of his whiskers; but my object was to give him an opportunity for a good look at my cabin. And then I could at last shut, with a clear conscience, the door of my stateroom and get my double back into the recessed part. There was nothing else for it. He had to sit still on a small folding stool, half smothered by the heavy coats hanging there. We listened to the steward going into the bathroom out of the saloon, filling the water bottles there, scrubbing the bath, setting things to rights, whisk, bang, clatter—out again into the saloon—turn the key—click. Such was my scheme for keeping my second self invisible. Nothing better could be contrived under the circumstances. And there we sat; I at my writing desk ready to appear busy with some papers, he behind me out of sight of the door. It would not have been prudent to talk in daytime; and I could not have stood the excitement of that queer sense of whispering to myself. Now and then, glancing over my shoulder, I saw him far back there, sitting rigidly on the low stool, his bare feet close together, his arms folded, his head hanging on his breast—and perfectly still. Anybody would have taken him for me.

I was fascinated by it myself. Every moment I had to glance over my shoulder. I was looking at him when a voice outside the door said:

"Beg pardon, sir."

"Well!" . . . I kept my eyes on him, and so, when the voice

outside the door announced, "There's a ship's boat coming our way, sir," I saw him give a start—the first movement he had made for hours. But he did not raise his bowed head.

"All right. Get the ladder over."

I hesitated. Should I whisper something to him? But what? His immobility seemed to have been never disturbed. What could I tell him he did not know already? . . . Finally I went on deck.

II

The skipper of the *Sephora* had a thin red whisker all round his face, and the sort of complexion that goes with hair of that color; also the particular, rather smeary shade of blue in the eyes. He was not exactly a showy figure; his shoulders were high, his stature but middling—one leg slightly more bandy[17] than the other. He shook hands, looking vaguely around. A spiritless tenacity was his main characteristic, I judged. I behaved with a politeness which seemed to disconcert him. Perhaps he was shy. He mumbled to me as if he were ashamed of what he was saying; gave his name (it was something like Archbold—but at this distance of years I hardly am sure), his ship's name, and a few other particulars of that sort, in the manner of a criminal making a reluctant and doleful confession. He had had terrible weather on the passage out—terrible—terrible—wife aboard, too.

By this time we were seated in the cabin and the steward brought in a tray with a bottle and glasses. "Thanks! No." Never took liquor. Would have some water, though. He drank two tumblerfuls. Terrible thirsty work. Ever since daylight had been exploring the islands round his ship.

"What was that for—fun?" I asked, with an appearance of polite interest.

"No!" He sighed. "Painful duty."

As he persisted in his mumbling and I wanted my double to hear every word, I hit upon the notion of informing him that I regretted to say I was hard of hearing.

[17]*bandy:* bow-legged

"Such a young man, too!" he nodded, keeping his smeary blue, unintelligent eyes fastened upon me. "What was the cause of it—some disease?" he inquired, without the least sympathy and as if he thought that, if so, I'd got no more than I deserved.

"Yes; disease," I admitted in a cheerful tone which seemed to shock him. But my point was gained, because he had to raise his voice to give me his tale. It is not worth while to record that version. It was just over two months since all this had happened, and he had thought so much about it that he seemed completely muddled as to its bearings, but still immensely impressed.

"What would you think of such a thing happening on board your own ship? I've had the *Sephora* for these fifteen years. I am a well-known shipmaster."

He was densely distressed—and perhaps I should have sympathized with him if I had been able to detach my mental vision from the unsuspected sharer of my cabin as though he were my second self. There he was on the other side of the bulkhead,[18] four or five feet from us, no more, as we sat in the saloon. I looked politely at Captain Archbold (if that was his name), but it was the other I saw, in a gray sleeping suit, seated on a low stool, his bare feet close together, his arms folded, and every word said between us falling into the ears of his dark head bowed on his chest.

"I have been at sea now, man and boy, for seven-and-thirty years, and I've never heard of such a thing happening in an English ship. And that it should be my ship. Wife on board, too."

I was hardly listening to him.

"Don't you think," I said, "that the heavy sea which, you told me, came aboard just then might have killed the man? I have seen the sheer weight of a sea kill a man very neatly, by simply breaking his neck."

"Good God!" he uttered, impressively, fixing his smeary blue eyes on me. "The sea! No man killed by the sea ever looked like that." He seemed positively scandalized at my

[18]*bulkhead:* partition

suggestion. And as I gazed at him, certainly not prepared for anything original on his part, he advanced his head close to mine and thrust his tongue out at me so suddenly that I couldn't help starting back.

After scoring over my calmness in this graphic way he nodded wisely. If I had seen the sight, he assured me, I would never forget it as long as I lived. The weather was too bad to give the corpse a proper sea burial. So next day at dawn they took it up on the poop, covering its face with a bit of bunting; he read a short prayer, and then, just as it was, in its oilskins and long boots, they launched it amongst those mountainous seas that seemed ready every moment to swallow up the ship herself and the terrified lives on board of her.

"That reefed foresail saved you," I threw in.

"Under God—it did," he exclaimed fervently. "It was by a special mercy, I firmly believe, that it stood some of those hurricane squalls."

"It was the setting of that sail which—" I began.

"God's own hand in it," he interrupted me. "Nothing less could have done it. I don't mind telling you that I hardly dared give the order. It seemed impossible that we could touch anything without losing it, and then our last hope would have been gone."

The terror of that gale was on him yet. I let him go on for a bit, then said, casually—as if returning to a minor subject:

"You were very anxious to give up your mate to the shore people, I believe?"

He was. To the law. His obscure tenacity on that point had in it something incomprehensible and a little awful; something, as it were, mystical, quite apart from his anxiety that he should not be suspected of "countenancing any doings of that sort." Seven-and-thirty virtuous years at sea, of which over twenty of immaculate command, and the last fifteen in the *Sephora*, seemed to have laid him under some pitiless obligation.

"And you know," he went on, groping shamefacedly amongst his feelings, "I did not engage that young fellow. His people had some interest with my owners. I was in a way forced to take him on. He looked very smart, very gentlemanly, and all that. But do you know—I never liked him, somehow. I am a plain man. You see, he wasn't exactly the sort for the chief mate of a ship like the *Sephora*."

I had become so connected in thoughts and impressions with the secret sharer of my cabin that I felt as if I, personally, were being given to understand that I, too, was not the sort that would have done for the chief mate of a ship like the *Sephora*. I had no doubt of it in my mind.

"Not at all the style of man. You understand," he insisted, superfluously, looking hard at me.

I smiled urbanely. He seemed at a loss for a while.

"I suppose I must report a suicide."

"Beg pardon?"

"Sui-cide! That's what I'll have to write to my owners directly I get in."

"Unless you manage to recover him before tomorrow," I assented, dispassionately. . . . "I mean, alive."

He mumbled something which I really did not catch, and I turned my ear to him in a puzzled manner. He fairly bawled:

"The land—I say, the mainland is at least seven miles off my anchorage."

"About that."

My lack of excitement, of curiosity, of surprise, of any sort of pronounced interest, began to arouse his distrust. But except for the felicitous[19] pretence of deafness I had not tried to pretend anything. I had felt utterly incapable of playing the part of ignorance properly, and therefore was afraid to try. It is also certain that he had brought some ready-made suspicions with him, and that he viewed my politeness as a strange and unnatural phenomenon. And yet how else could I have received him? Not heartily! That was impossible for psychological reasons, which I need not state here. My only object was to keep off his inquiries. Surlily? Yes, but surliness might have provoked a point-blank question. From its novelty to him and from its nature, punctilious[20] courtesy was the manner best calculated to restrain the man. But there was the danger

[19]*felicitous:* aptly chosen
[20]*punctilious:* careful or scrupulous

of his breaking through my defense bluntly. I could not, I think, have met him by a direct lie, also for psychological (not moral) reasons. If he had only known how afraid I was of his putting my feeling of identity with the other to the test! But, strangely enough—(I thought of it only afterward)—I believe that he was not a little disconcerted by the reverse side of that weird situation, by something in me that reminded him of the man he was seeking—suggested a mysterious similitude to the young fellow he had distrusted and disliked from the first.

However that might have been, the silence was not very prolonged. He took another oblique step.

"I reckon I had no more than a two-mile pull to your ship. Not a bit more."

"And quite enough, too, in this awful heat," I said.

Another pause full of mistrust followed. Necessity, they say, is mother of invention, but fear, too, is not barren of ingenious suggestions. And I was afraid he would ask me point-blank for news of my other self.

"Nice little saloon, isn't it?" I remarked, as if noticing for the first time the way his eyes roamed from one closed door to the other. "And very well fitted out, too. Here, for instance," I continued, reaching over the back of my seat negligently and flinging the door open, "is my bathroom."

He made an eager movement, but hardly gave it a glance. I got up, shut the door of the bathroom, and invited him to have a look around, as if I were very proud of my accommodation. He had to rise and be shown round, but he went through the business without any raptures whatever.

"And now we'll have a look at my stateroom," I declared, in a voice as loud as I dared to make it, crossing the cabin to the starboard side with purposely heavy steps.

He followed me in and gazed around. My intelligent double had vanished. I played my part.

"Very convenient—isn't it?"

"Very nice. Very comf . . ." He didn't finish, and went out brusquely as if to escape from some unrighteous wiles of mine. But it was not to be. I had been too frightened not to feel vengeful; I felt I had him on the run, and I meant to keep him on the run. My polite insistence must have had something menacing in it, because he gave in suddenly. And I did not let him off a single item; mates' room, pantry, storerooms, the very sail locker which was also under the poop—he had to look into them all. When at last I showed him out on the quarter-deck he drew a long, spiritless sigh, and mumbled dismally that he must really be going back to his ship now. I desired my mate, who had joined us, to see to the captain's boat.

The man of whiskers gave a blast on the whistle which he used to wear hanging round his neck, and yelled, "*Sephora's* away!" My double down there in my cabin must have heard, and certainly could not feel more relieved than I. Four fellows came running out from somewhere forward and went over the side, while my own men, appearing on deck too, lined the rail. I escorted my visitor to the gangway ceremoniously, and nearly overdid it. He was a tenacious beast. On the very ladder he lingered, and in that unique, guiltily conscientious manner of sticking to the point:

"I say . . . you . . . you don't think that—"

I covered his voice loudly:

"Certainly not. . . . I am delighted. Good-by."

I had an idea of what he meant to say, and just saved myself by the privilege of defective hearing. He was too shaken generally to insist, but my mate, close witness of that parting, looked mystified and his face took on a thoughtful cast. As I did not want to appear as if I wished to avoid all communication with my officers, he had the opportunity to address me.

"Seems a very nice man. His boat's crew told our chaps a very extraordinary story, if what I am told by the steward is true. I suppose you had it from the captain, sir?"

"Yes. I had a story from the captain."

"A very horrible affair—isn't it, sir?"

"It is."

"Beats all these tales we hear about murders in Yankee ships."

"I don't think it beats them. I don't think it resembles them in the least."

"Bless my soul—you don't say so! But of course I've no acquaintance whatever with American ships, not I, so I couldn't go against your knowledge. It's horrible enough for me. . . . But the queerest part is that those fellows seemed to have some idea the man was hidden aboard here. They had really. Did you ever hear of such a thing?"

"Preposterous—isn't it?"

We were walking to and fro athwart the quarter-deck. No one of the crew forward could be seen (the day was Sunday), and the mate pursued:

"There was some little dispute about it. Our chaps took offense. 'As if we would harbor a thing like that,' they said. 'Wouldn't you like to look for him in our coalhole?' Quite a tiff. But they made it up in the end. I suppose he did drown himself. Don't you, sir?"

"I don't suppose anything."

"You have no doubt in the matter, sir?"

"None whatever."

I left him suddenly. I felt I was producing a bad impression, but with my double down there it was most trying to be on deck. And it was almost as trying to be below. Altogether a nerve-trying situation. But on the whole I felt less torn in two when I was with him. There was no one in the whole ship whom I dared to take into my confidence. Since the hands had got to know his story, it would have been impossible to pass him off for anyone else, and an accidental discovery was to be dreaded now more than ever. . . .

The steward being engaged in laying the table for dinner, we could talk only with our eyes when I first went down. Later in the afternoon we had a cautious try at whispering. The Sunday quietness of the ship was against us; the stillness of air and water around her was against us; the elements, the men were against us—everything was against us in our secret partnership; time itself—for this could not go on forever. The very trust in Providence was, I suppose, denied to his guilt. Shall I confess that this thought cast me down very much? And as to the chapter of accidents which counts for so much in the book of success, I could only hope that it was closed. For what favorable accident could be expected?

"Did you hear everything?" were my first words as soon as we took up our position side by side, leaning over my bed-place.

He had. And the proof of it was his earnest whisper, "The man told you he hardly dared to give the order."

I understood the reference to be that saving foresail.

"Yes. He was afraid of it being lost in the setting."

"I assure you he never gave the order. He may think he did, but he never gave it. He stood there with me on the break of the poop after the main-topsail blew away, and whimpered about our last hope—positively whimpered about it and nothing else—and the night coming on! To hear one's skipper go on like that in such weather was enough to drive any fellow out of his mind. It worked me up into a sort of desperation. I just took it into my own hands and went away from him, boiling, and—But what's the use telling you? *You* know! . . . Do you think that if I had not been pretty fierce with them I should have got the men to do anything? Not it! The bo's'n perhaps? Perhaps! It wasn't a heavy sea—it was a sea gone mad! I suppose the end of the world will be something like that; and a man may have the heart to see it coming once and be done with it—but to have to face it day after day—I don't blame anybody. I was precious little better than the rest. Only—I was an officer of that old coal wagon, anyhow—"

"I quite understand," I conveyed that sincere assurance into his ear. He was out of breath with whispering; I could hear him pant slightly. It was all very simple. The same strung-up force which had given twenty-four men a chance, at least, for their lives, had, in a sort of recoil, crushed an unworthy mutinous existence.

But I had no leisure to weigh the merits of the matter—footsteps in the saloon, a heavy knock. "There's enough wind to get under way with, sir." Here was the call of a new claim upon my thoughts and even upon my feelings.

"Turn the hands up," I cried through the door. "I'll be on deck directly."

I was going out to make the acquaintance of my ship. Before I left the cabin our eyes met—the eyes of the only two strangers on board. I pointed to the recessed part where the little camp-stool awaited him and laid my finger on my lips. He made a gesture—somewhat vague—a little mysterious, accompanied by a faint smile, as if of regret.

This is not the place to enlarge upon the sensations of a man who feels for the first time a ship move under his feet to his own independent word. In my case they were not unalloyed. I was not wholly alone with my command; for there was that stranger in my cabin. Or rather, I was not completely and wholly with her. Part of me was absent. That mental feeling of being in two places at once affected me physically as if the mood of secrecy had penetrated my very soul. Before an hour had elapsed since the ship had begun to move, having occasion to ask the mate (he stood by my side) to take a compass bearing of the pagoda, I caught myself reaching up to his ear in whispers. I say I caught myself, but enough had escaped to startle the man. I can't describe it otherwise than by saying that he shied. A grave, preoccupied manner, as though he were in possession of some perplexing intelligence, did not leave him henceforth. A little later I moved away from the rail to look at the compass with such a stealthy gait that the helmsman noticed it—and I could not help noticing the unusual roundness of his eyes. These are trifling instances, though it's to no commander's advantage to be suspected of ludicrous eccentricities. But I was also more seriously affected. There are to a seaman certain words, gestures, that should in given conditions come as naturally, as instinctively as the winking of a menaced eye. A certain order should spring on to his lips without thinking; a certain sign should get itself made, so to speak, without reflection. But all unconscious alertness had abandoned me. I had to make an effort of will to recall myself back (from the cabin) to the conditions of the moment. I felt that I was appearing an irresolute commander to those people who were watching me more or less critically.

And, besides, there were the scares. On the second day out, for instance, coming off the deck in the afternoon (I had straw slippers on my bare feet) I stopped at the open pantry door and spoke to the steward. He was doing something there with his back to me. At the sound of my voice he nearly jumped out of his skin, as the saying is, and incidentally broke a cup.

"What on earth's the matter with you?" I asked, astonished.

He was extremely confused. "Beg your pardon, sir. I made sure you were in your cabin."

"You see I wasn't."

"No, sir. I could have sworn I had heard you moving in there not a moment ago. It's most extraordinary . . . very sorry, sir."

I passed on with an inward shudder. I was so identified with my secret double that I did not even mention the fact in those scanty, fearful whispers we exchanged. I suppose he had made some slight noise of some kind or other. It would have been miraculous if he hadn't at one time or another. And yet, haggard as he appeared, he looked always perfectly self-controlled, more than calm—almost invulnerable. On my suggestion he remained almost entirely in the bathroom, which, upon the whole, was the safest place. There could be really no shadow of an excuse for anyone ever wanting to go in there, once the steward had done with it. It was a very tiny place. Sometimes he reclined on the floor, his legs bent, his head sustained on one elbow. At others I would find him on the camp-stool, sitting in his gray sleeping suit and with his cropped dark hair like a patient, unmoved convict. At night I would smuggle him into my bed-place, and we would whisper together, with the regular foot-falls of the officer of the watch passing and repassing over our heads. It was an infinitely miserable time. It was lucky that some tins of fine preserves were stowed in a locker in my stateroom; hard bread I could always get hold of; and so he lived on stewed chicken, *pâté de foie gras,*[21] asparagus, cooked oysters, sardines—on all sorts of abominable sham delicacies out of tins. My early morning coffee he always drank; and it was all I dared do for him in that respect.

Every day there was the horrible maneuvering to go through so that my room and then the bathroom should be done in the usual way. I came to hate the sight of the steward, to abhor the voice of that harmless man. I felt that it was he who would bring on the disaster of discovery. It hung like a sword over our heads.

[21]*pâté de foie gras:* expensive paste made of goose liver and truffles

The fourth day out, I think (we were then working down the east side of the Gulf of Siam, tack for tack,[22] in light winds and smooth water)—the fourth day, I say, of this miserable juggling with the unavoidable, as we sat at our evening meal, that man, whose slightest movement I dreaded, after putting down the dishes ran up on deck busily. This could not be dangerous. Presently he came down again; and then it appeared that he had remembered a coat of mine which I had thrown over a rail to dry after having been wetted in a shower which had passed over the ship in the afternoon. Sitting stolidly at the head of the table I became terrified at the sight of the garment on his arm. Of course he made for my door. There was no time to lose.

"Steward," I thundered. My nerves were so shaken that I could not govern my voice and conceal my agitation. This was the sort of thing that made my terrifically whiskered mate tap his forehead with his forefinger. I had detected him using that gesture while talking on deck with a confidential air to the carpenter. It was too far to hear a word, but I had no doubt that this pantomime could only refer to the strange new captain.

"Yes, sir," the pale-faced steward turned resignedly to me. It was this maddening course of being shouted at, checked without rhyme or reason, arbitrarily chased out of my cabin, suddenly called into it, sent flying out of his pantry on incomprehensible errands, that accounted for the growing wretchedness of his expression.

"Where are you going with that coat?"

"To your room, sir."

"Is there another shower coming?"

"I'm sure I don't know, sir. Shall I go up again and see, sir?"

"No! never mind."

My object was attained, as of course my other self in there would have heard everything that passed. During this interlude my two officers never raised their eyes off their respective plates; but the lip of that confounded cub, the second mate, quivered visibly.

I expected the steward to hook my coat on and come out at

[22]*tack for tack:* zigzag course against the wind

once. He was very slow about it; but I dominated my nervousness sufficiently not to shout after him. Suddenly I became aware (it could be heard plainly enough) that the fellow for some reason or other was opening the door of the bathroom. It was the end. The place was literally not big enough to swing a cat in. My voice died in my throat and I went stony all over. I expected to hear a yell of surprise and terror, and made a movement, but had not the strength to get on my legs. Everything remained still. Had my second self taken the poor wretch by the throat? I don't know what I could have done next moment if I had not seen the steward come out of my room, close the door, and then stand quietly by the sideboard.

"Saved," I thought. "But, no! Lost! Gone! He was gone!"

I laid my knife and fork down and leaned back in my chair. My head swam. After a while, when sufficiently recovered to speak in a steady voice, I instructed my mate to put the ship round at eight o'clock himself.

"I won't come on deck," I went on. "I think I'll turn in, and unless the wind shifts I don't want to be disturbed before midnight. I feel a bit seedy."

"You did look middling bad a little while ago," the chief mate remarked without showing any great concern.

They both went out, and I stared at the steward clearing the table. There was nothing to be read on that wretched man's face. But why did he avoid my eyes, I asked myself. Then I thought I should like to hear the sound of his voice.

"Steward!"

"Sir!" Startled as usual.

"Where did you hang up that coat?"

"In the bathroom, sir." The usual anxious tone. "It's not quite dry yet, sir."

For some time longer I sat in the cuddy. Had my double vanished as he had come? But for his coming there was an explanation, whereas his disappearance would be inexplicable. . . . I went slowly into my dark room, shut the door, lighted the lamp, and for a time dared not turn round. When at last I did I saw him standing bolt upright in the narrow recessed part. It would not be true to say I had a shock, but an irresistible doubt of his bodily existence flitted through my mind. Can it be, I asked myself, that he is not visible to other eyes than mine? It was like being haunted. Motionless, with a grave face, he raised his hands slightly at me in a gesture which meant clearly, "Heavens! What a narrow escape!" Narrow indeed. I think I had come creeping quietly as near insanity as any man who has not actually gone over the border. That gesture restrained me, so to speak.

The mate with the terrific whiskers was now putting the ship on the other tack. In the moment of profound silence which follows upon the hands going to their stations I heard on the poop his raised voice: "Hard alee!" and the distant shout of the order repeated on the main deck. The sails, in that light breeze, made but a faint fluttering noise. It ceased. The ship was coming round slowly; I held my breath in the renewed stillness of expectation; one wouldn't have thought that there was a single living soul on her decks. A sudden brisk shout, "Mainsail haul!" broke the spell, and in the noisy cries and rush overhead of the men running away with the main brace we two, down in my cabin, came together in our usual position by the bed-place.

He did not wait for my question. "I heard him fumbling here and just managed to squat myself down in the bath," he whispered to me. "The fellow only opened the door and put his arm in to hang the coat up. All the same—"

"I never thought of that," I whispered back, even more appalled than before at the closeness of the shave, and marveling at that something unyielding in his character which was carrying him through so finely. There was no agitation in his whisper. Whoever was being driven distracted, it was not he. He was sane. And the proof of his sanity was continued when he took up the whispering again.

"It would never do for me to come to life again."

It was something that a ghost might have said. But what he was alluding to was his old captain's reluctant admission of the theory of suicide. It would obviously serve his turn—if I had understood at all the view which seemed to govern the unalterable purpose of his action.

"You must maroon me as soon as ever you can get amongst these islands off the Cambodge shore," he went on.

"Maroon you! We are not living in a boy's adventure tale," I protested. His scornful whispering took me up.

"We aren't indeed! There's nothing of a boy's tale in this. But there's nothing else for it. I want no more. You don't suppose I am afraid of what can be done to me? Prison or gallows or whatever they may please. But you don't see me coming back to explain such things to an old fellow in a wig and twelve respectable tradesmen, do you? What can they know whether I am guilty or not—or of *what* I am guilty, either? That's my affair. What does the Bible say? 'Driven off the face of the earth.' Very well, I am off the face of the earth now. As I came at night so I shall go."

"Impossible!" I murmured. "You can't."

"Can't? . . . Not naked like a soul on the Day of Judgment, I shall freeze on to this sleeping suit. The Last Day is not yet—and . . . you have understood thoroughly. Didn't you?"

I felt suddenly ashamed of myself. I may say truly that I understood—and my hesitation in letting that man swim away from my ship's side had been a mere sham sentiment, a sort of cowardice.

"It can't be done now till next night," I breathed out. "The ship is on the off-shore tack and the wind may fail us."

"As long as I know that you understand," he whispered. "But of course you do. It's a great satisfaction to have got somebody to understand. You seem to have been there on purpose." And in the same whisper, as if we two whenever we talked had to say things to each other which were not fit for the world to hear, he added, "It's very wonderful."

We remained side by side talking in our secret way—but sometimes silent or just exchanging a whispered word or two at long intervals. And as usual he stared through the port. A breath of wind came now and again into our faces. The ship might have been moored in dock, so gently and on an even keel she slipped through the water, that did not murmur even at our passage, shadowy and silent like a phantom sea.

At midnight I went on deck, and to my mate's great surprise put the ship round on the other tack. His terrible whiskers flitted round me in silent criticism. I certainly should not have done it if it had been only a question of getting out of that sleepy gulf as quickly as possible. I believe he told the second mate, who relieved him, that it was a great want of judgment. The other only yawned. That intolerable cub shuffled about so sleepily and lolled against the rails in such a slack, improper fashion that I came down on him sharply.

"Aren't you properly awake yet?"

"Yes, sir! I am awake."

"Well, then, be good enough to hold yourself as if you were. And keep a lookout. If there's any current we'll be closing with some islands before daylight."

The east side of the gulf is fringed with islands, some solitary, others in groups. On the blue background of the high coast they seem to float on silvery patches of calm water, arid and gray, or dark green and rounded like clumps of evergreen bushes, with the larger ones, a mile or two long, showing the outlines of ridges, ribs of gray rock under the dark mantle of matted leafage. Unknown to trade, to travel, almost to geography, the manner of life they harbor is an unsolved secret. There must be villages—settlements of fishermen at least—on the largest of them, and some communication with the world is probably kept up by native craft. But all that forenoon, as we headed for them, fanned along by the faintest of breezes, I saw no sign of man or canoe in the field of the telescope I kept on pointing at the scattered group.

At noon I gave no orders for a change of course, and the mate's whiskers became much concerned and seemed to be offering themselves unduly to my notice. At last I said:

"I am going to stand right in. Quite in—as far as I can take her."

The stare of extreme surprise imparted an air of ferocity also to his eyes, and he looked truly terrific for a moment.

"We're not doing well in the middle of the gulf," I continued, casually. "I am going to look for the land breezes tonight."

"Bless my soul! Do you mean, sir, in the dark amongst the lot of all them islands and reefs and shoals?"

"Well—if there are any regular land breezes at all on this coast one must get close inshore to find them, mustn't one?"

"Bless my soul!" he exclaimed again under his breath. All that afternoon he wore a dreamy, contemplative appearance which in him was a mark of perplexity. After dinner I went into my stateroom as if I meant to take some rest. There we two bent our dark heads over a half-unrolled chart lying on my bed.

"There," I said. "It's got to be Koh-ring. I've been looking at it ever since sunrise. It has got two hills and a low point. It must be inhabited. And on the coast opposite there is what looks like the mouth of a biggish river—with some town, no doubt, not far up. It's the best chance for you that I can see."

"Anything. Koh-ring let it be."

He looked thoughtfully at the chart as if surveying chances and distances from a lofty height—and following with his eyes his own figure wandering on the blank land of Cochin China, and then passing off that piece of paper clean out of sight into uncharted regions. And it was as if the ship had two captains to plan her course for her. I had been so worried and restless running up and down that I had not had the patience to dress that day. I had remained in my sleeping suit, with straw slippers and a soft floppy hat. The closeness of the heat in the gulf had been most oppressive, and the crew were used to see me wandering in that airy attire.

"She will clear the south point as she heads now," I whispered into his ear. "Goodness only knows when, though, but certainly after dark. I'll edge her in to half a mile, as far as I may be able to judge in the dark—"

"Be careful," he murmured, warningly—and I realized suddenly that all my future, the only future for which I was fit, would go irretrievably to pieces in any mishap to my first command.

I could not stop a moment longer in the room. I motioned him to get out of sight and made my way on the poop. That unplayful cub had the watch. I walked up and down for a while thinking things out, then beckoned him over.

"Send a couple of hands to open the two quarter-deck ports," I said, mildly.

He actually had the impudence, or else so forgot himself

in his wonder at such an incomprehensible order, as to repeat:

"Open the quarter-deck ports! What for, sir?"

"The only reason you need concern yourself about is because I tell you to do so. Have them open wide and fastened properly."

He reddened and went off, but I believe made some jeering remark to the carpenter as to the sensible practice of ventilating a ship's quarter-deck. I know he popped into the mate's cabin to impart the fact to him because the whiskers came on deck, as it were by chance, and stole glances at me from below—for signs of lunacy or drunkenness, I suppose.

A little before supper, feeling more restless than ever, I rejoined, for a moment, my second self. And to find him sitting so quietly was surprising, like something against nature, inhuman.

I developed my plan in a hurried whisper.

"I shall stand in as close as I dare and then put her round. I will presently find means to smuggle you out of here into the sail locker, which communicates with the lobby. But there is an opening, a sort of square for hauling the sails out, which gives straight on the quarter-deck and which is never closed in fine weather, so as to give air to the sails. When the ship's way is deadened in stays[23] and all the hands are aft at the main-braces you will have a clear road to slip out and get overboard through the open quarter-deck port. I've had them both fastened up. Use a rope's end to lower yourself into the water so as to avoid a splash—you know. It could be heard and cause some beastly complication."

He kept silent for a while, then whispered, "I understand."

"I won't be there to see you go," I began with an effort. "The rest . . . I only hope I have understood, too."

"You have. From first to last"—and for the first time there seemed to be a faltering, something strained in his whisper. He caught hold of my arm, but the ringing of the supper bell made me start. He didn't, though; he only released his grip.

[23]*deadened in stays:* motionless while changing directions

After supper I didn't come below again till well past eight o'clock. The faint, steady breeze was loaded with dew; and the wet, darkened sails held all there was of propelling power in it. The night, clear and starry, sparkled darkly, and the opaque, lightless patches shifting slowly against the low stars were the drifting islets. On the port bow there was a big one more distant and shadowily imposing by the great space of sky it eclipsed.

On opening the door I had a back view of my very own self looking at a chart. He had come out of the recess and was standing near the table.

"Quite dark enough," I whispered.

He stepped back and leaned against my bed with a level, quiet glance. I sat on the couch. We had nothing to say to each other. Over our heads the officer of the watch moved here and there. Then I heard him move quickly. I knew what that meant. He was making for the companion; and presently his voice was outside my door.

"We are drawing in pretty fast, sir. Land looks rather close."

"Very well," I answered. "I am coming on deck directly."

I waited till he was gone out of the cuddy, then rose. My double moved too. The time had come to exchange our last whispers, for neither of us was ever to hear each other's natural voice.

"Look here!" I opened a drawer and took out three sovereigns. "Take this anyhow. I've got six and I'd give you the lot, only I must keep a little money to buy some fruit and vegetables for the crew from native boats as we go through Sunda Straits."

He shook his head.

"Take it," I urged him, whispering desperately. "No one can tell what—"

He smiled and slapped meaningly the only pocket of the sleeping jacket. It was not safe, certainly. But I produced a large old silk handkerchief of mine, and tying the three pieces of gold in a corner, pressed it on him. He was touched, I suppose, because he took it at last and tied it quickly round his waist under the jacket, on his bare skin.

Our eyes met; several seconds elapsed, till, our glances still mingled, I extended my hand and turned the lamp out. Then I passed through the cuddy, leaving the door of my room wide open. . . . "Steward!"

He was still lingering in the pantry in the greatness of his zeal, giving a rub-up to a plated cruet[24] stand the last thing before going to bed. Being careful not to wake up the mate, whose room was opposite, I spoke in an undertone.

He looked round anxiously. "Sir!"

"Can you get me a little hot water from the galley?"

"I am afraid, sir, the galley fire's been out for some time now."

"Go and see."

He fled up the stairs.

"Now," I whispered, loudly, into the saloon—too loudly, perhaps, but I was afraid I couldn't make a sound. He was by my side in an instant—the double captain slipped past the stairs—through the tiny passage . . . a sliding door. We were in the sail locker, scrambling on our knees over the sails. A sudden thought struck me. I saw myself wandering barefooted, bare-headed, the sun beating on my dark poll. I snatched off my floppy hat and tried hurriedly in the dark to ram it on my other self. He dodged and fended off silently. I wonder what he thought had come to me before he understood and suddenly desisted. Our hands met gropingly, lingered united in a steady, motionless clasp for a second. . . . No word breathed by either of us when they separated.

I was standing quietly by the pantry door when the steward returned.

"Sorry, sir. Kettle barely warm. Shall I light the spirit lamp?"

"Never mind."

I came out on deck slowly. It was now a matter of conscience to shave the land as close as possible—for now he must go overboard whenever the ship was put in stays. Must! There could be no going back for him. After a moment I walked over to leeward and my heart flew into my mouth at

[24]*cruet:* spice bottle

the nearness of the land on the bow. Under any other circumstances I would not have held on a minute longer. The second mate had followed me anxiously.

I looked on till I felt I could command my voice.

"She will weather," I said then in a quiet tone.

"Are you going to try that, sir?" he stammered out incredulously.

I took no notice of him and raised my tone just enough to be heard by the helmsman.

"Keep her good full."

"Good full, sir."

The wind fanned my cheek, the sails slept, the world was silent. The strain of watching the dark loom of the land grow bigger and denser was too much for me. I had shut my eyes—because the ship must go closer. She must! The stillness was intolerable. Were we standing still?

When I opened my eyes the second view started my heart with a thump. The black southern hill of Koh-ring seemed to hang right over the ship like a towering fragment of the everlasting night. On that enormous mass of blackness there was not a gleam to be seen, not a sound to be heard. It was gliding irresistibly toward us, and yet seemed already within reach of the hand. I saw the vague figures of the watch grouped in the waist, gazing in awed silence.

"Are you going on, sir?" inquired an unsteady voice at my elbow.

I ignored it. I had to go on.

"Keep her full. Don't check her way. That won't do now," I said warningly.

"I can't see the sails very well," the helmsman answered me, in strange, quavering tones.

Was she close enough? Already she was, I won't say in the shadow of the land, but in the very blackness of it, already swallowed up, as it were, gone too close to be recalled, gone from me altogether.

"Give the mate a call," I said to the young man who stood at my elbow as still as death. "And turn all hands up."

My tone had a borrowed loudness reverberated from the height of the land. Several voices cried out together: "We are all on deck, sir."

Then stillness again, with the great shadow gliding closer, towering higher, without a light, without a sound. Such a hush had fallen on the ship that she might have been a bark of the dead floating in slowly under the very gate of Erebus.[25]

"My God! Where are we?"

It was the mate moaning at my elbow. He was thunderstruck, and as it were deprived of the moral support of his whiskers. He clapped his hands and absolutely cried out, "Lost!"

"Be quiet," I said, sternly.

He lowered his tone, but I saw the shadowy gesture of his despair. "What are we doing here?"

"Looking for the land wind."

He made as if to tear his hair, and addressed me recklessly. "She will never get out. You have done it, sir. I knew it'd end in something like this. She will never weather, and you are too close now to stay. She'll drift ashore before she's round. O my God!"

I caught his arm as he was raising it to batter his poor devoted head, and shook it violently.

"She's ashore already," he wailed, trying to tear himself away.

"Is she? . . . Keep good full there!"

"Good full, sir," cried the helmsman in a frightened, thin, childlike voice.

I hadn't let go the mate's arm and went on shaking it. "Ready about, do you hear? You go forward"—shake—"and stop there"—shake—"and hold your noise"—shake—"and see these headsheets properly overhauled"—shake, shake—shake.

And all the time I dared not look toward the land lest my heart should fail me. I released my grip at last and he ran forward as if fleeing for dear life.

I wondered what my double there in the sail locker thought of this commotion. He was able to hear everything—and perhaps he was able to understand why, on my conscience, it

[25]*Erebus:* in Greek myth, the dark region through which the dead passed before entering Hades

had to be thus close—no less. My first order "Hard alee!" re-echoed ominously under the towering shadow of Koh-ring as if I had shouted in a mountain gorge. And then I watched the land intently. In that smooth water and light wind it was impossible to feel the ship coming-to. No! I could not feel her. And my second self was making now ready to slip out and lower himself overboard. Perhaps he was gone already . . . ?

The great black mass brooding over our very mastheads began to pivot away from the ship's side silently. And now I forgot the secret stranger ready to depart, and remembered that I was a total stranger to the ship. I did not know her. Would she do it? How was she to be handled?

I swung the main yard and waited helplessly. She was perhaps stopped, and her very fate hung in the balance, with the black mass of Koh-ring like the gate of the everlasting night towering over her taffrail. What would she do now? Had she way on her yet? I stepped to the side swiftly, and on the shadowy water I could see nothing except a faint phosphorescent flash revealing the glassy smoothness of the sleeping surface. It was impossible to tell—and I had not learned yet the feel of my ship. Was she moving? What I needed was something easily seen, a piece of paper, which I could throw overboard and watch. I had nothing on me. To run down for it I didn't dare. There was no time. All at once my strained, yearning stare distinguished a white object floating within a yard of the ship's side. White on the black water. A phosphorescent flash passed under it. What was that thing? . . . I recognized my own floppy hat. It must have fallen off his head . . . and he didn't bother. Now I had what I wanted—the saving mark for my eyes. But I hardly thought of my other self, now gone from the ship, to be hidden forever from all friendly faces, to be a fugitive and a vagabond on the earth, with no brand of the curse on his sane forehead to stay a slaying hand . . . too proud to explain.

And I watched the hat—the expression of my sudden pity for his mere flesh. It had been meant to save his homeless head from the dangers of the sun. And now—behold—it was saving the ship, by serving me for a mark to help out the ignorance of my strangeness. Ha! It was drifting forward, warning me just in time that the ship had gathered sternway.

"Shift the helm," I said in a low voice to the seaman standing still like a statue.

The man's eyes glistened wildly in the binnacle light as he jumped round to the other side and spun round the wheel.

I walked to the break of the poop. On the overshadowed deck all hands stood by the forebraces waiting for my order. The stars ahead seemed to be gliding from right to left. And all was so still in the world that I heard the quiet remark "She's round," passed in a tone of intense relief between two seamen.

"Let go and haul."

The foreyards ran round with a great noise, amidst cheery cries. And now the frightful whiskers made themselves heard giving various orders. Already the ship was drawing ahead. And I was alone with her. Nothing! no one in the world should stand now between us, throwing a shadow on the way of silent knowledge and mute affection, the perfect communion of a seaman with his first command.

Walking to the taffrail, I was in time to make out, on the very edge of a darkness thrown by a towering black mass like the very gateway of Erebus—yes, I was in time to catch an evanescent glimpse of my white hat left behind to mark the spot where the secret sharer of my cabin and of my thoughts, as though he were my second self, had lowered himself into the water to take his punishment: a free man, a proud swimmer striking out for a new destiny.

FOR DISCUSSION

1. In the captain's decision to harbor the stranger, what is at stake for himself, for the crew, and for the ship? Why does he decide to take the risk? Does he have a right to take it?
2. What past events have influenced the relationship between the captain and the crew? What actions of the captain arouse the suspicions of the mate, the second mate, and the steward? How

does the relationship between the captain and the members of the crew change during the course of the story?

3. Compare the character of the captain with that of his guest. Who is the secret sharer? What is being shared? What effect does hiding Leggatt have on the captain's seamanship and on his personality?
4. Why does Leggatt decide to leave the ship? How does the captain react? What alternatives are possible? How well were you prepared for the ending of the story by earlier hints? Cite examples of foreshadowing.
5. Compare the views of the captain, of the skipper of the *Sephora*, and of Leggatt himself about his crime. What is your own view?
6. Describe the mood of the story and the way in which the setting helps to establish it. How are the feelings of the captain as he views the sea related to the theme of the isolation of man? What relation is there between this theme and the ending of the story?
7. If the opening paragraph describes the physical world and also suggests the inner world of the captain's thoughts and feelings, what conclusion can you draw about the problem the captain faces? What is his state of mind, and how does it affect his decision to harbor Leggatt?
8. At the opening of the story, the captain wonders how far he would "turn out faithful to that ideal conception of one's own personality every man sets up for himself secretly." What do you think is the captain's ideal? How well does he live up to it?

FOR COMPOSITION

1. Write an essay analyzing "The Secret Sharer" as a story about the discovery of the real self, or of the search for one's real identity.
2. Discuss in an essay the use to which Conrad puts shadows and darkness in this story. Explain in the process why Leggatt is initially so shadowy a figure.
3. Write an essay entitled "The Sea as a Symbolic Force in Conrad's 'The Secret Sharer.'"

THE PRECURSORS

The narrative has been popular in every age, for man's story-telling faculties have been intrinsic to him from the earliest time. Even the most experimental novel or short story of today must recognize the heritage out of which it came. This story-telling heritage has its roots in the Anglo-Saxon epic poem *Beowulf*, in medieval romances, in Chaucer's *exempla* or moral tales of the fourteenth century, in Malory's fifteenth-century legends of King Arthur, and, three centuries later, Swift's account of the travels of Gulliver. Today's narratives and those of the past share the common characteristic of telling a story, although they may vary considerably in their purpose and method.

Sir Gawain and the Green Knight, one of four poems contained in a single manuscript, is believed to have been written about 1370 by someone known to us only as the Pearl poet (so-called because one of the four poems is entitled "The Pearl"). *Sir Gawain and the Green Knight* is one of the most popular of the medieval romances. Among its many striking qualities is its feeling for the drama, the color, and the pageantry of medieval life. Another is the concreteness and realism of the descriptions, which always move the story forward rather than interrupt it. Still another is the uncommon skill with which the poet combined two plots: the Beheading

Game and the Temptation. The poet used one to reinforce the other—the Beheading Game provides the occasion for the Temptation, which in turn allows for the resolution of the Beheading Game.

Although only scholars can read the original, which was written in alliterative verse and Midland dialect, the enduring virtues of this romance—its color, vividness, atmosphere, and suspense—have been preserved with remarkable accuracy and artistry in the modern prose translation in this volume.

SIR THOMAS MALORY'S *Le Morte d'Arthur*, a collection of legends about King Arthur, is the best-known literary work of fifteenth-century England. Perhaps to relieve the boredom of being in prison, Malory undertook the enormous task of creating from old versions and pieces an inclusive account of eight important episodes in the history of King Arthur and his Knights of the Round Table. This account contrasted sharply with previous accounts, both in its rapid presentation of events, and in its direct, terse, and vigorous style.

Perhaps Malory felt that the simple, noble life idealized in the Arthurian legends was preferable to the turbulent life of his own time. This was certainly the case with William Caxton, England's first printer, who prepared the first printed editions of *Le Morte d'Arthur*, of Chaucer's poetry, and of numerous medieval romances, histories, and philosophical works. Thus printing, which was to bring a revolution in England's cultural and intellectual life, started with a nostalgic return to the life, thought, and legends of the Middle Ages. Unwittingly, both Malory and Caxton were salvaging the cultural heritage of their nation.

JOHN BUNYAN'S *The Pilgrim's Progress* (1678), an account of the spiritual journey of a man who encounters various adventures as he travels toward his heavenly goal, is literature's most vivid product of the Puritan temperament. One critic has written:

> The Puritan imagination saw the life of the spirit as pilgrimage and battle. The images of wayfaring and warfaring which fill the Old Testament had been exploited by that fighting itinerant,

> Paul, and by generations upon generations of subsequent evangelists. Reaching the pulpits of the seventeenth century by a hundred channels, they there underwent new and peculiarly vigorous development. The Christian was a traveler through a strange country and a soldier in battle.[1]

When Bunyan began his famous allegory of Christian self-realization, he was in prison, a victim of religious persecution under Charles II. He had already seen service in the Parliamentary Army and had spent twelve years in prison for "illegal" preaching. Like the author, the hero of *The Pilgrim's Progress* was a man of humble origin but of extraordinarily profound convictions. The Calvinist doctrine that dominated Bunyan's thinking could make even the saintliest man feel that he was never free from sin. "He was a fighting, not an innocent, soul."[2] Because he considered himself a soldier of the cross rather than a writer, Bunyan was not consciously a literary artist as Milton, a more widely educated Puritan, was. But artist he was, nevertheless, with an uncommon gift for narration in vigorous, unadorned prose. He drew literary inspiration from medieval allegories, from a contemporary work called *The Plain Man's Path-way to Heaven*, from Foxe's *Book of Martyrs*, and, above all, from the King James Version of the Bible, the last great project on which both Anglican and Puritan churchmen had cooperated before the civil wars.

Bunyan's powers of narrative and description and his skill with dialogue are recognized by scholars of English literary history as being significant in the development of the English novel.

JONATHAN SWIFT, a master prose writer, found in satire a keen and effective weapon for ridiculing those who violated the rules of common sense. He usually directed his attacks against individuals. "I hate and detest that animal called man," he once wrote, "although I heartily love John, Peter, Thomas, and so forth." He opposed the Deists and

[1]William Haller, *The Rise of Puritanism*, as quoted in E.M.W. Tillyard, *The English Epic and Its Background* (London: Chatto and Windus, 1954), p. 433.

[2]E.M.W. Tillyard, *The English Epic and Its Background* (London: Chatto and Windus, 1954), p. 433.

others who would reduce the teachings of Christianity to a mild trust in nature. "We have just enough religion to make us hate," he complained, "but not enough to make us love one another." His objections to scientific inquiry sprang from a fear that the humanistic wisdom of the past was being foolishly thrown away in a frenzy of experimentation. His attacks on human cruelty and stupidity were often vicious, but he inveighed against evil because he had a deep faith that men could improve themselves through their ability to reason. Swift's satire was effective because it was withering and angry, yet comic; it was powerful because it had "at its core a moral idealism expressing itself in righteous indignation."[3] But in addition to its superb satire, Swift's masterpiece, *Gulliver's Travels*, is excellent narrative. Swift maintained a plausible and clear story line that in itself provides excellent entertainment.

Despite enormous differences in style and purpose, one can see in the examples found in this section the beginnings for the great burst of English fiction that would come in the eighteenth, nineteenth, and twentieth centuries.

[3]Louis I. Bredvold, "The Gloom of the Tory Satirists," *Eighteenth Century English Literature*, ed. James L. Clifford (New York: Oxford University Press, 1959), p. 11.

Sir Gawain and the Green Knight

This romance is based on two old Celtic legends, known elsewhere in medieval legendry but combined here by the "Pearl poet" to create an original and superbly plotted story. The first legend is referred to as the Beheading Game; the second, as the Temptation. So skillfully are the two combined that the first leads inescapably into the second, which in turn provides the solution to the first.

I

It was Christmas.

King Arthur lay[1] at Camelot, and with him were many noble knights, brothers of the Round Table. All day long they would joust[2] at the tournament grounds; then they would ride to the castle for singing and dancing. For a full fortnight this rich revelry continued; in the morning and afternoon a delightful din, glorious to hear; in the evening, dancing, and the finest foods that the court could devise. At Camelot, at that moment, dwelt the most renowned knights in Christ's earthly kingdom, the loveliest ladies who ever lived, and the comeliest king who ever ruled a court. (It would be hard to match any of them today, in any castle in any land; for that was in the old time, the happiest under heaven.)

Now when New Year was so fresh that it was newly come, on that day the festivities were twice as merry. The king and his knights came into the hall; the priests ended the singing of the Mass; everywhere echoed the cry, "Noel!" All the people ran forward, shouting "New Year's Gift!" and talking busily the while. Afterwards they washed their hands and went to the dining tables, seating themselves according to rank, as was fitting.

At the center of the high table sat Queen Guenever under a canopy of rich red silk; beneath her feet lay an embroidered

[1]*lay:* was staying
[2]*joust:* battle with lances

carpet, a tapestry adorned with the finest gems. Beside her was Arthur, talking graciously to those around him. On his left was his nephew Agravain; on his right, as said, was Guenever; and next to her was Gawain, Arthur's nephew also. At the head of the table sat Bishop Baldwin; at the foot, Iwain, Urien's son. The other knights were at side tables.

A cracking of trumpets, a drumming of drums, a piping of pipes—wild warbles and loud—announced the first course. Serving men entered with an abundance of fresh foods on silver platters. Every two people had twelve silver dishes, and also good beer and bright wine. Now I will say no more of their table service; everyone must know that there was no want there.

Once again the trumpets blared, the drums rolled, the pipes piped, a signal to the company to begin eating. But they had scarcely touched the food when in at the hall door rides a knight, a gigantic knight, surely the greatest on earth in stature. He is so squarely built, so thick from his neck to his middle, and his loins and his limbs are so long and so great, that I think he may well be half giant. At any rate, I declare him to be the largest of men and the most splendid. All who see him have wonder of his color, set plain in his face. He is everywhere—bright green.

Completely green[3] is this knight, as also are his garments. A green straight coat sticks full tightly to his sides; above it is a merry mantle lined with the finest of furs, as also is his hood, which is caught back from his locks and lies on his shoulders. Green hose cling to his calves; below are shining spurs of bright gold, and shoes with long pointed toes. Truly, all his garments are green, even the bars adorning his belt and the jewels sprinkled about his array and upon his saddle, which sits upon embroidered silks. It would be hard to tell even half of what is embroidered on those silks: the gayest birds and bees, green gold always in the midst. The pendants[4] of his horse's breast trappings, the proud crupper,[5] the studs of the bit, these are all enameled green. The stirrups, the sad-

[3]*green:* color symbolic of the supernatural
[4]*pendants:* hanging objects
[5]*crupper:* part of the harness

dle bows, and the rump trappings are all stained the same color. The whole harness glimmers and gleams with green stones.

And the horse himself is green! A green horse, great and thick, a steed full hard to restrain—well suited to the man on his back.

The green hair of the man's head fans out and covers his shoulders. His great beard is like a bush in color and size. Hair and beard are clipped all around like the eaves of a roof and fall in an "O" right above his elbows, so that half his arms are enclosed after the fashion of a king's capados.[6]

The green mane of the great horse is crisped and combed and tied into many knots. Gold threads are folded in; for each strand of green hair there is a strand of gold. The forelock and tail are plaited to match each other and are bound with bands of bright green ornamented with precious stones; to each is tied a thong in an intricate knot, from which bells of burnished gold ring.

Such a horse and such a man were never seen in that hall before. All who saw that knight swore he shone as bright as lightning. No one, they felt, might endure for long under his blows!

Yet he has no armor at all—neither helmet nor hauberk,[7] nor breast armor nor arm armor, nor shaft nor shield. In one hand he holds a holly branch,[8] in the other an axe.

This axe is a monstrous one, a cruel battle-axe indeed. The head is forty-five inches in length; the spike is of green steel and gold and the bit is razor-sharp and burnished bright. The handle is a stiff green staff intricately carved and wound with iron; about it loops a thong, which is fastened at the head with tassels attached to buttons of bright green.

The knight holds the horse in and guides him to the high table. He greets no one. High over all he looks. He calls out:

"Who rules in this house?"

He casts his eyes to the knights and struts himself up and down. Then he stops and studies them. The whole court

[6]*capados:* short leather tunic
[7]*hauberk:* long tunic of ring or chain mail
[8]*holly branch:* sign of peace

stares at him. They stalk nearer to him. Thinking he may be a phantom from faery land, many of them are afraid to answer him.

Now Arthur speaks, "Knight, welcome! I am King Arthur. Alight from your horse, I pray you. Afterwards we can learn what your will is."

"Nay," declines the knight, "I am not here to visit. I am here because your glory, Prince, is lifted so high, and because your knights are held to be the best—the strongest to ride on steeds in steel armor. And always ready to take part in any pure sport! You may be sure by this holly branch that I come in peace. If I had gone in fighting-wise—well, I have a hauberk at home, and a helmet, and a shield and a sharp spear, and other weapons besides. But because I wish no trouble my clothing is softer. Now, if you are as bold as men say you are, you will grant me the sport that I ask."

Arthur replies, "Sir, if you want bare battle, you will not fail to find it here."

"Nay," says the knight, "I ask for no fight, I tell you. These are but beardless children about on the bench. I crave only a Christmas game, for it is Yule and the New Year. If there is anyone in this house who will dare to strike one blow for another, he shall have the rich battle-axe as my Christmas present—and I shall take the first blow as bare as I sit here. If any of you is so brave as to test what I have said, let him come here to me and catch this weapon. I will quit-claim it forever, he can keep it as his own; and I shall stand him a stroke, right here on this floor. However, a twelvemonth to the day from now you must allow me to return the stroke. Who dares say anything?"

The knight turns in his saddle, runishly[9] rolls his red eyes about, and bends his bristling green brows. He looks around to see who will rise. When no one does, he coughs, stretches himself richly, and demands:

"What? Is this Arthur's house, the fame of which runs through so many realms? Where now are your pride and your conquests, your fierceness and your wrath, your bold

[9]*runishly:* fiercely

speeches? Now are the revelry and the renown of the Round Table overthrown by the words of one man—for all of you cower in fear without a blow being shown!"

He grows as wrathful as the wind; so do all the knights. The king moves near him:

"Sir, by Heaven, your request is foolish; and as you have foolishly asked so it behooves you to find. I know no man who is frightened by your great words. For God's sake, give me your axe and I shall grant your wish."

Arthur leaps to him and grabs the axe by the handle. The knight lights upon his feet and stands towering above him, higher than any in the castle by a head and more. He strokes his beard and draws down his tunic.

Gawain looks to the king and cries, "I beg you that this contest may be mine! While so many bold knights sit about you on the bench, it does not seem fitting that you should answer this request. Grant it to me, since this business is so foolish that it does not become you and since I have asked you first."

Arthur commands him to rise. Gawain comes to him, kneels, and catches the weapon. Then, axe in hand, he goes to the knight, who speaks to him boldly:

"Before we pass further, let us restate our agreement. But first, knight, tell me your name."

"In good faith," Gawain replies, "I am named Gawain—and I shall give you a blow and take another from you a twelvemonth from now, with whatsoever weapon you wish."

"Sir Gawain!" exclaimed the Green Knight. "It indeed pleases me that I shall receive from your hand that which I have asked here. And you have repeated the agreement fairly, except that you must assure me, knight, that you will seek me yourself, wherever you think I may be found."

"Where shall I find you, where is your place?" Gawain queries. "I do not know where you live—nor do I know you, knight. If you will tell me your name, I shall spend all my wit to find my way to you. That I swear to you."

The Green Knight answers, "It will be sufficient if I tell you after you have struck me. If I can say nothing then, why so much the better for you! In that event, you can stay in your land and search no further. But enough of this. Let's see how you can strike."

"Gladly," replies Gawain. He caresses the axe.

The Green Knight prepares himself. He bows his head a little, lays his long lovely locks over his crown, and lets his naked neck show bare. Gawain grips the axe and, with both hands, gathers it on high. The blade comes down, sundering the bones, shrinking through the bright flesh, and biting into the ground. The green head hits the earth and rolls. The people thrust at it with their feet.

Blood spurts forth from the body, gleaming red on the green. But the knight does not falter or fall. He starts forth stoutly on stiff shanks, runishly reaches out where the knights stand, and picks up his lovely head. Then he goes to his horse, catches hold of the bridle, steps into the stirrup-irons, and strides aloft. He holds his head by the hair. Many feel fear in their hearts by the time it has begun to speak.

Holding the head up in his hand, he turns its face to those at the table. The head lifts up its eyelids, stares at Gawain full broadly, and speaks thus with its mouth:

"Look you, Gawain, that you be ready to go as you promised, that you seek me faithfully till you find me, as you have sworn to do. I charge you: go to the Green Chapel, there to receive such a blow as you have given me, on next New Year's morn. I am the Knight of the Green Chapel. Many men know me. You will find me if you ask. Come, or be called recreant!"[10]

With a runish roar he turns the reins and hales out at the hall door, his head in his hands. The fire flies under his horse's hooves. To what land he went no one knew, no more than they knew whence he came.

Arthur had wonder in his heart, but he let no sign of it show. He said most courteously to his lovely queen, "Dear lady, do not be frightened. Such tricks as this are fitting at Christmas time—the playing of interludes, laughing, singing, the comely carols of knights and ladies. I will now turn to my dinner. But that I have seen a wonder I will not deny."

Looking at Gawain, he said, "Now, sir, hang up your axe. You have cut enough."

[10]*recreant:* coward

They hung it on a tapestry above the high table, so that all men might see it and marvel. Then with all sort of food and minstrelsy they spent the rest of that day with joy, till it came to an end in the land.

II

A year runs full quickly, and seldom does the end match the beginning. After Christmas comes the crabbed Lent, which tries the flesh with fish and food more simple. Then the weather of the world contends with winter: the cold shrinks away, the clouds lift up, the bright rain falls in showers full warm, falls upon the fair meadow-lands. Flowers appear. The earth and the trees are clothed in green; birds begin to build and to sing for joy of the soft summer which follows; blossoms swell to bloom. Now comes summer with its soft winds; Zephirus[11] whistles gently over seeds and herbs. Happy are the plants that live out of doors, when the danking dew drops from the leaves, to await a look from the warm sun. Then autumn nighs[12] and hardens them, warns them to wax full ripe, and drives with drought the dust to fly full high from the face of the earth. Wrathful winds wrestle with the sun, leaves lance from the trees, the grass grays that before was green. Now all ripens and rots that rose in the beginning, and thus runs the year in yesterdays many.

Michaelmas moon[13] is come, with its pledge of winter, and now Gawain prepares for his wearisome voyage. Yet he lingers with Arthur till All Saints' Day.[14]

The best of the castle—Iwain and Errik, Sir Dodinal le Sauvage, the Duke of Clarence, Lancelot and Lionel, and Lucan the good, Sir Bors and Sir Bedivere, big men both, Sir Mador de la Port, and many another noble knight—come to counsel him, with grief in their hearts. They sorrow that one so worthy as Gawain should go on that errand, to suffer a doleful[15] blow and give none in return. But Gawain makes

[11]*Zephirus:* personification of the west wind
[12]*nighs:* draws near
[13]*Michaelmas moon:* the harvest moon, September 29
[14]*All Saints' day:* November 1
[15]*doleful:* sorrowful

light of their anxiety. He says, "What is there to fear? Some fates are hard, some easy. All a man can do is try."

When the morning comes he asks early for his arms, and they are brought to him. First, a carpet of red silk is spread on the floor; on it a mound of gold gear gleams. Gawain steps forward, wearing a doublet of Turkestan silk and a capados lined with bright white fur. His squires set the steel shoes on his feet. They place the polished steel greaves[16] on his legs, with the knee pieces attached, and fasten them with knots of gold. Then, with thongs, they tie on the goodly thigh-pieces, that cunningly enclose his thick brawny thighs. Then they set on him the rest of his armor: the broad corslet of bright steel rings, the well-burnished arm-pieces, the elbow-pieces, the gloves of plate steel, the rich coat-armor,[17] the trustworthy sword, fastened to his side with a silken sash. His armor is rich; every latchet and loop shines of gold.

Then clanking in his armor he goes to Mass and worships at the high altar. Then he meets with the king and the lords and ladies, who kiss him and walk with him, commending him to Christ.

By this time Gringolet is ready. His saddle is red and studded with gold nails, specially prepared. His red bridle is barred and bound with gold. The breast trappings, the crupper, the proud skirts, the cloth, the saddle bows are all red; against this red background everywhere glint the rich gold nails.

Gawain takes up his helmet and kisses it. It sits high on his head. Over the beaver is a silken covering adorned with gems and embroidery—true-love knots, preening parrots, turtle doves. His shield is red and has a pentangle[18] depicted on it in pure gold. His squires hand him the shield and he hangs it about his neck by its strap.

Even though I shall delay the story, I want to tell you why the pentangle belongs to Sir Gawain. The pentangle was created by Solomon[19] to represent truth. It has five points

[16]*greaves:* shin armor
[17]*rich coat-armor:* vest of rich material worn over the armor
[18]*pentangle:* five-pointed star
[19]*created by Solomon:* Solomon's seal was a pentangle in a circle

and each line interlocks with the others, so that everywhere it is endless. The English generally call it "the endless knot." It befitted Gawain because he was faithful in five ways and in each way five times:

First, he was perfect in his five wits, and secondly in his five fingers, which never failed him. Third, all his trust was in the five wounds Christ received on the Cross, as the Creed tells. Fourth, all his fierceness in battle derived from the five joys of the Virgin Mary, which she had of her child (Gawain had her image painted on the inner side of his shield, so that when he looked at her his courage would not fail). The fifth five were these: generosity, love for fellow man, purity, chivalric courtesy, and compassion, which surpasses all virtues—these qualities were more evident in Gawain than in any other knight. Now all these various "fives" were to be found in Gawain, each joined to the other, so that they had no end; therefore this pentangle, this endless knot, was painted on his shield, in red gold on red.

Now Gawain is ready to go. He catches his lance, and gives them all good day—thinking it is to be for ever. He spurs his horse, which springs forward so vigorously that fire strikes from the stones. Those who look at him departing sigh in their hearts.

He made no stay anywhere but swiftly went his way. He rode by many a bewildering path, as the book tells. . . .

Riding always alone he climbed many a cliff; at every waterfall he found an enemy, each so foul and fierce that he had to fight him. Sometimes he fought with dragons, sometimes with wolves, sometimes with the forest trolls who dwell in the crags; at other times he fought with bulls and bears and boars, and also with ogres, who puffed at him from the high rocks. But the winter weather was even worse than the fighting, what with the clear cold water shedding from the clouds and freezing before it could reach the earth. Nearly dead from the sleet, he slept in his armor more nights than enough up among the naked rocks, with the cold streams clattering down from the crests and hanging high over his head in hard icicles. In constant peril and pain, he rode on until Christmas Eve.

He prayed to Mary to direct him to some dwelling: "I beseech thee, Lord, and Mary, that is the mildest of mothers, that you send me to some lodging where I may hear Mass, and thy Matins[20] in the morning, and for that I pray my Pater Noster and Ave and Creed."

He rode on, signing himself and saying, "Christ's Cross speed me!" But he had scarcely crossed himself three times when he became aware of a dwelling on a knoll in a glade. Set as it was in a meadow, with a park all about, it was as fine a castle as knight ever owned. It shimmered and shone through the bright oaks. Gawain took off his helmet and thanked Jesus and Saint Julian,[21] who both are gentle. "Now good lodging," he said, "I beseech you to grant!" He spurred Gringolet and was at the main gate in no time at all.

But the drawbridge was raised, the gate fast shut. The walls sank wondrously deep in the moat and rose wondrously high. Of hard-hewn stone, that castle feared no wind's blast! Nor man's. It had watch towers evenly spaced and loop holes for the archers that locked closed. He had never seen a better fortress.

Within he could see the hall itself. Chalk-white chimneys and towers gleamed in the lights. So many white pinnacles were powdered about everywhere that the castle seemed cut out of paper. He thought it would be well indeed if he could spend the holy day within those walls. He called out and a porter appeared.

"Good Sir," Gawain shouted, "will you go to the lord of this castle and beg lodging for me?"

"Gladly, by St. Peter," said the porter.

He returned promptly, bringing others with him, who let down the great drawbridge and ran across it. They knelt down courteously on the cold earth to welcome Gawain, who bade them rise and then rode over the bridge. While he dismounted, the men held his saddle and knights and squires came to bring him with joy into the hall. When he raised his helmet they rushed forward to take it from his hand; they took

[20]*Matins:* morning prayers
[21]*Saint Julian:* patron saint of hospitality

his sword and shield. He greeted each one of them; and then, still in his armor, he was taken to the hall, where a fine fire burned. The lord of the castle came out of his chamber to meet him with honor, and said,

"What is here is your own, to have at your will and to control."

"Gramercy,"[22] Gawain replied, "may Christ reward you."

Each folded the other in his arms. Gawain looked at the knight who greeted him so warmly. He was a huge man with a broad, beaver-hued beard. He was in the prime of life. His face was as fierce as the fire and his speech was noble. Standing firm on stalwart legs, he seemed well fit to be lord of such a castle.

The lord commanded that a servant be assigned to Gawain and went back into his chamber. Gawain was led to a bright room, where the furnishings were princely: curtains of pure silk with gold hems, elegant coverlets adorned with white fur and inset with embroidered panels, tapestries on the walls and also on the floor. There he was relieved of the rest of his armor and rich robes brought for him to change into. When he had chosen a robe which became him especially, one with fur up by the face and wide flowing skirts, he seemed to them the handsomest knight that ever Christ made, a warrior without peer wherever men fought. Cushions and quilted coverings were laid on a chair before the fireplace, and he sat and warmed himself. A table was set on trestles and covered with a clean white cloth; a salt cellar and silver spoons were put on it, and he was served most plentifully with various stews, seasoned in the best fashion, and with many kinds of fishes: one was baked in bread, a second was grilled on the coals, a third was boiled, a fourth came in a broth savored with spices. With all these were most cunningly compounded sauces.

Over and over Gawain called it a feast; but the knights, equally graciously, replied: "No, it is a penance,[23] but amends

[22]*Gramercy:* originally, "God grant you mercy"; figuratively, "Thanks."
[23]*penance:* On Christmas Eve no meat was served; to that extent the meal is a penance.

shall be made in due time." Gawain was merry because of the wine, which went to his head.

Then he was questioned, tactfully. He told that noble Arthur of the Round Table was his ruler and that he himself was Gawain, come among them by chance at Christmas time.

When the lord learned who he was he laughed loud. All the knights were delighted also to be in the presence of Gawain, the most famous on earth for prowess and refined manners. Each said softly to his companion: "We have caught the very father of courtesy. Now we shall see true courtly manners, and hear the spotless terms of noble conversation. In truth, God has granted us his grace most wondrously, that we have such a guest as Gawain at this time when men sit and sing for joy at Christ's birth."

It was nearly night before the dinner was over. Chaplains then led the way to the chapel, ringing their bells to call them to the devout Evensong. The lord went into the chapel, as did his lady also. She entered a closed pew, but the lord caught Gawain by a fold of his robe, took him to a seat aside, spoke familiarly to him, calling him by his name, and told him he was the most welcome man in all the world. Gawain thanked him from his heart and each saluted the other and sat soberly together throughout the service.

When it was over, the lady wished to see Gawain. Followed by many young maidens, she came from her pew. Another lady—much older than she, and highly honored by all the nobles about—led her by the left hand. The two ladies were most unlike: Whereas the one was young and fresh, the other was withered and yellow. A rich rod appeared everywhere on the one. Rough wrinkled cheeks rolled on the other. The one had kerchiefs on her head and many shining pearls; her breast and her bright throat were bare and shone whiter than the snow that falls on the hills. The other was swathed up the neck with a gorget;[24] her chin was wrapped around with chalk-white veils, so that only her black brows, her two eyes, her nose, and her lips were visible—and these were sour to see and wondrously bleared. A true *grande dame*[25] one might

[24]*gorget:* collar
[25]*grande dame:* elderly lady of impressive appearance

call her, by God! Her body was short and thick; her buttocks jutted out like a bay window! The one she had in tow was the more delicious to taste. Of all women she was the fairest of skin, of flesh, of face, of figure, of expression—fairer even, he thought, than Guenever. He went through the chancel to salute them.

Gawain greeted the old woman first, bowing full low, and then clasped the younger a little in his arms and kissed her courteously. He spoke to them in a knightly fashion, asking to be allowed to be their servant. They took him between them and, conversing, led him to their sitting-room, where they called for spices and wine.

The lord of the castle leaped up graciously many a time, exhorting everyone to be merry. In high good humor, he seized off his hood, hung it on a spear, and waved it at them, putting it up as a prize to be won by whoever made the most mirth that Christmas season. "And I shall try," he said, "to contend with the best of you! Before I lose my clothes with the help of my friends!" Thus with laughing speeches the lord made merry, to amuse Sir Gawain, till it was time for bed.

On the morn joy grew in every dwelling in the world, as each person called to mind Him who for our salvation was born to die. There was much joy that day and the next and the next—St. John's day, the last of the games. There were guests who were leaving on the gray morrow, and hence they all reveled marvelously late into the night, drinking wine and dancing carols.[26] When Gawain went to take leave, the lord detained him, leading him to his own room and there thanking him for the great honor he had done them in visiting his house at that high season. He tried hard to persuade him to stay longer, but Gawain said that there was no way he might:

"I am bound for a place I know not where in all the world to go to find! Yet, so help me God, I would not fail to be there on New Year's morn for all the land in England. Tell me if you have ever heard of the Green Chapel, what ground it stands on; or of the Green Knight who keeps it. By solemn agreement we established a tryst[27] between us, to meet, if I might live,

[26]*carols:* Originally the carol was a dance and a song combined.
[27]*tryst:* meeting

at the Green Chapel on New Year's Day—and of the New Year it now lacks but a little. I have barely three days in which to busy myself, and I would as soon fall dead as fail to be there."

The lord laughed at that. "Let the Green Chapel bother you no more! You can be in your bed, man, at your ease, until well on into New Year's Day, and ride there by mid-morn! Stay until New Year's Day, then rise and leave. One of my men will set you on the way. The Green Chapel is not two miles hence!"

Then Gawain was full glad and said, "Above everything else I thank you for this! Now I shall dwell here at your will and do as you see fit."

The lord held him with his arms and called for the ladies. He made such merry sounds that he seemed out of his wits. Finally he managed to speak:

"You have promised to do as I ask? Is that true, will you keep this promise right now, right at this moment?"

"Yes. While I remain at your castle I shall do as you wish."

"Well, you have had a hard journey and have since reveled with me. You are not fully recovered yet. Tomorrow you shall stay in your bed until Mass and eat when you will. My wife will keep you company. As for me, I shall rise early and go hunting."

Gawain agreed, bowing graciously.

The lord continued, "Furthermore, we shall make an agreement between us. Whatever I get hunting shall be yours; whatever you get here shall be mine. Sweet sir, so shall we swap. Swear!"

"By God," said Gawain, "I do!"

"Then the bargain is made!" cried the lord.

They drank and made merry, these lords and ladies, and afterwards with many fair speeches kissed most courteously and took their leave. Gleaming torches brought them all to bed at last.

III

Before daylight, the new day began. The guests who were leaving called their servants, who quickly saddled the horses, arranged the gear, and trussed the bags. Dressed in the richest fashion, the guests leaped on their horses, seized the bridles, and were on their way.

After he had heard Mass the lord of the castle ate a sop hastily; then, amid the sound of bugles, he and many others set out for the hunting fields. By daybreak he and his knights were high on their horses. The houndsmen leashed the dogs together in pairs, then opened the kennel door and called them out. They blew three long notes on the bugles, at which the braches[28] bayed, making a wonderful music. The houndsmen then went to the hunting stations and unleashed the greyhounds. A great and fine noise rose in the forest!

At the first sound of the hunt the wild animals quaked for dread. Mad for fear, the deer fled to the valleys, ran to the high grounds, but were quickly turned back by the shouts of a ring of beaters. They let the high-antlered harts[29] pass through, and the broad-palmed bucks, for the lord had forbidden the hunting of the males during the closed season. They held in the hinds and the does with "Hay!" and with "Ho!" and drove them into the deep valleys, where men might see the slanting of arrows as they shot by. Under every branch whapped an arrow. The deer cried out; they bled; they died on the slopes—and ever the hounds chased on in a rush. Blowing on horns, the hunters pursued them with such a cracking cry as though the cliffs had burst.

The lord was carried away for bliss. He galloped about. He alighted to the ground. He drove that day with joy to the dark night.

All this time Gawain lay abed, snug under a fine coverlet, curtained about. As he lay dozing, he heard a little noise at the door. He raised his hand out of the bed clothes and lifted a corner of the curtain, watching warily to see what it might be. It was the lady—and lovely she was! She closed the door after her and went to the bed. Gawain, embarrassed, lay down and pretended to sleep. Stepping silently, the lady stole to his bed, lifted the curtain, and crept within. She

[28]*braches:* hunting dogs
[29]*harts:* stags

sat down softly on the edge of the bed and waited for him to wake. Gawain pondered what her meaning might be. It seemed very strange to him—but then he said to himself, "It would be more becoming to ask straightway what she wants." He stretched himself and pretended to be amazed, crossing himself with his hand.

"Good morning, Sir Gawain!" she cried, laughing. "You are captured! Unless we make a truce, I shall bind you in your bed, that you may be sure."

"Good morning!" said Gawain. "I surrender completely and cry after grace! Now, lovely lady, if you will only free your prisoner, he will get up and make himself presentable to talk with you."

"Nay—forsooth, fair sir," she answered. "I shall fasten you here on the other side also, and speak with my knight whom I have captured. I know who you are. You are Sir Gawain, whom all the world worships, whose honor and courtliness are praised by knights and ladies everywhere."

"Madame, the honor which people give me they exaggerate beyond my deserts. Here the honor is rather to you, who are unable to think anything but good."

Thus they talked until it was past nine, and always the lady behaved as if she were much in love with him. Gawain kept on the defensive, but with the greatest courtesy.

"Though I were the loveliest of women," she thought to herself, "the less love-making would he bring with him now—because of the disaster that he seeks, the blow that will strike him down." She said good day, and laughed. Then she stood up and spoke very severely.

"Now may he who rewards every speech reward you for *this* entertainment! That you really are Gawain is debated in my mind."

"Wherefore?" said Gawain quickly, fearing that somehow he had spoken amiss.

But she blessed him, saying, "One so courteous as Gawain never could have remained so long with a lady without begging for a kiss, through his courtesy, at least at some place in the conversation."

"As a knight should," replied Gawain, "I kiss at your

command. And, as a further reason, not to displease you."

She caught him in her arms and kissed him. Then they commended each other to Christ, and she went out the door without another word.

All this time the lord of the castle had been occupied with his games, and by sundown he had slain such a quantity of does and hinds that it was wondrous to consider them. The huntsmen quickly made a *curée*[30] of the killed deer. Then the nobles took over.[31] They gathered up the fattest animals and had them cut open. They tested them and found that even the poorest had two fingers' breadth of fat on her. Then they slit the throat, pulled out the first stomach, scraped it with a knife, and sewed it together; next they cut off the legs, tore away the hide, opened the belly, and threw out the bowels; they gripped the throat and drew out the guts; then they cut out the shoulders, lifting them by a little hole to keep the sides complete. They carved the breast and then went back to the throat, slitting it to the fork in the legs. Next they removed all the edible organs in the front part and then took out the backbone; they raised it out whole, as far as the haunch. Then they removed the numbles,[32] the thighs, the head, and the neck. At the last they detached the sides from the backbone and threw the ravens' fee[33] into the trees. They fed the hounds with the liver and lights, the tripe, and bread soaked in blood; this they spread out on a skin.

The huntsmen then blew the horns. The dogs bayed. Then the huntsmen seized the meat and turned to go home; all the way they sounded stoutly many fine notes. By the time daylight was done all were back at the castle, where Gawain waited by a bright fire.

The lord joyfully commanded everyone to gather in the hall, the ladies with their maids as well as the men, and had his share of venison brought in. He called to Gawain, showing

[30]*made a curée:* In a *curée* the slain deer are arranged with their heads pointing in one direction only, each deer's feet to the other's back.

[31]*Then . . . over:* It was the duty of the nobility to be skilled in the butchering of game.

[32]*numbles:* heart, lungs, liver, etc., of a deer

[33]*ravens' fee:* gristle, which custom required to be thrown in the trees for the ravens and crows

him the tally of the deer slain and the ribs of bright meat. "Does this please you?" he asked; "do I not deserve your praise and thanks?"

Gawain replied, "Yes, in truth."

"I give it all to you, Gawain," said the lord, "according to our agreement."

"I say the same to you," returned Gawain; "what I have won in this house is yours." He took the lord in his arms and kissed him as nicely as he could, saying: "Take now my winnings!"

"Many thanks," the lord said. "It may well be that the kiss is the better gain of the two—if you will tell me where you got it."

"That was not in the bargain," Gawain replied, laughing.

After supper, as they sat by the fire, they agreed to the same covenant as before: to exchange, when they met the next night, whatever winnings chance awarded them. Wine was brought forth, and they pledged the agreement before the whole court, then took leave of each other courteously. Each man went quickly to his bed.

By the time the cock had crowed no more than thrice the lord had leaped from his bed. The company was on its way to the hunt before day sprang. Blowing on horns, they rode across level fields until they came to thickets in a marsh. They unleashed some of the hounds there, who soon fell on a scent. Shouting, the huntsmen urged them on and unleashed others. Forty hounds landed on the trail at once, and such a din rose from them that the rocks rang.

The pack swayed together between a pool and a crag, and rushed on to a rock-heap below a cliff, at the side of the marsh. Their baying told the huntsmen that the beast must be there, and they searched both the rock-heap and the crag, beating on the bushes and calling to him to come forth. Suddenly a boar swung out. Long since away from the herd, he was of great age and very fierce, and of tremendous size. He charged wildly at the men in his path and sent three of them to the earth, then rushed onward. The hunters cried "High!" and "Hay, hay!" They put their horns to their mouths and blew the recall. Many were the merry mouths of men and dogs that pursued this boar to the kill.

The boar stood at bay. He thrust at the pack, hurting the dogs so that they yelled in pain. The men shot at him, but his hide was so tough the arrows split and shivered. Even so, the blows hurt him; and, brain-mad for a fight, he rushed at the hunters. He injured some of them; many drew back in fear. But not the lord, who, blowing boldly on his bugle, raced after him on a light horse.

All this time our courteous prince, Sir Gawain, lay at home in his richly-hued bed. The lady did not forget him but set out early to change his mind. Raising the curtain, she peeped in at him. He welcomed her graciously, and she sat by his side with a lovely look. Laughingly, she said:

"Sir, if you are Gawain, I think it is a wonder that you do not know the proper observances of good company. And if someone shows them to you, you cast them out of your mind. Have you forgotten already what I taught you yesterday?"

"What is that?" asked Gawain. "Truly, I do not know what you mean."

"Why, I taught you of kissing."

"That I dared not do," Gawain parried; "I thought you might refuse me."

"My faith, you cannot be refused!" the merry lady replied. "You are strong enough to take by force—if any could be so rude as to refuse you!"

"In my land," Gawain countered, "force does no good to the user, nor any gift that is not given with good will. I am at your command, to kiss when you like."

She bent down and kissed him, and then complained: "I would like to know why I have never heard from your mouth words that belong to love. In the romances of chivalry, the service of love is everything; it is both the title and text of these books. So it is with true knights: they adventure their lives for their loves, endure for them grievous times, free them from care, and bring them to bliss. You are young, you are active, you are renowned far and wide for your knighthood. Yet I have sat by you on two separate times."

Gawain answered, "It is a great happiness to me that you should trouble yourself with so poor a man as I. But to take it upon myself to expound to you true love, to you who have twice the skill in that art that a hundred such as I combined have, or ever shall have, would be a great folly!"

She made trial of him, tested him often, tried to win him to sin (whatever she may have intended besides). But he defended himself so gracefully that there was no fault to be seen, nor any sinful act, on either side: nothing but happiness. At the last she kissed him and went her way, and Gawain rose to go to Mass. He played with the ladies all day.

But the lord dashed about over the countryside chasing his unlucky boar, who had bitten in two the backs of his best hounds. Finally the boar was forced out in the open by the archers, who showered him with their arrows. He was so tired he could run no more. He tried to escape to a hole by a rock on the bank of a stream. He got the bank at his back and began to paw the ground. His mouth foamed; he whet his white tusks. None of the hunters dared to close with him, he was so fierce and so frenzied and had hurt so many already.

Then the lord came himself, urging his horse on. He saw the animal at bay with his men beside him. He jumped down from the saddle, took out his bright sword, and strode forward with firm steps. He waded through the ford to where the beast stood. The boar saw him and raised up his bristles. He snorted so ferociously that the men feared for their lord's life. The boar charged.

Man and boar met in the swiftest part of the stream, but the boar had the worst of it. The lord marked him well, set his blade at the hollow just above the breastbone, and drove it in to the hilt.

Now there was a blowing of horns, a hallooing of men, a baying of dogs! A man skilled in woodcraft began to cut up the boar. First he chopped his head off and set it on high; then he slit him along the backbone and pulled out the bowels. These he broiled on coals and mixed with bread, and with them he rewarded the dogs. Then he cut the flesh in broad bright slabs, tore out the haslets,[34] fastened the two

[34]*haslets:* heart, lungs, liver, etc. of a pig

sides together, and hung them on a pole. Then the huntsmen turned home. They carried the boar's head on high.

The lord could hardly wait to see Gawain. They greeted each other with much laughter and loud talking. Then the ladies were brought, and the company gathered. The lord described to them the great size of the boar and the terribleness of the fighting. Gawain called the boar a prize, saying he had never before seen such a beast. He admired the great head.

"Now, Gawain," said the lord, "this boar is all yours, by the terms of our agreement."

"That is true," Gawain replied; "and now I shall give you my winnings." He seized the knight by the neck and kissed him graciously twice. "Now are we even," said Gawain, "of all the agreements we have made."

"By St. Giles," the lord answered, "you are the luckiest man I know! You will be rich before long if you draw such bargains."

Later, by the fireplace, they drank and made merry, and the lord proposed the same agreement for New Year's eve. But Gawain begged to be allowed to ride on in the morning, for it was near the time when he needs must go. The lord restrained him:

"As I am a true knight, I give you my word you shall be at the Green Chapel long before prime[35] on New Year's morn. Therefore lie in your bed and take your ease, and I shall hunt in the woods and keep the agreement to exchange with you the winnings when I return. I have tested you twice and have found you faithful. Now—'third time turns out best,' as they say."

Gawain agreed to stay and that night slept full still and soft.

The lord rose early. He and his men took a bit of food after Mass, and then he called for his mount. It was a fine morning. The earth was frost-covered; the sun rose red upon the clouds coasting through the sky. Soon, the dogs fell on the trail of a fox and ran this way and that to find where the scent was strongest. One of them cried out; all the huntsmen shouted; the rest of the pack ran to him and they all raced forth. The

[35]*prime:* early morning

fox flitted on, ever before them. When the dogs saw him with their eyes they chased on even faster and denounced him with their angry barks. The fox dodged and turned across rough ground, doubled back along hedges, stopped and listened, and at last leapt over a thorn hedge by a little ditch and stole out quietly along the border of a small wood. He thought he had eluded them—but before he knew it he was at a hunting station, where three great hounds attacked him at once. He swerved quickly. With all the woe in the world upon him he went back into the woods.

Then was it life as you like it to hear the hounds! What a cursing was set on that fox's head! He was "hallooed" when the huntsmen saw him; he was damned and called thief. The greyhounds were always on his tail, so that he could never pause a moment. But he was wily, this Reynard, and he led the lord and his men a chase till midday, while at home our courteous knight slept within his comely curtains that cold morn.

But the lady did not sleep. She rose quickly and went to him. She came, closing the door after her, and swung open a window, calling, "Ah, man! how can you sleep? This morning is so bright and clear!"

In the heavy gloom of a dream Gawain muttered, like a man troubled with many grim matters, as indeed he was: how destiny should that next day award him his fate, when he would receive the blow without struggle. He recovered his wits, swung out of the dream, and answered her with haste. She came to him laughing softly. She bent low over his face and kissed him. When he saw her so glorious, so gaily attired, so faultless in her features, a strong welling joy warmed his heart. Smiling courteously and gently, they fell into mirth.

He cared much for chivalric manners and for his reputation as a knight; but even more that he should sin and be a traitor to the man in whose house he was a guest.

"God forbid," he said, "that shall not happen!" With a laughing speech, he gently laid aside all the words of love that came from her mouth.

Sighing, she bent down and kissed him; then she separated herself from him and, standing, asked:

"Now, beloved, do this much for me at this parting. Give

me something of yours, your glove, perhaps, that I may remember you by, to lessen my grief."

Gawain replied, "I would that I had here the dearest thing I possess; you have deserved more reward than I can give. But to give you only a glove is not to your honor. I am here on a mission in a strange country, and have no men with me with bags of valuable things. Each man must do as he is circumstanced—do not take it illy."

"Nay," she said, "though I have nothing of yours, yet you shall have something of mine."

She handed him a ring of red gold with a great standing stone that blazed like the bright sun. But he refused it, saying:

"I will have no gifts at this time. I have none to give you nor will I take any."

Then she sighed and spoke, "If you will not take my ring, because it seems too rich to you, then I shall give you my belt. It is worth very little."

She took off a girdle that was knotted about her. It was made of green silk and gold and ornamented with pendants of gold.

"It is unworthy," she said, "but take it."

He told her he would take nothing until God granted him the achievement of his quest. "Therefore I pray you," he said, "be not displeased. Now stop pressing me, for I shall never consent. But I will always be your true servant."

"You refuse this silk because it is so simple?" she asked. "Lo, it is little, and so the less is it valuable; but anyone who knew the qualities knit into it might consider it of value, perhaps. Whoever is girt with this green belt cannot be slain by any means whatsoever. While he has it fastened about him, there is no man under heaven who can kill him."

Gawain mused a moment, and in his mind he realized what a jewel the girdle would be when he reached the Green Chapel. He suffered her to speak. She pressed the belt on him. He granted her her wish. She gave the belt to him and besought him, for her sake, never to reveal the gift, but to conceal it loyally from her lord.

He agreed that no one should ever know. She thanked him over and over, and by then she had kissed him for the third time.

When she was gone, Sir Gawain arose and dressed himself

in noble array. He put away the love-token where he might find it again and then went to the chapel. He privately approached a priest and asked him to tell him how he might save his soul when he should go hence, confessed his misdeeds, besought mercy, and called for absolution. The priest absolved him, making him as clean as though Doomsday were to come that morning. Then Gawain was merrier with the ladies, with carols and all sorts of joy, than he had ever been. All were delighted with him and said, "Surely he was never so merry since he came here."

Now let us leave him in that comfortable place, surrounded by love. The lord is still in the field leading his men. He has killed the fox which he followed so long. As the lord leaped over a hedge to see the rascal, Reynard came running through the woods with the pack at his heels. The lord drew out his bright blade and cast it at him, but the fox swerved. He would have started back, except that a hound rushed him. Then the dogs all fell on him, right under the horse's hooves. The lord leaped down and snatched him from their jaws. He held him high over his head and shouted loudly. The hunters ran to him, blowing the recall on their horns. All those who had bugles blew them at once, those who did not shouted aloud, and the hounds bayed. It was a fine noise that was raised for Reynard's soul.

They rewarded the hounds, stroking them and rubbing their heads. Then they took Reynard and stripped him of his coat. As it was now nearly night, they turned towards home, blowing stoutly on horns all the way.

The lord found Sir Gawain by the fire. He wore a coat of blue that reached to the floor; his surcoat was softly furred, and a matching hood hung on his shoulder; both were bordered with white fur all about. Saying "I shall first fulfill the agreement," he embraced the good lord and, with much relish and vigor, kissed him three times.

"By St. Giles," said his host, "I think you got pleasure in buying this merchandise, if the price was not too high."

"No matter the price," said Gawain. "The bargain that I owed you is now fully paid."

"Marry," replied the lord, "mine is not worth much. I have

hunted all day and have only this foul-smelling fox's skin—the Fiend may have it—which is poor exchange for the three kisses you have pressed so warmly on me here."

"It is enough," cried Gawain. "I thank you, by the Cross."

With mirth and with minstrelsy, with the laughter of the ladies, with food as they liked it, Gawain and the lord passed the evening. Then Gawain humbly took his leave. First he spoke to the lord:

"May God reward you for the wonderful hospitality you have shown me at this high feast-time. I must, as you know, leave on the morrow. If you will do as you promised, give me someone to guide me to the Green Chapel, I will indeed give you myself to become one of your men."

"In good faith," the lord replied, "I shall do all that I promised you I would." At once he assigned him a servant to set him on the way.

Gawain thanked him, and then took his leave from the fair ladies. With sorrow and with kissing he spoke to them, urging upon them his heartfelt thanks. With sad sighings they commended him to Christ, and he left. He thanked each man he met for the various troubles he had gone to to serve him, and each man was as sorry to see him go as if he had lived there forever.

Surrounded by people, he was lighted to his chamber and brought merrily to bed to be at his rest. I dare not say whether he slept soundly. He had much to think of, if he would.

IV

It is now almost New Year. The night passes, daylight drives away the darkness, as God commands. Outside it is storming wildly. The clouds cast to the earth the cold snow which, with all the bitterness of the north in it, sifts down, cruelly nipping all the naked wild things. From the heights the shrill wind rushes and fills every valley with great drifts of snow.

Gawain lies in his bed and listens. He sleeps very little. The crowing of each cock reminds him of his ordeal, and long before day he springs up. There is a lamp lighted in his chamber, and he calls for his groom, who brings him his armor. First he puts on his clothing, to ward off the cold; then his armor, the rings of the corslet and the plates all burnished like new; and finally his coat with the embroidered badge set upon velvet. Gawain does not forget the belt, the lady's gift. After fastening on his sword, he winds this love-token about him; the green silk shines against the red and the gold.

Now he goes to where the household is gathered. He thanks them all. Gringolet is brought in ready to gallop. Gawain looks at the fine condition of the horse's coat and says to himself, "The people in this castle truly think about courtesy. May the man who maintains them have joy, and may the dear lady have love in this life!" He steps into the stirrup and swings aloft; he spurs Gringolet with his gilt heels. The great horse leaps forward.

Gawain cries: "I commend this castle to Christ! May he ever give it good fortune!"

He crosses himself quickly and rides over the bridge. He compliments the porter who, kneeling before him, gives him good day and prays that God may save him. Now he is on his way alone, save for the man who is to take him to the dismal place where he will receive the blow.

The way leads along hillsides covered with bare trees, along cliffs where the cold is intense. Mist drizzles on the moors, melts on the mountains. Every hill wears a hat, a cloud-cap. The brooks boil and foam white as they rush down.

Now the two riders are on a high hill, and the sun rises. White snow lies around them. The man bids Gawain wait:

"You are now near the place that you have so specially asked after. But I must say the truth to you, since I know you and love you well. Take my advice and be the better for it. In that wasteland lives a man who is the very worst on earth. He is strong and stern, he loves to kill. He is larger than any man on earth, larger than the best four knights in Arthur's house, Hector,[36] or any other. He is a merciless man and a violent one. None passes by that place—churl or chaplain, monk or masspriest—who is not killed by a blow from his

[36]*Hector:* Trojan hero

hand. As surely as you sit here, you will be killed if you go there. So, good Sir Gawain, let the man alone! Go by some other way! Ride through some other land, and may Christ bless you! I promise you that I shall swear by God and all his saints that you never fled from any man I ever knew of."

Gawain turns to him: "May it be well with you who so wish my good! I believe that you would keep the secret, but no matter. If I fled from here I would be a cowardly knight; there could be no excuse. I will go on to the chapel and speak with that man, for good or for ill. He may indeed be a grim fellow to deal with. But God can save His servants, if it is His will."

"Marry!" says the man. "If you wish to lose your life I cannot prevent you. Take your helmet and spear and ride down that path by the side of that rock till you come to the bottom of the valley; then look on your left and you shall see both the Green Chapel and the man who keeps it. Now farewell, noble Gawain, and God be with you! For all the gold in the earth I would not go with you one foot further!"

Gawain turns his bridle, hits his horse with his heels as hard as he can, and leaves his guide on the hill-top alone. "Before God," he says to himself, "I shall not falter; I am obedient to His will and I hold myself at one with Him."

Now he spurs Gringolet again and picks up the path, going in by a steep bank at the side of a small wood. He rides down into the valley and then looks about him, but sees no sign of the chapel: only high banks on each side, rough knuckled crags above him, clouds grazing along their tops. He holds in his horse and looks for the chapel.

Now he sees a sort of knoll in the middle of a little glade, a smooth-swelling mound. It is on the bank of a stream just below a waterfall, and the stream bubbles as though it is boiling.

He urges on his horse and approaches the mound. Now he dismounts, ties the reins to a tree, and walks about the mound, debating with himself as to what it may be. It has a hole in the end on either side, and it is overgrown everywhere with green grass in clumps. Inside it is all hollow. "It is nothing but an old cave," he thinks, "or perhaps the crevice of an old crag." He does not know quite what to call it.

"Can this be the Green Chapel?" he asks himself. "It looks a fitting place for the devil to say his Matins in at midnight! And it would well suit the Green Knight, to perform his devotions here in devil's wise. I do feel it is the Fiend—feel it in all my five wits—who has forced this appointment on me, to destroy me! This is the Chapel of Disaster, the cursedest kirk[37] I ever came in."

Helmet on head, lance in hand, he makes his way to the roof. Now he hears coming from the rocks beyond the brook, a noise, as though someone were grinding a scythe on a grindstone.

Whack! it clatters against the cliff!

Whack! it whirrs and whets!

Whack! it rushes and rings!

"By God," he says, "that is being prepared as a welcome for me! However, let God work His will. Even though I lose my life, moaning will not help me; and besides, no noise is going to make me afraid."

He calls out: "Who is here to keep an appointment with me? For now is Gawain walking right here! If a man wishes anything with him, let him come quickly, either now or never!"

"Hold!" bellows a voice from the bank over his head. "You shall soon have everything I promised you!"

The man who spoke keeps on with his noise-making. Whack! Whack! Whack!

Suddenly he whirls out of an opening in a crag. He holds before him a frightful weapon, a Danish axe newly made, with a blade, filed sharp on the whetstone, four feet wide; and he is dressed in green. Green is his face and his legs, his hair and his beard—all just as before, except that now full fairly on his feet he hastens over the earth. He comes to the water, vaults over it on his axe, and strides across the snow.

Sir Gawain stands to meet him; he does not bow. The green man speaks: "Sweet sir, a man can see you keep your word!

[37] *kirk:* church

You have timed your journey like a true man, and you know the agreement between us: twelve months ago you had your opportunity, and now, at this New Year, I have mine. We are completely alone here; there are no knights to separate us; we can fight as we like. Take off your helmet and receive your payment. Give me no more resistance than I did you when you lopped off my head at one blow!"

Gawain speaks: "By God who gave me a soul, I bear you no ill will. If you limit yourself to one stroke, I shall stand still and let you work as you like."

He bows his head; the skin of his neck shows bare. He acts as though he fears nothing.

Now the Green Knight gathers up his grim tool and with all the force in his body raises it aloft. He takes aim. As the axe comes down, Gawain glances at it and flinches a little. The Green Knight swerves and withholds the axe. He rebukes Gawain with proud words:

"You are not Gawain, who is held to be so worthy! Who never showed fear before any army in valley or hill! For you flinch for fright before you even feel pain. Such cowardice of Gawain I never heard tell. Nor did I shrink when you aimed at me in Arthur's house. My head flew to my feet and yet I never moved. And you, you are frightened out of your wits before you receive any harm. Now who is the better man?"

Gawain replies:

"I flinched once, but I will not do it again. However, if you cut off *my* head *I* cannot put it back on again. But hurry; come to the point; deal me my fate, and do it out of hand! I shall stand you the stroke and flinch no more till your axe has hit me. Here is my word."

"Here goes then!" cries the other. He heaves the axe aloft, and looks about angrily. He aims, but he does not cut. He withholds his hand. Gawain waits; he does not flinch, but stands still as a stone, or a stump fixed in rocky ground by a hundred roots. Now the green man calls out merrily:

"So—now that you have your heart again, it behooves me to hit. Hold now the high hood that Arthur gave you, and keep your neck at this stroke—if it can recover from it!"

Gawain speaks wrathfully:

"Thrash on, you fierce fellow. You threaten too long. I suspect you have frightened your own self."

"Ah," says the other, "you speak so boldly now that I need wait no longer."

He takes his stance to strike and puckers his lips and his forehead. He raises his weapon and sends it down with all his vigor, but the blade merely nicks the skin! The bright blood shoots over Gawain's shoulder. He sees it gleaming on the snow and springs forth in a great leap, more than a spear's length, grabs his helmet, puts it on his head, raises his shield in front of him, draws out his bright sword, and cries:

"No more! I have taken one stroke, and if you offer me another I shall pay you back readily—you may trust it!—and fiercely. One stroke only belonged to you—the agreement in Arthur's house said so. Now therefore, knight, cease!"

The Green Knight rests on his axe and looks at him, how he stands armed, boldly, without fear. In his heart he is pleased with him. Now he speaks merrily, in his great, ringing voice:

"Bold fellow, do not be so fierce! No man has treated you discourteously or misused you. As the agreement had it, I promised you one stroke and you have received it; consider yourself well paid. If I had been more nimble, I might have given you a harsher blow. But here is what I did: First I threatened you, but did not hurt you. That was for the agreement we made on the first night, which you held to faithfully, giving me all you got. The second blow, also a pretended one, I gave you for the second morning on which you kissed my wife—the kisses you gave to me. If an honest man pays back honestly, he need fear no danger. But on the third day you did fail me, and therefore you took that little tap. For it is my garment that you wear, that girdle. My own wife gave it to you—I know that well. I know all about the kissing and your knightly behavior, about my wife's tempting you. I brought that all about myself. I sent her to test you, and to speak truly you seem to me to be more faultless than any other knight. But in accepting the girdle you were at fault—although you did it only because you loved your life, so I blame you very little."

Gawain stands still in a deep study. Now the blood rushes to his face and he winces for shame. He cries out in anguish:

"May cowardice and covetousness be cursed for always!"

He catches at the knot, undoes it, and flings the girdle at the Green Knight:

"Lo, there lies my broken faith! For fear of your blow cowardice taught me to join hands with covetousness and forsake my own nature, which is the generosity and loyalty that belongs to a knight. Now I am false, I who have always feared treachery and untruth! Let me win back your good will."

The other laughs and says amiably:

"Any harm that I had I consider completely healed. You are confessed so clean, and have your penance so evident, that I hold you as pure as if you had never done wrong. I will give you the girdle, for it is green like my garments. It will be an excellent token of the adventure at the Green Chapel. But now you shall go back to my castle, and we shall revel away the rest of the New Year festivities. I think we can reconcile you with my wife, who was your bitter enemy!"

"No," says Gawain, "I have stayed long enough. May happiness betide you. Commend me to your comely wife—to my honored ladies, both of them, who have thus beguiled their knight with their trick. But is it any wonder if a fool be won to sorrow through the wiles of women? Adam was beguiled by one, Solomon by many, Samson—Delilah gave him his—and David was blinded by Bathsheba. These were all brought to disaster by their wiles. It would be a great gain to love women well and to believe them not, if a man could. But your girdle: God reward you for that! I will keep it gladly as a reminder of my transgression, to teach me how tender is the flesh. When pride shall prick me for my prowess at arms, I shall look at it. Now, one more word I beg of you: tell me your right name."

"Bercilak de Hautdesert," replies the Green Knight. "Through the power of Morgan le Fay,[38] who lives in my house, and the cunning of her magic, I went to Arthur's

[38]*Morgan le Fay:* enchantress beloved by Merlin, the wizard of King Arthur's court, who taught her his magic

castle to put the renown of the Round Table to a test. She hoped to take away your reason and to cause Guenever to die in terror of the green man who spoke so ghostily with his head in his hand. It is she who is at home, the ancient lady. She is also your aunt, Arthur's half-sister, the daughter of the Duchess of Tyntagel, whom noble Uther[39] afterwards had Arthur upon. Therefore I entreat you to come to your aunt and make merry in my house. All my household loves you, and I myself wish you as much good in this life as any man under God, for your great fidelity."

"No," says Gawain, "not by any means."

Now they embrace, they kiss, they commend each other to the Prince of Paradise. Now they part right there in the cold.

The knight in bright green went whithersoever he would, but Gawain rode back to Arthur's castle. He had many an adventure, but I shall not at this time recount them. The cut in his neck healed, and he wore the shining girdle slantwise as a baldric,[40] knotted under his left arm, as a sign that he was guilty of a fault. And thus he came back to the court.

Joy wakened in the castle when they knew good Gawain had returned. The king kissed him. The queen kissed him also. Then many a knight greeted him and asked him of his journey. He told it all: about the hardships that he had, the adventure of the Green Chapel, the behavior of the knight, the love of the lady, and last of all, about the girdle. The blood shot to his face when he had to tell of it.

"Lo," said he, fingering the girdle, "this is the band of cowardice and covetousness, the symbol of perfidy—and I needs must wear it as long as I live. No man can hide his harm when it is one of the spirit."

They all laughed loudly at that and they all agreed—all the brotherhood of the Round Table—to wear, all of them, a baldric of the same bright green for Gawain's sake. And ever afterwards, to wear such a baldric was an honor, as is written down in the best books of romance.

[39]*noble Uther:* King Uther Pendragon, father of Arthur
[40]*baldric:* belt worn over one shoulder and across the chest

In Arthur's day this adventure took place, as the books bear witness. Since Brutus,[41] that bold knight, first came hither,

Many knightly adventures
Have fallen such as this;
Now may he who bore the crown of thorn
Bring us to his bliss.
Amen.

Honi soit qui mal y pense.[42]

[41]*Brutus:* Aeneas' grandson, traditionally believed to be the founder of Britain

[42]*Honi . . . pense:* Evil to him who evil thinks (motto of the Order of the Garter).

FOR DISCUSSION

1. Although *Sir Gawain and the Green Knight,* like other romances, portrays an idealized way of life, it is nevertheless a rich and accurate picture of medieval customs and ceremony. Which passages and details particularly evoke the times? What do these passages contribute to the fabric of the romance?
2. A medieval audience would immediately recognize that the arrival of the Green Knight was the signal for the beginning of some adventure that would form the core of the romance. In what ways is his arrival made dramatic? Why are the courtly revelers justified in thinking him "a phantom from faery land"? What is the purpose of the Green Knight's visit? Why does Gawain claim the contest? What is strange about the terms of the agreement?
3. When Gawain accepts the Green Knight's challenge, he becomes, unknowingly, the defender of "the renown of the Round Table." As such, what knightly ideals will he have to exemplify in his actions and manners? On which occasions do you think he succeeds? On which occasions do you think he falls short of being "the ideal knight"? Do you think that the "Pearl poet"

intended to portray Gawain as less than perfect? If so, what reason might he have had for doing so?

4. In describing Gawain's preparations for his journey to the Green Chapel, the author digresses to discuss the pentangle. Why is this article a suitable adornment for Gawain? What does the digression suggest about the interests of the medieval audience?
5. How does the reception that Gawain receives at the castle on the knoll fulfill the demands of hospitality and courtesy characteristic of the romance? For diversion, the lord of the castle suggests a series of exchanges. What are the terms of these exchanges? What purpose do the accounts of the hunts serve in the over-all framework of the story? What conflict does Gawain experience in fulfilling the requirements of the exchanges? How do you interpret the concluding paragraph of Part III?
6. At the beginning of Part IV, what mood is created for the forthcoming encounter? Which details contribute to the mood? By what means does the author dramatize the second meeting between Gawain and the Green Knight?
7. What explanation of the three trials at the castle and of the three blows does the Green Knight offer? Why does he blame Gawain very little and hold him as pure as though he had never done wrong (page 110)? What is Gawain's reaction to the Green Knight's words? What purpose is served by revealing at this point the reasons for the Green Knight's visit to King Arthur's court and for the subsequent challenge?
8. Compare Gawain and the Green Knight in character and chivalric behavior. To what extent are they, and other characters in the story, one-dimensional or flat characters rather than credible representations of human beings? Why is such characterization appropriate to a romance?
9. The structure of the romance is designed to achieve the maximum in excitement and suspense. For this purpose, two legends —the Beheading Game and the Temptation—are employed in "Sir Gawain and the Green Knight." In what ways are the four parts of the romance related to one or both of the old Celtic legends? By what means does the author combine the two legends in his story? Which legend serves as the main plot and which the subplot? Who are the protagonist and antagonist in each? What conflict is basic to each plot, and how are the conflicts resolved?

FOR COMPOSITION

1. As a moral romance, "Sir Gawain and the Green Knight" presented the medieval audience with both a picture of an idealized society and with values to incorporate into their own lives. In a well-organized essay, discuss the life and values presented in this romance. Which aspects of life in Arthur's court obviously appealed to the audience? What values were offered as models? Which character most clearly embodied the ideal man?
2. The story of Gawain is greatly enhanced by the "Pearl poet's" descriptive skill. To the delight of the medieval audience, whole passages of narrative are devoted to descriptions of festive celebrations and courtly behavior. Choose several such passages and briefly discuss the reasons for their effectiveness.
3. The two characters who dominate attention in the romance are the Green Knight and Gawain. In a brief essay, tell which character interested you more and why. Explain his importance in the narrative and cite references from the story to support your opinion.

Sir Thomas Malory

Malory's *Le Morte d'Arthur* was one of the most historically and literarily important books published by England's first printer, William Caxton. It has been a favorite since its first appearance in 1485, partly because of the charming stories themselves and partly because of the exceptional style in which they were written. His contemporaries strove to "decorate" the English language as much as possible, and to prove their own learning through their long and intricately paralleled sentences. But Malory preferred brief, simple sentences that are straightforward and direct. He loved strong action words that produced an impact: his knights were not *struck*, they were *walloped.* Because Malory transmitted so excellently his admiration of knighthood, jousting, and chivalry, his works have continued to influence English culture. From Tennyson's *Idylls of the King* to American technicolor movies, evidence continues to mount of the fascination exerted by Malory's tales about Celtic King Arthur of Wales, his queen, and his Knights of the Round Table.

from Le Morte d'Arthur

In these episodes, as in the entire work, Sir Thomas Malory transports the reader "to a strange country in a distant world, unreal, impossible, and yet imaginatively coherent—a country where all is tourneys and battles, where the only dwellings reared are castles; a country without agricultural life or trade, a region of mirage in which the marvelous is at home, and fantastic personages are plausible."* All the romance and excitement of this "strange country" and these "fantastic personages" are preserved in this modern version by an English poet.

*Emile Legouis and Louis Cazamian, *A History of English Literature* (rev. ed.; New York: The Macmillan Company, 1957), p. 197.

ARTHUR BECOMES A KING

Two years later King Uther[1] fell sick, and his enemies once more overran his kingdom, inflicting heavy losses on him as they advanced. Merlin[2] prophesied that they could be checked only by the presence of the king himself on the battle field, and suggested that he should be conveyed there on a horse litter. King Uther's army met the invader on the plain at St. Albans, and the king duly appeared on the horse litter. Inspired by his presence, and by the lively leadership of Sir Brastius and Sir Jordanus, his army quickly defeated the enemy and the battle finished in a rout. The king returned to London to celebrate the victory.

But his sickness grew worse, and after he had lain speechless for three days and three nights Merlin summoned the nobles to attend the king in his chamber on the following morning. "By the grace of God," he said, "I hope to make him speak."

In the morning, when all the nobles were assembled, Merlin addressed the king: "Sire, is it your will that Arthur shall succeed to the throne, together with all its prerogatives?"

The king stirred on his bed, and then spoke so that all could hear: "I bestow on Arthur God's blessing and my own, and Arthur shall succeed to the throne on pain of forfeiting my blessing." Then King Uther gave up the ghost. He was buried and mourned the next day, as befitted his rank, by Igraine[3] and the nobility of Britain.

During the years that followed the death of King Uther, while Arthur was still a child, the ambitious barons fought one another for the throne, and the whole of Britain stood in jeopardy.[4] Finally the day came when the Archbishop of Canterbury, on the advice of Merlin, summoned the nobility to London for Christmas morning. In his message the Arch-

[1]*King Uther:* ruler of Britain
[2]*Merlin:* prophet and magician in the King's court
[3]*Igraine:* queen of Britain and mother of the two-year-old Arthur
[4]*jeopardy:* danger

bishop promised that the true succession to the British throne would be miraculously revealed. Many of the nobles purified themselves during their journey, in the hope that it would be to them that the succession would fall.

The Archbishop held his service in the city's greatest church (St. Paul's), and when matins[5] were done the congregation filed out to the yard. They were confronted by a marble block into which had been thrust a beautiful sword. The block was four feet square, and the sword passed through a steel anvil which had been struck in the stone, and which projected a foot from it. The anvil had been inscribed with letters of gold:

> Whoso pulleth oute this Swerd of this Stone and Anvyld is rightwys Kynge borne of all Brytaygne.

The congregation was awed by this miraculous sight, but the Archbishop forbade anyone to touch the sword before mass had been heard. After mass, many of the nobles tried to pull the sword out of the stone, but none was able to, so a watch of ten knights was set over the sword, and a tournament proclaimed for New Year's Day, to provide men of noble blood with the opportunity of proving their right to the succession.

Sir Ector, who had been living on an estate near London, rode to the tournament with Arthur and his own son Sir Kay, who had been recently knighted. When they arrived at the tournament, Sir Kay found to his annoyance that his sword was missing from its sheath, so he begged Arthur to ride back and fetch it from their lodging.

Arthur found the door of the lodging locked and bolted, the landlord and his wife having left for the tournament. In order not to disappoint his brother, he rode on to St. Paul's, determined to get for him the sword which was lodged in the stone. The yard was empty, the guard also having slipped off to see the tournament, so Arthur strode up to the sword, and, without troubling to read the inscription, tugged it free. He then rode straight back to Sir Kay and presented him with it.

Sir Kay recognized the sword, and taking it to Sir Ector,

[5]*matins:* morning prayers and worship

said, "Father, the succession falls to me, for I have here the sword that was lodged in the stone." But Sir Ector insisted that they should all ride to the churchyard, and once there bound Sir Kay by oath to tell how he had come by the sword. Sir Kay then admitted that Arthur had given it to him. Sir Ector turned to Arthur and said, "Was the sword not guarded?"

"It was not," Arthur replied.

"Would you please thrust it into the stone again?" said Sir Ector. Arthur did so, and first Sir Ector and then Sir Kay tried to remove it, but both were unable to. Then Arthur, for the second time, pulled it out. Sir Ector and Sir Kay both knelt before him.

"Why," said Arthur, "do you both kneel before me?"

"My lord," Sir Ector replied, "there is only one man living who can draw the sword from the stone, and he is the true-born King of Britain." Sir Ector then told Arthur the story of his birth and upbringing.

"My dear father," said Arthur, "for so I shall always think of you—if, as you say, I am to be king, please know that any request you have to make is already granted."

Sir Ector asked that Sir Kay should be made Royal Seneschal,[6] and Arthur declared that while they both lived it should be so. Then the three of them visited the Archbishop and told him what had taken place.

All those dukes and barons with ambitions to rule were present at the tournament on New Year's Day. But when all of them had failed, and Arthur alone had succeeded in drawing the sword from the stone, they protested against one so young, and of ignoble[7] blood, succeeding to the throne.

The secret of Arthur's birth was known only to a few of the nobles surviving from the days of King Uther. The Archbishop urged them to make Arthur's cause their own; but their support proved ineffective. The tournament was repeated at Candlemas and at Easter, and with the same outcome as before.

[6]*Royal Seneschal:* administrator in the King's household
[7]*ignoble:* of common origin

Finally at Pentecost, when once more Arthur alone had been able to remove the sword, the commoners arose with a tumultuous cry and demanded that Arthur should at once be made king. The nobles, knowing in their hearts that the commoners were right, all knelt before Arthur and begged forgiveness for having delayed his succession for so long. Arthur forgave them, and then, offering his sword at the high altar, was dubbed first knight of the realm. The coronation took place a few days later, when Arthur swore to rule justly, and the nobles swore him their allegiance.

GAWAIN, TORRE, AND PELLINORE

It was natural that King Arthur, having sought Merlin's advice during the early years of his reign, while enforcing his sovereignty over the petty kings of the north and west of Britain who had challenged his right to the succession, should again seek Merlin's advice in the matter of marriage, which his loyal barons were urging upon him now that peace had been established.

"Certainly a king should marry," said Merlin. "But tell me, is there already a lady who has captured your heart?"

"There is," Arthur replied. "The daughter of my friend King Lodegreaunce of Camylarde. I mean, of course, the incomparably innocent and beautiful Gwynevere."

"She is certainly as beautiful as one could wish, and if indeed you are set on making her your queen, I suppose that you must do so, although many more as beautiful, and more happily destined, could be found."

"Why do you say that?"

"Because Gwynevere is destined to love Sir Launcelot, and he her, and many disasters will result from their love. However, provide me with a royal escort and I will go to King Lodegreaunce and tell him that you are in love with Gwynevere and would like to marry her."

King Lodegreaunce was overjoyed when Merlin disclosed the purpose of his visit. "What greater honor could I receive," he said, "than that so illustrious a king as Arthur should choose my daughter for his queen?"

Instead of the usual lands or riches for a wedding gift, King Lodegreaunce decided to give King Arthur the Round Table which he had received from King Uther, and to place under Arthur's command the hundred knights who served him. This would leave empty at the table fifty seats, which had belonged to knights who had been killed or captured in King Lodegreaunce's service in the course of the years.

When Merlin and his escort, with the Round Table, and accompanied by Gwynevere and the hundred knights, returned to Camelot, he was received by Arthur with unabashed delight; and orders were given to prepare for the royal wedding and the coronation of Gwynevere.

Merlin then scoured the country for suitable knights to occupy the empty seats at the table, and found twenty-eight, who were sworn in to Arthur's service by the Archbishop of Canterbury. When the ceremony was over it was seen that each place at the table was now marked in gold letters with the name of the knight to which it belonged; but two places were left blank, and the one between them was marked: "Siege Perelous."[8]

King Arthur had issued a proclamation that on the day of the feast all reasonable petitions would be granted, and the first to take advantage of this was Gawain, King Lot's son, who begged to be knighted. Gawain was Arthur's nephew, and he readily assented. The next was a poor cowherd called Aryes, who came to make the same request on behalf of his son Torre, who accompanied him.

"This is a large request for you to make," said Arthur. "Please tell me your name, and whose wish it is that your son should be knighted: yours or his."

"Sire, my name is Aryes the cowherd, I have thirteen sons, and they all work for me willingly enough but this one, Torre. Since he was a child he would have none of it, but was always practicing with the sword or shooting with the bow, or running off to watch tournaments."

Arthur looked carefully at Torre. He did not resemble his father in any way; he was large, well built, of fine features and fearless expression, about eighteen years of age.

[8]*Siege Perelous:* perilous seat (Archaic English)

"I should like to see his brothers," said Arthur. They were sent for, and when they were all together before Arthur, he noticed how they all resembled their father but Torre.

"Have you a sword?" Arthur said to Torre.

"Sire, I have," Torre replied.

"Then give it to me, kneel down, and request to be knighted." Torre did so and Arthur dubbed him. At this moment Merlin appeared.

"Merlin," said Arthur, "I have knighted this young man Torre. Have I done wisely?"

"You have," Merlin replied. . . .

At last the day of the feast arrived, and the royal wedding and the coronation of Gwynevere took place in the church of St. Stephens, and were conducted with befitting solemnity by the Archbishop of Canterbury. When it was over, King Arthur with his queen and their suite repaired to the Round Table for the banquet.

"Tell me, Merlin," said Arthur, "why those two seats are blank, and why the one between them is marked: 'Siege Perelous.'"

"Sire, because it would be death for any but the appointed knight to sit at the Siege Perelous, and only a little less disastrous at the unmarked seats on either side. The knight who shall sit at the Siege Perelous has not yet been born; the names of the knights who shall sit at the other two seats will appear when they arrive at the court. However, I suggest that King Pellinore, as the senior knight present, should take the seat adjacent to them."

Sir Gawain, who had been knighted that morning, was furious when he heard this, and whispered to Gaheris, his brother, who was acting as his squire, "Why should King Pellinore be so honored? You know that he killed our father at the battle of Terrabyl. Well, with this good sword of mine, I am going to avenge his death."

"But not now," said Gaheris, "not at King Arthur's own table. We must bide our time; anyhow, I want to avenge his death myself as soon as I am knighted."

The banquet was nearly over, and the guests about to

rise from their seats, when Merlin addressed the company at large: "My lords and ladies, pray keep your seats, for you are about to witness an unusual event."

And just as he spoke, a white hart[9] galloped into the hall, pursued by a white brachet[10] and thirty pairs of black hounds. The brachet kept snapping at the hart's haunches, and finally succeeded in tearing off a piece of flesh. The hart made a tremendous leap and, in doing so, overturned a knight who was sitting at one of the side tables. The knight jumped up, seized the brachet, and made off with her.

Almost immediately a young noblewoman rode into the hall on a white palfrey.[11] She was sobbing with anger and dismay, and rode straight up to Arthur. "Sire," she cried, "summon the knight who has stolen my brachet at once, for I cannot be without it."

"I may not summon him now," Arthur replied.

Next, a knight appeared, fully armed and riding a powerful charger. He rode up to the young noblewoman and, despite her screams, seized her around the waist, threw her across the withers of his horse, and galloped out of the hall again. Arthur was relieved that the hubbub was over; however, Merlin spoke up once more.

"Sire, you cannot let these matters rest here. It would go ill for your marriage, and your court would be dishonored."

"Very well," said Arthur. "Sir Gawain, I request you to retrieve the hart; you, Sir Torre, to retrieve the brachet, and capture or kill the knight who stole her; and you, King Pellinore, the lady, and capture or kill her captor. None of you is to return to the court before your quest is accomplished."

Sir Gawain and Gaheris were the first to set off, and they galloped through the forest until they came upon two knights fighting each other on foot. Sir Gawain rode his horse between them. "What is your quarrel?" he cried.

Both knights looked up sheepishly. "We are fighting," said one of them, "to prove which of us is the bigger, and

[9]*hart:* stag
[10]*brachet:* female hound
[11]*palfrey:* horse

should therefore be the one to pursue a white hart which ran by a short time ago. It came from the direction of King Arthur's court, and we thought that one of us could win fame by chasing it down. We are brothers."

"That is a silly quarrel indeed," said Sir Gawain, "and now either you will have to accept my challenge, or go to King Arthur and yield to him, saying that you are prisoners of the knight on the quest of the white hart. But tell me first, what are your names?"

"Our names are Sorlus and Bryan of the Forest. We will be your prisoners rather than fight any more, we are so weary."

Sir Gawain and Gaheris could still hear the yapping of the hounds in the distance, and so they turned eagerly to their quest once more. Coming to a river they were challenged by a knight on the further bank. "Sir, you may not pursue the white hart without first fighting me," he shouted.

Sir Gawain swam his horse across the river. They jousted[12] and Sir Gawain threw his opponent off his horse at the first encounter, and demanded that he should yield. "Not until we have fought on foot with our swords," said the knight.

"Please tell me, what is your name?" Sir Gawain asked him.

"Sir Alardyne of the Outer Isles."

Sir Gawain drew his sword and with one stroke chopped clean through Sir Alardyne's helmet and skull. "That was a fine stroke for a young knight," said Gaheris appreciatively.

The brothers galloped off again in pursuit of the hart, and were soon joined by three pairs of greyhounds who slipped out from the undergrowth. Together they pursued their quarry until it fled into a castle; the greyhounds raced in first and made their kill in the hall.

Sir Gawain and Gaheris arrived at the entrance to the hall in time to see a knight emerge from an inner room and set about the greyhounds with his sword. He killed two of them and the remainder fled.

"Alas, my white hart!" the knight exclaimed, "gift that you were from my sovereign lady; but at least you shall not go unavenged."

[12]*jousted:* battled with lances

He withdrew to the inner room and a moment later reappeared in full armor. "Sir," said Sir Gawain, "why kill the greyhounds, whose nature it is to devour their quarry? Why not try to kill me instead?"

"I will," said the knight.

They fought, and both were severely wounded before Sir Gawain sent his opponent reeling to the ground with a blow on the helmet. He begged Sir Gawain to spare his life.

"I will not," Sir Gawain replied. "You killed my greyhounds."

"For those I can surely make amends," said the knight.

But Sir Gawain felt no mercy and dragged off his helmet. He was just poised to behead him when the knight's lady appeared and threw herself between them. Unable to restrain the blow, Sir Gawain beheaded the lady. He was completely dismayed.

"Arise, I grant you your life," he said to the knight.

"I think little of your mercy now," the knight replied, "since with your cowardly stroke you have killed my lady, who was far more dear to me than my own life."

"In truth, it was you I meant to kill," said Sir Gawain. "But go now to King Arthur: tell him what has befallen you, and say that you are a prisoner of the knight on the quest of the white hart. Before you go, please tell me, what is your name?"

"Sir Blamoure de la Maryse," the other replied.

Sir Blamoure strapped the two greyhounds to his horse, one on either side of the saddle, and departed for Camelot. Sir Gawain and Gaheris meanwhile prepared to rest overnight in the castle. Sir Gawain started to disarm.

"What, would you disarm here?" asked Gaheris. "Surely we must be surrounded by enemies."

No sooner had he spoken than four knights in full armor rushed into the hall and attacked them.

"You should be ashamed," one of them shouted, "that you, a newly made knight, have already dishonored the order of knighthood by killing a lady. However, you need expect no mercy from us."

Sir Gawain and Gaheris fought desperately, but were no match for their attackers. Soon Sir Gawain received a crippling wound in the arm, and they were both at death's door when four ladies appeared and begged the knights to spare their lives.

They spent the night bemoaning their fate, as prisoners in one of the castle cells. Sir Gawain was particularly troubled by his arm, and feared that he had lost the use of it. In the morning one of the ladies came to them.

"Good knight, what cheer?" she said.

"No cheer," Sir Gawain replied.

"The fault is your own," she said, "but please tell me your name and from whose court you have come."

"Sir Gawain, son of King Lot of Lowthean and Orkney, and of Magawse, sister to King Arthur. I am a knight of the Round Table, and King Arthur is my liege."

The lady was impressed. "Since you are related to King Arthur," she said, "I will intercede on your behalf with the four knights."

Sir Gawain and Gaheris were released soon afterward, on condition that Sir Gawain should bear the corpse of the lady on his own body throughout the journey to Camelot, and that he should report to Arthur truthfully all that had occurred. He was allowed to take the hart's head as proof that he had accomplished his quest.

King Arthur and Queen Gwynevere listened attentively to Sir Gawain's account of his adventures, and when he had finished, Queen Gwynevere rebuked him sternly, commanding that henceforth he should always spare those who begged for mercy, and always put the service of ladies foremost. Sir Gawain swore on the gospel to do so, and so ended his first quest.

Sir Torre had set off on the quest of the brachet, and had not ridden far through the forest when a dwarf appeared before him and struck his horse on the nose with his staff, so that the horse started backward by a spear's length.

"Why did you do that?" Sir Torre demanded.

"Because no knight may ride this way without first fighting my masters," the dwarf replied.

"I am on a quest and have no time for idle jousting," said

Sir Torre; but the dwarf blew on his horn and two knights appeared from their pavilions.[13]

Sir Torre jousted and fought with each in turn, and overcame them both. "What are your names?" he demanded.

"Sir Phelot of Langeduke," said one.

"Sir Petipace of Winchilsee," said the other.

"Go then to King Arthur, and say that you are prisoners of the knight on the quest of the knight with the white brachet."

They left, and the dwarf asked Sir Torre, "Sir, will you grant me a wish?"

"Ask and you shall have it," Sir Torre replied.

"May I now serve you instead of those two rascally knights whom you just defeated? If you accept me, I can lead you to the lady who now has the white brachet."

Sir Torre accepted the dwarf, and they rode together through the forest until they came to two pavilions hard by a priory.[14] Outside each was a shield, one red and one white. Sir Torre dismounted, gave his spear into the keeping of the dwarf, and looked first into the pavilion with the white shield; there he saw three maids asleep on a paillasse.[15] He then looked inside the other pavilion and saw a lady asleep, and by her the white brachet. He seized the animal, despite its furious barks, and strode out of the pavilion with it.

By the time that Sir Torre had given the brachet to his dwarf and remounted, the lady and her three maids had emerged from their pavilions. "Sir, why do you take my brachet?" the lady cried.

"My lady, I am obliged to, since my liege King Arthur has commanded me to bring it to his court."

"Beware, then, for I shall be avenged by a knight who will prove more than your match," she replied.

"By the grace of God I shall suffer such adventures as He shall provide," said Sir Torre, and rode away with the dwarf toward Camelot. It was already dusk, and Sir Torre asked the

[13]*pavilions:* large tents
[14]*priory:* monastery
[15]*paillasse:* pad filled with straw

dwarf if he knew of a lodging nearby. "Only a poor hermitage," the dwarf replied.

The hermit, however, made them welcome, gave fodder to their horses, and provided a frugal supper for Sir Torre and the dwarf. They left early in the morning after hearing mass and receiving the hermit's blessing. They rode for many miles through the forest and then were confronted by a handsome knight, fully armed and mounted on a fine charger.

"Sir, you must yield to me the brachet which you have stolen from my lady," he demanded of Sir Torre.

Sir Torre refused, and they fought. The jousting brought both horses and men to the ground, and there followed a long and savage sword fight in which the armor and hauberk[16] of each were hacked to pieces. At last, when both were thoroughly bloodied and gasping, the knight, whose name was Abellyus, fell faint. Sir Torre pressed his advantage and sent him staggering to the ground with a final blow on the helmet.

"Now yield," he said.

"Never, while there is breath in my body, and while you have the brachet," Sir Abellyus replied.

At this moment a lady galloped up to them on a palfrey and cried out aloud to Sir Torre.

"My lady, what can I do for you?" Sir Torre responded.

"In the name of King Arthur, grant me my wish."

"Name it and it shall be granted."

"May God reward you!" she said. "It is that you kill this treacherous knight before you."

"I am loath[17] to do that," said Sir Torre. "Surely, if he has wronged you, he can make amends?"

"He cannot. He killed my brother in front of my eyes. My brother was the better knight, and they were fighting only for sport. For half an hour I knelt in the mire before Abellyus, pleading for my brother's life, and then he beheaded him. If you do not grant my wish I shall shame you before King Arthur and all of his court."

Sir Abellyus grew frightened when he heard this, and at once began begging for mercy. "It is impossible now," said

[16]*hauberk:* long tunic of ring or chain mail
[17]*loath:* reluctant

Sir Torre, "for me to go back on the promise I made to this lady; if you had only yielded in the first place, I should not have to kill you."

Sir Torre then seized his helmet and dragged it off, but Sir Abellyus managed to struggle free and fled into the forest. Sir Torre gave chase, and soon returned bearing the knight's head.

"Sir," said the lady, "would you allow my lord and me to give you lodging for the night?"

"I would gladly," Sir Torre replied. "Both my horse and I have fared badly since we left Camelot."

The lady and her husband, a handsome elderly knight, entertained them hospitably at their comfortable manor, and both men and horses were at their ease. They took their leave in the morning after hearing mass and breaking their fast. The lady asked Sir Torre his name. He told her, and how he had been newly knighted, and what his quest had been.

"Good knight," said his host, "do please remember us when you are in this part of the country again, and know how welcome you will always be at our poor manor."

Three days later, Sir Torre, with his dwarf, arrived at Camelot, and was received joyfully at the court by King Arthur and Queen Gwynevere. Sir Torre had left poorly equipped for his quest, supplied with an old suit of armor by Arthur, and a very old courser[18] by King Pellinore; but now, when he had described his adventure, Merlin praised him so highly and prophesied such distinction for him in the future that Arthur rewarded him with an earldom. So ended Sir Torre's first quest.

King Pellinore, who had been commanded to bring back the young noblewoman (whose name was Nyneve), had set out at the same time as Sir Torre. He rode through the forest and came to a valley where he found another young noblewoman seated with a wounded knight in her arms. On seeing King Pellinore she cried out aloud:

"Good knight, for the love of Jesus, help me, I beseech you!"

[18]*courser:* steed

But King Pellinore was so eager in the pursuit of his quest that he did no more than salute the young noblewoman (whose name was Alyne) and continue on his path. Alyne cursed him bitterly when he had passed, praying to God that when he was most in need, he too should be denied all succor. The knight, her lover, died in her arms a few hours later, and Alyne, crazy with grief, killed herself with his sword.

Further along the valley, King Pellinore came upon a laborer and, halting his horse, asked if he had seen a knight with a captive lady.

"I have," the laborer replied. "The knight was challenged by one of two brothers, whose pavilions you will find further down the valley, and who claim to be her cousins. They were fighting when I left, and if you ride fast you should find them still there."

"I thank you," said King Pellinore, and galloped away.

King Pellinore found the knights still fighting, and Nyneve standing by the two pavilions, together with the two squires. He rode straight up to Nyneve.

"My lady, I am commanded by my liege, King Arthur, to bring you to his court."

"Sir," said one of the squires, "you will have to challenge the two knights who are already fighting for her, if she is to accompany you."

"That is fair," said King Pellinore, and rode up to the two combatants, who were fighting on foot, and drove his horse between them. "What is the cause of your quarrel?" he demanded.

Sir Meliot, Nyneve's cousin, replied first. "Sir, I am fighting to protect my kinswoman (she is my aunt's daughter) against this knight who has taken her by force, and against her will."

"Sir," said Sir Outelake, her captor, "I won the lady by force of arms, and by force of arms I shall keep her."

"That is a lie," said King Pellinore. "I was present when you made off with her; we were banqueting and none had the chance to challenge you. But now I am commanded by King Arthur to bring her back with me to the court, so I challenge you both."

Sir Outelake accepted the challenge, and then suddenly thrust his spear into King Pellinore's horse and killed it. King Pellinore managed to leap clear, and Sir Outelake said:

"Now we can fight on equal footing."

"You shall pay for that thrust," King Pellinore replied, and drawing his sword, killed Sir Outelake with a single stroke, which split open his head. Sir Meliot at once knelt before King Pellinore and yielded.

"Sir, I will not fight with a knight of your prowess," he said, "but I beg you not to dishonor my cousin."

"As I am a true knight you need have no fear for that," King Pellinore replied, "but now I am in need of a horse, so I will take Sir Outelake's."

"Sir, if you will do me the honor of lodging with me tonight, I will give you a horse that I promise will please you more."

"I will gladly accept," said King Pellinore.

Sir Meliot regaled King Pellinore and Nyneve with excellent food and wine, and they spent the evening merrily together. In the morning Sir Meliot gave King Pellinore a splendid bay courser, and they exchanged names before leave-taking. Sir Meliot also gave his brother's name, which was Sir Bryan of the Isles.

"I wonder that your brother did not offer to fight for Nyneve," said King Pellinore.

"My brother is an excellent knight, but he will fight only when he is challenged, or when he is absolutely certain that the cause is a just one."

"Why not bring him to King Arthur's court?" said King Pellinore. "You both would be most welcome."

"I thank you; we will come together one day," Sir Meliot replied.

King Pellinore and Nyneve departed for Camelot. They were riding through a rocky valley, where the path was strewn with stones, when Nyneve's horse stumbled and threw her. She fell heavily on her arm, bruising it painfully, and fainted. When she came to she begged that they should rest a while, so they both lay beneath a tree and slept until dusk. King Pellinore then prepared to continue the journey, but Nyneve said:

"In this light we shall not know whether we are riding forward or backward."

King Pellinore agreed, and so they settled down to bivouac for the night, and King Pellinore disarmed. A little before midnight they were awakened by the sound of two horses approaching from opposite directions. King Pellinore hastily rearmed, and warned Nyneve to keep silent. The two riders met within earshot of them, one from the direction of Camelot, one from the north. They hailed each other.

"What news from Camelot?" said one.

"Bad news," the other replied. "I have just been spying on King Arthur's court, and I have to report to my chieftains in the north that he now has the flower of the chivalry at his command, in the fellowship of the Round Table. There is good reason for their fame, and I fear that we shall never break them."

"As for that, I cannot agree. I have in my wallet a deadly poison, and at Arthur's court we have a sworn accomplice, who, for the immense rewards that my chieftains have offered, will administer it to Arthur willingly enough."

"Then you must beware of Merlin; with his devil's craft he always seems to find out what is going on."

"I do not fear Merlin," the other replied, and with that they parted.

King Pellinore and Nyneve continued their journey in the morning, and came to the well where Alyne had besought King Pellinore's aid. Of Alyne, all that remained now was her still beautiful head, with its long golden hair; of her lover, a mangled corpse, for they had been preyed upon by wild animals. King Pellinore was overwhelmed by remorse. "Alas! that I did not save them," he said.

"Why do you complain now?" asked Nyneve.

"Because she was young and beautiful, and it was in my power to save her, but I was too eager to accomplish my quest."

"Then why not take the remains of the knight to the nearest hermitage and have him decently buried, and yourself bear the head of the lady to King Arthur's court?"

They did this, and King Pellinore rewarded the hermit by allowing him to keep the knight's armor. They arrived at

Arthur's court at noon on the same day and were received by the king and queen who commanded King Pellinore to recount, under oath, all that had happened to him. When he had come to the end of his story the queen rebuked him for deserting the young noblewoman.

"Ma'am, I repent it," said King Pellinore.

"You have cause to," said Merlin. "They were on their way to Camelot to serve King Arthur, when he was treacherously attacked by Sir Lorayne, Now, it is ordained that you yourself shall be deserted by the man you have trusted most, at the moment of your death."

"May God show His mercy yet," King Pellinore responded.

King Arthur, now that the three quests were accomplished, established each of the knights of the Round Table with sufficient lands and wealth to maintain the dignity of the fellowship; and every time the feast of Pentecost came round, the oath was renewed, which was: only to fight in just causes, at all times to be merciful, at all times to put the service of ladies foremost.

THE DEATH OF ARTHUR

Then, on the night of Trinity Sunday, Arthur was vouchsafed a strange dream:

He was appareled in gold cloth and seated in a chair which stood on a pivoted scaffold. Below him, many fathoms deep was a dark well, and in the water swam serpents, dragons, and wild beasts. Suddenly the scaffold tilted and Arthur was flung into the water, where all the creatures struggled toward him and began tearing him limb from limb.

Arthur cried out in his sleep and his squires hastened to waken him. Later, as he lay between waking and sleeping, he thought he saw Sir Gawain, and with him a host of beautiful noblewomen. Arthur spoke:

"My sister's son! I thought you had died; but now I see you live, and I thank the lord Jesu! I pray you, tell me, who are these ladies?"

"My lord, these are the ladies I championed in righteous

quarrels when I was on earth. Our lord God has vouchsafed that we visit you and plead with you not to give battle to Sir Modred tomorrow, for if you do, not only will you yourself be killed, but all your noble followers too. We beg you to be warned, and to make a treaty with Sir Modred, calling a truce for a month, and granting him whatever terms he may demand. In a month Sir Launcelot will be here, and he will defeat Sir Modred."

Thereupon Sir Gawain and the ladies vanished, and King Arthur once more summoned his squires and his counselors and told them this vision. Sir Lucas and Sir Bedivere were commissioned to make a treaty with Sir Modred. They were to be accompanied by two bishops and to grant, within reason, whatever terms he demanded.

The ambassadors found Sir Modred in command of an army of a hundred thousand and unwilling to listen to overtures of peace. However, the ambassadors eventually prevailed on him, and in return for the truce granted him suzerainty[19] of Cornwall and Kent, and succession to the British throne when King Arthur died. The treaty was to be signed by King Arthur and Sir Modred the next day. They were to meet between the two armies, and each was to be accompanied by no more than fourteen knights.

Both King Arthur and Sir Modred suspected the other of treachery, and gave orders for their armies to attack at the sight of a naked sword. When they met at the appointed place the treaty was signed and both drank a glass of wine.

Then, by chance, one of the soldiers was bitten in the foot by an adder which had lain concealed in the brush. The soldier unthinkingly drew his sword to kill it, and at once, as the sword flashed in the light, the alarums were given, trumpets sounded, and both armies galloped into the attack.

"Alas for this fateful day!" exclaimed King Arthur, as both he and Sir Modred hastily mounted and galloped back to their armies. There followed one of those rare and heartless battles in which both armies fought until they were destroyed.

[19]*suzerainty:* political control

King Arthur, with his customary valor, led squadron after squadron of cavalry into the attack, and Sir Modred encountered him unflinchingly. As the number of dead and wounded mounted on both sides, the active combatants continued dauntless until nightfall, when four men alone survived.

King Arthur wept with dismay to see his beloved followers fallen; then, struggling toward him, unhorsed and badly wounded, he saw Sir Lucas the Butler and his brother, Sir Bedivere.

"Alas!" said the king, "that the day should come when I see all my noble knights destroyed! I would prefer that I myself had fallen. But what has become of the traitor Sir Modred, whose evil ambition was responsible for this carnage?"[20]

Looking about him King Arthur then noticed Sir Modred leaning with his sword on a heap of the dead.

"Sir Lucas, I pray you give me my spear, for I have seen Sir Modred."

"Sire, I entreat you, remember your vision—how Sir Gawain appeared with a heaven-sent message to dissuade you from fighting Sir Modred. Allow this fateful day to pass; it is ours, for we three hold the field, while the enemy is broken."

"My lords, I care nothing for my life now! And while Sir Modred is at large I must kill him: there may not be another chance."

"God speed you, then!" said Sir Bedivere.

When Sir Modred saw King Arthur advance with his spear, he rushed to meet him with drawn sword. Arthur caught Sir Modred below the shield and drove his spear through his body; Sir Modred, knowing that the wound was mortal, thrust himself up to the handle of the spear, and then, brandishing his sword in both hands, struck Arthur on the side of the helmet, cutting through it and into the skull beneath; then he crashed to the ground, gruesome and dead.

King Arthur fainted many times as Sir Lucas and Sir Bedi-

[20]*carnage:* bloodshed

vere struggled with him to a small chapel nearby, where they managed to ease his wounds a little. When Arthur came to, he thought he heard cries coming from the battlefield.

"Sir Lucas, I pray you, find out who cries on the battle-field," he said.

Wounded as he was, Sir Lucas hobbled painfully to the field, and there in the moonlight saw the camp followers stealing gold and jewels from the dead, and murdering the wounded. He returned to the king and reported to him what he had seen, and then added:

"My lord, it surely would be better to move you to the nearest town?"

"My wounds forbid it. But alas for the good Sir Launcelot! How sadly I have missed him today! And now I must die—as Sir Gawain warned me I would—repenting our quarrel with my last breath."

Sir Lucas and Sir Bedivere made one further attempt to lift the king. He fainted as they did so. Then Sir Lucas fainted as part of his intestines broke through a wound in the stomach. When the king came to, he saw Sir Lucas lying dead with foam at his mouth.

"Sweet Jesu, give him succor!"[21] he said. "This noble knight had died trying to save my life—alas that this was so!"

Sir Bedivere wept for his brother.

"Sir Bedivere, weep no more," said King Arthur, "for you can save neither your brother nor me; and I would ask you to take my sword Excalibur to the shore of the lake and throw it in the water. Then return to me and tell me what you have seen."

"My lord, as you command, it shall be done."

Sir Bedivere took the sword, but when he came to the water's edge, it appeared so beautiful that he could not bring himself to throw it in, so instead he hid it by a tree, and then returned to the king.

"Sir Bedivere, what did you see?"

"My lord, I saw nothing but the wind upon the waves."

"Then you did not obey me; I pray you, go swiftly again, and this time fulfill my command."

[21]*succor:* aid

Sir Bedivere went and returned again, but this time too he had failed to fulfill the king's command.

"Sir Bedivere, what did you see?"

"My lord, nothing but the lapping of the waves."

"Sir Bedivere, twice you have betrayed me! And for the sake only of my sword: it is unworthy of you! Now I pray you, do as I command, for I have not long to live."

This time Sir Bedivere wrapped the girdle around the sheath and hurled it as far as he could into the water. A hand appeared from below the surface, took the sword, waved it thrice, and disappeared again. Sir Bedivere returned to the king and told him what he had seen.

"Sir Bedivere, I pray you now help me hence, or I fear it will be too late."

Sir Bedivere carried the king to the water's edge, and there found a barge in which sat many beautiful ladies with their queen. All were wearing black hoods, and when they saw the king, they raised their voices in a piteous lament.

"I pray you, set me in the barge," said the king.

Sir Bedivere did so, and one of the ladies laid the king's head in her lap; then the queen spoke to him:

"My dear brother, you have stayed too long: I fear that the wound on your head is already cold."

Thereupon they rowed away from the land and Sir Bedivere wept to see them go.

"My lord King Arthur, you have deserted me! I am alone now, and among enemies."

"Sir Bedivere, take what comfort you may, for my time is passed, and now I must be taken to Avalon[22] for my wound to be healed. If you hear of me no more, I beg you pray for my soul."

The barge slowly crossed the water and out of sight while the ladies wept. Sir Bedivere walked alone into the forest and there remained for the night.

In the morning he saw beyond the trees of a copse[23] a small hermitage. He entered and found a hermit kneeling

[22]*Avalon:* in Celtic mythology, the happy underworld of the dead where Morgan le Fay was said to live and from which Arthur was expected to return

[23]*copse:* grove

down by a fresh tomb. The hermit was weeping as he prayed, and then Sir Bedivere recognized him as the Archbishop of Canterbury, who had been banished by Sir Modred.

"Father, I pray you, tell me, whose tomb is this?"

"My son, I do not know. At midnight the body was brought here by a company of ladies. We buried it, they lit a hundred candles for the service, and rewarded me with a thousand bezants."[24]

"Father, King Arthur lies buried in this tomb."

Sir Bedivere fainted when he had spoken, and when he came to he begged the Archbishop to allow him to remain at the hermitage and end his days in fasting and prayer.

"Father, I wish only to be near to my true liege."

"My son, you are welcome; and do I not recognize you as Sir Bedivere the Bold, brother to Sir Lucas the Butler?"

Thus the Archbishop and Sir Bedivere remained at the hermitage, wearing the habits of hermits and devoting themselves to the tomb with fasting and prayers of contrition.

Such was the death of King Arthur as written down by Sir Bedivere. By some it is told that there were three queens on the barge: Queen Morgan le Fay, the Queen of North Galys, and the Queen of the Waste Lands; and others include the name of Nyneve, the Lady of the Lake who had served King Arthur well in the past, and had married the good knight Sir Pelleas.

In many parts of Britain it is believed that King Arthur did not die and that he will return to us and win fresh glory and the Holy Cross of our Lord Jesus Christ; but for myself I do not believe this, and would leave him buried peacefully in his tomb at Glastonbury, where the Archbishop of Canterbury and Sir Bedivere humbled themselves, and with prayers and fasting honored his memory. And inscribed on his tomb, men say, is this legend:

Hic iacet Arthurus, rex quondam rexque futurus.[25]

[24]*bezants:* gold coins
[25]*Hic iacet . . .futurus:* Here lies Arthur, the once and future King.

FOR DISCUSSION

1. In his preface to Malory's *Le Morte d'Arthur,* Caxton stated that he agreed to print his work "to the intent that noble men may see and learn the noble acts of chivalry, the gentle and virtuous deeds that some knights used in those days, by which they came to honor; and how they that were vicious were punished and oft put to shame and rebuke." Point out, in the legends you have just read, examples of these acts and deeds and instances in which vicious knights were punished, shamed, or rebuked.
2. Both Christian and pagan beliefs are represented in *Le Morte d'Arthur.* What evidence of both do you find in these legends? How do you explain the attitude toward taking the life of another person? What oath do Knights of the Round Table take? How well do the knights in these legends abide by this oath?
3. After the death of King Uther, why does the whole of Britain stand in jeopardy? Why is the nobility summoned to London? Do you think Merlin and the Archbishop believe (1) that Arthur is not the "true successor" or (2) that the miraculous revelation will prove to everyone that he is? Discuss.
4. Why is a tournament proclaimed? How is it directly related to Arthur's winning recognition as the "true successor"? What information is unknown to Arthur and to many of the dukes and barons? How are the nobles finally persuaded to swear allegiance to Arthur?
5. What reservations does Merlin have about King Arthur's marriage to Gwynevere? How does her father demonstrate his appreciation of the great honor King Arthur had paid him? How does Merlin fill most of the empty seats? What circumstances lead to the knighting of Gawain and Torre? Why is Gawain angered by the honor shown King Pellinore? What seats remain empty and why?
6. In what ways is the event witnessed by the guests "unusual"? In response to Merlin's warning, whom does Arthur name to defend the honor of his court, and what quest does each have to accomplish? What are the consequences if he should fail?
7. Although Sir Gawain accomplishes his quest, he receives from Queen Gwynevere a stern rebuke. Why? What series of events lead Sir Blamoure to beg for mercy? Why does one of Bla-

moure's defenders accuse Gawain of dishonoring the order of knighthood? How are he and Gaheris saved on two occasions by the ladies of the castle? On what condition is Gawain allowed to return to Camelot?

8. How is Sir Torre assisted in his quest? What warning does he receive from the lady in the pavilion? Why couldn't he grant the knight's plea for mercy? How is he rewarded both by the lady whose wish he had granted and by King Arthur?
9. King Pellinore also receives a rebuke from Queen Gwynevere when he returns from his quest. What has he done to deserve it? How does he deal with the knight who has seized the lady in King Arthur's court? What secret plot against King Arthur does he overhear? Why does he say to Merlin, "May God show His mercy yet"?
10. That Malory names his account *Le Morte d'Arthur* is clear evidence of the popularity of the legend about King Arthur's tragic death. What is Arthur warned against, and by whom? How does "chance" undo all his efforts to avoid combat with Sir Modred? Why does he turn a deaf ear to the entreaties of his two remaining knights? How does he receive his fatal wound?
11. What last command does King Arthur give Sir Bedivere that this loyal knight is reluctant to obey? The hand that rose out of the lake could hardly be real. What about the barge and its occupants? How do you account for the seeming contradiction between Arthur's statement to Bedivere as the barge leaves the shore and the Archbiship's statement at the tomb? What belief, held by many Britons, was not shared by Malory? Which belief is supported by the legend inscribed on Arthur's tomb?
12. The three major elements of a good narrative are setting, plot, and character. In these legends, which of tho three is dominant?
13. As a rule, the main characters in a story are portrayed by what they say, think, and do, by what other characters say about them, and by the comments the author makes. A well-portrayed character "comes to life" as a flesh-and-blood individual whom you can picture in your mind and whose thoughts and feelings you can share vicariously. In your opinion, how well are the main characters in these legends portrayed? What, if anything, would you like to know about them but are not told? Is it essential to the kind of account Malory wrote? Discuss.

FOR COMPOSITION

1. In a short composition tell why, in your opinion, the miraculous events recounted in these legends do, or do not, seem plausible. If they do, explain how you think Malory made them seem plausible.
2. Select the two or three incidents recounted in these legends which impressed you the most. Perhaps they were especially dramatic, blood-curdling, appealing to the emotions, fantastic. In several paragraphs describe them briefly and explain what impressed you and why.
3. Merlin seems to be "the power behind the throne." Write a paragraph explaining (1) what part he played in the events recounted in these legends, and (2) what seemed to be the relationship between him and Arthur.
4. If you have read *Sir Gawain and the Green Knight*, you are aware that the Gawain portrayed by the "Pearl poet" is quite different from the Gawain portrayed by Malory. In a short composition, point out what you believe the difference is. Support your opinion with evidence based on your reading of each account.

John Bunyan

Although John Bunyan's purpose was to serve God rather than the Muses, his literary output was impressive in both quantity and quality. The number of works he wrote is estimated to be from forty to fifty, with three or four of them enjoying a popular success that more literary-minded writers might well envy. Even in his own lifetime *The Pilgrim's Progress* sold over 100,000 copies. It became, next to the Bible, the most widely read book in all of English literature.

The success of this self-made writer can be attributed partly to the universality of his theme: the spiritual journey of a man who encounters various adventures as he travels toward his heavenly goal. Bunyan brought to this story, with its strong resemblance to the trials of Everyman in medieval allegory, an untutored but vigorous genius for making the religious parable come alive. One critic has written:

> As a writer, Bunyan has a natural gift that is undeniable; he feels and perceives with the greatest keenness; he knows how to express what he perceives; he knows how to tell a tale, to link up incidents in a drama; his style, racy and full of sap, has nevertheless ease, lucidity, order, a sense of construction quite unexpected in one of so little culture.*

*Legouis and Cazamian, *op. cit.*, p. 719.

from The Pilgrim's Progress

The full title of the work from which these passages are taken is *The Pilgrim's Progress from This World to That Which Is to Come.* The entire story is told as a dream allegory, with Christian as the central figure. The opening passage reveals how he came to "set forth" from his home in the City of Destruction in search of "eternal life."

CHRISTIAN SETS FORTH

As I walked through the wilderness of this world, I lighted on a certain place where was a Den, and I laid me down in that place to sleep; and, as I slept, I dreamed a dream. I dreamed, and behold I saw a man clothed with rags, standing in a certain place, with his face from his own house, a book in his hand, and a great burden upon his back. I looked and saw him open the book and read therein; and, as he read, he wept, and trembled; and not being able longer to contain, he brake out with a lamentable cry, saying, "What shall I do?"

In this plight, therefore, he went home and refrained himself as long as he could, that his wife and children should not perceive his distress; but he could not be silent long, because that his trouble increased. Wherefore at length he brake[1] his mind to his wife and children; and thus he began to talk to them. O my dear wife, said he, and you the children of my bowels, I, your dear friend, am in myself undone by reason of a burden that lieth hard upon me; moreover, I am for certain informed that this our city will be burned with fire from heaven, in which fearful overthrow both myself, with thee, my wife, and you my sweet babes, shall miserably come to ruin, except (the which yet I see not) some way of escape can be found, whereby we may be delivered. At this his relations were sore[2] amazed; not for that they believed that what he had said to them was true, but because they

[1]*brake:* unburdened
[2]*sore:* greatly

thought that some frenzy distemper had got into his head; therefore, it drawing towards night, and they hoping that sleep might settle his brains, with all haste they got him to bed. But the night was as troublesome to him as the day; wherefore, instead of sleeping, he spent it in sighs and tears. So, when the morning was come, they would know how he did. He told them, Worse and worse; he also set to talking to them again: but they began to be hardened. They also thought to drive away his distemper by harsh and surly carriages[3] to him; sometimes they would deride, sometimes they would chide, and sometimes they would quite neglect him. Wherefore he began to retire himself to his chamber, to pray for and pity them, and also to condole[4] his own misery; he would also walk solitarily in the fields, sometimes reading, and sometimes praying: and thus for some days he spent his time.

Now, I saw, upon a time, when he was walking in the fields, that he was, as he was wont,[5] reading in his book, and greatly distressed in his mind; and as he read, he burst out, as he had done before, crying, "What shall I do to be saved?"

I saw also that he looked this way and that way, as if he would run; yet he stood still, because, as I perceived, he could not tell which way to go. I looked then, and saw a man named Evangelist coming to him, who asked, Wherefore dost thou cry?

He answered, Sir, I perceive by the book in my hand that I am condemned to die, and after that to come to judgment, and I find that I am not willing to do the first, nor able to do the second.

> *Christian* no sooner leaves the World but meets
> *Evangelist*, who lovingly him greets
> With tidings of another; and doth show
> Him how to mount to that from this below.

Then said Evangelist, Why not willing to die, since this life is attended with so many evils? The man answered,

[3]*carriages:* conduct
[4]*condole:* lament
[5]*wont:* accustomed

d saw every day the flowers appear in the earth, and heard e voice of the turtle[7] in the land. In this country the sun ineth night and day; wherefore this was beyond the Valley the Shadow of Death, and also out of the reach of Giant espair, neither could they from this place so much as see oubting Castle. Here they were within sight of the city ey were going to, also here met them some of the inhabi-nts thereof; for in this land the Shining Ones commonly alked, because it was upon the borders of heaven. In this nd also, the contract between the bride and the bride-room was renewed; yea, here, "As the bridegroom rejoiceth ver the bride, so did their God rejoice over them." Here hey had no want of corn and wine, for in this place they met vith abundance of what they had sought for in all their ilgrimage. Here they heard voices from out of the city, oud voices, saying, "Say ye to the daughter of Zion, behold, hy salvation cometh! Behold, his reward is with him!" Here all the inhabitants of the country called them, "The ıoly people, The redeemed of the Lord, Sought out," etc.

Now, as they walked in this land, they had more rejoicing than in parts more remote from the kingdom to which they were bound; and drawing near to the city, they had yet a more perfect view thereof. It was builded of pearls and precious stones, also the street thereof was paved with gold; so that by reason of the natural glory of the city, and the reflection of the sunbeams upon it, Christian with desire fell sick; Hopeful also had a fit or two of the same disease. Wherefore, here they lay by it a while, crying out, because of their pangs, "If ye find my beloved, tell him that I am sick of love."

But, being a little strengthened, and better able to bear their sickness, they walked on their way, and came yet nearer and nearer, where were orchards, vineyards, and gardens, and their gates opened into the highway. Now, as they came up to these places, behold the gardener stood in the way, to whom the pilgrims said, Whose goodly vineyards and gardens are these? He answered, They are the King's, and are planted here for his own delight, and also for the solace of pilgrims. So

[7]*turtle:* turtle-dove

Because I fear that this burden that is upon n
sink me lower than the grave, and I shall fall i
And, sir, if I be not fit to go to prison, I am not fit
ment, and from thence to execution; and the thou
things make me cry.

Then said Evangelist, If this be thy condition, w
thou still? He answered, Because I know not wh
Then he gave him a parchment roll, and there
within, "Flee from the wrath to come."

The man therefore read it, and looking upon
very carefully, said, Whither must I fly? Then said
pointing with his finger over a very wide field, I
yonder wicket-gate? The man said, No. Then said
Do you see yonder shining light? He said, I think
said Evangelist, Keep that light in your eye, and go
thereto: so shalt thou see the gate; at which w
knockest it shall be told thee what thou shalt do.
in my dream that the man began to run. Now, he ha
far from his own door, but his wife and children per
began to cry after him to return; but the man put his
his ears, and ran on, crying, Life! life! eternal lif
looked not behind him, but fled towards the midd
plain.

THE CELESTIAL CITY

After many trials, obstacles, hardships, and temptations
tian, with his friend Hopeful, comes at last within sight
Celestial City.

Now I saw in my dream, that by this time the pilgrim
got over the Enchanted Ground, and entering into the c
of Beulah, whose air was very sweet and pleasant, th
lying directly through it, they solaced themselves the
a season. Yea, here they heard continually the singing of

[6]*Tophet:* Hell

the gardener had them into the vineyards, and bid them refresh themselves with the dainties. He also showed them there the King's walks, and the arbors where he delighted to be; and here they tarried and slept.

Now I beheld in my dream, that they talked more in their sleep at this time than ever they did in all their journey; and being in a muse thereabout, the gardener said even to me, Wherefore musest thou at the matter? It is the nature of the fruit of the grapes of these vineyards to go down so sweetly as to cause the lips of them that are asleep to speak.

So I saw that when they awoke, they addressed themselves to go up to the city; but, as I said, the reflection of the sun upon the city (for "the city was pure gold,") was so extremely glorious, that they could not, as yet, with open face behold it, but through an instrument made for that purpose. So I saw, that as I went on, there met them two men, in raiment that shone like gold; also their faces shone as the light.

These men asked the pilgrims whence they came; and they told them. They also asked them where they had lodged, what difficulties and dangers, what comforts and pleasures they had met in the way; and they told them. Then said the men that met them, You have but two difficulties more to meet with, and then you are in the city.

Christian then, and his companion, asked the men to go along with them; so they told them they would. But, said they, you must obtain it by your own faith. So I saw in my dream that they went on together, until they came in sight of the gate.

Now, I further saw, that betwixt them and the gate was a river, but there was no bridge to go over: the river was very deep. At the sight, therefore, of this river, the pilgrims were much stunned; but the men that went with them said, You must go through, or you cannot come at the gate.

The pilgrims then began to inquire if there was no other way to the gate; to which they answered, Yes; but there hath not any, save two, to wit, Enoch and Elijah,[8] been permitted to tread that path, since the foundation of the world, nor

[8]*Enoch and Elijah:* prophets

shall, until the last trumpet shall sound. The pilgrims then, especially Christian, began to despond[9] in their minds, and looked this way and that, but no way could be found by them, by which they might escape the river. Then they asked the men if the waters were all of a depth. They said, No; yet they could not help them in that case; for, said they, you shall find it deeper or shallower, as you believe in the King of the place.

They then addressed themselves to the water; and entering, Christian began to sink, and crying out to his good friend Hopeful, he said, I sink in deep waters; the billows go over my head, all his waves go over me! Selah.[10]

Then said the other, Be of good cheer, my brother, I feel the bottom, and it is good. Then said Christian, Ah! my friend, "the sorrows of death have compassed me about"; I shall not see the land that flows with milk and honey; and with that a great darkness and horror fell upon Christian, so that he could not see before him. Also here he in great measure lost his senses, so that he could neither remember, nor orderly talk of any of those sweet refreshments that he had met with in the way of his pilgrimage. But all the words that he spake still tended to discover that he had horror of mind, and heart fears that he should die in that river, and never obtain entrance in at the gate. Here also, as they that stood by perceived, he was much in the troublesome thoughts of the sins that he had committed, both since and before he began to be a pilgrim. It was also observed that he was troubled with apparitions of hobgoblins and evil spirits, for ever and anon he would intimate so much by words. Hopeful, therefore, here had much ado to keep his brother's head above water; yea, sometimes he would be quite gone down, and then, ere a while, he would rise up again half dead. Hopeful also would endeavor to comfort him, saying, Brother, I see the gate, and men standing by to receive us; but Christian would answer, It is you, it is you they wait for; you have been Hopeful ever since I knew you. And so have you, said he to Christian. Ah, brother! said he, surely if I was right he would now arise to help me; but for my sins he hath brought me into the snare,

[9]*despond:* lose courage
[10]*Selah:* Amen

and hath left me. Then said Hopeful, My brother, you have quite forgot the text, where it is said of the wicked, "There are no bands[11] in their death, but their strength is firm. They are not in trouble as other men, neither are they plagued like other men." These troubles and distresses that you go through in these waters are no sign that God hath forsaken you; but are sent to try you, whether you will call to mind that which heretofore you have received of his goodness, and live upon him in your distresses.

Then I saw in my dream, that Christian was as in a muse a while. To whom also Hopeful added this word, Be of good cheer. Jesus Christ maketh thee whole; and with that Christian brake out with a loud voice, Oh! I see him again, and he tells me, "When thou passest through the waters, I will be with thee; and through the rivers, they shall not overflow thee." Then they both took courage, and the enemy was after that as still as a stone, until they were gone over. Christian therefore presently found ground to stand upon, and so it followed that the rest of the river was but shallow. Thus they got over. Now, upon the bank of the river, on the other side, they saw the two shining men again, who there waited for them; wherefore, being come out of the river, they saluted them saying, We are ministering spirits, sent forth to minister for those that shall be heirs of salvation. Thus they went along towards the gate.

> Now, now look how the holy pilgrims ride,
> Clouds are their Chariots, Angels are their Guide:
> Who would not here for him all hazards run,
> That thus provides for his when this world's done.

Now you must note that the city stood upon a mighty hill, but the pilgrims went up that hill with ease, because they had these two men to lead them up by the arms; also, they had left their mortal garments behind them in the river, for though they went in with them, they came out without them. They, therefore, went up here with much agility and speed, though the foundation upon which the city was framed was higher

[11]*bands:* honors

than the clouds. They, therefore, went up through the regions of the air, sweetly talking as they went, being comforted, because they safely got over the river, and had such glorious companions to attend them.

The talk they had with the Shining Ones was about the glory of the place; who told them that the beauty and glory of it was inexpressible. There, said they, is the "Mount Zion, the heavenly Jerusalem, the innumerable company of angels, and the spirits of just men made perfect." You are going now, said they, to the paradise of God, wherein you shall see the tree of life, and eat of the never-fading fruits thereof; and when you come there, you shall have white robes given you, and your walk and talk shall be every day with the King, even all the days of eternity. There you shall not see again such things as you saw when you were in the lower region upon the earth, to wit, sorrow, sickness, affliction, and death, "for the former things are passed away." You are now going to Abraham, to Isaac, and Jacob, and to the prophets—men that God hath taken away from the evil to come, and that are now resting upon their beds, each one walking in his righteousness. The men then asked, What must we do in the holy place? To whom it was answered, You must there receive the comforts of all your toil, and have joy for all your sorrow; you must reap what you have sown, even the fruit of all your prayers, and tears, and sufferings for the King by the way. In that place you must wear crowns of gold, and enjoy the perpetual sight and vision of the Holy One, for "there you shall see him as he is." There also you shall serve him continually with praise, with shouting, and thanksgiving, whom you desired to serve in the world, though with much difficulty, because of the infirmity of your flesh. There your eyes shall be delighted with seeing, and your ears with hearing the pleasant voice of the Mighty One. There you shall enjoy your friends again, that are gone thither before you; and there you shall with joy receive, even every one that follows into the holy place after you. There also shall you be clothed with glory and majesty, and put into an equipage[12] fit to ride out with the King of glory. When he shall come with the sound of trumpet in the

[12]*equipage:* carriage

clouds, as upon the wings of the wind, you shall come with him; and when he shall sit upon the throne of judgment, you shall sit by him; yea, and when he shall pass sentence upon all the workers of iniquity,[13] let them be angels or men, you also shall have a voice in that judgment, because they were his and your enemies. Also, when he shall again return to the city, you shall go too, with sound of trumpet, and be ever with him.

Now while they were thus drawing towards the gate, behold a company of the heavenly host came out to meet them; to whom it was said, by the other two Shining Ones, These are the men that have loved our Lord when they were in the world, and that have left all for his holy name; and he hath sent us to fetch them, and we have brought them thus far on their destined journey, that they may go in and look their Redeemer in the face with joy. Then the heavenly host gave a great shout, saying, "Blessed are they which are called unto the marriage supper of the Lamb." There came out also at this time to meet them, several of the King's trumpeters, clothed in white and shining raiment, who, with melodious noises, and loud, made even the heavens to echo with their sound. These trumpeters saluted Christian and his fellow with ten thousand welcomes from the world; and this they did with shouting, and sound of trumpet.

This done, they compassed them round on every side; some went before, some behind, and some on the right hand, some on the left (as it were to guard them through the upper regions), continually sounding as they went, with melodious noise, in notes on high: so that the very sight was to them that could behold it, as if heaven itself was come down to meet them. Thus, therefore, they walked on together; and as they walked, ever and anon these trumpeters, even with joyful sound, would, by mixing their music with looks and gestures, still signify to Christian and his brother, how welcome they were into their company, and with what gladness they came to meet them; and now were these two men, as it were, in heaven, before they came at it, being swallowed up with the sight of angels, and with hearing of their melodious notes.

[13]*iniquity:* wickedness

Here also they had the city itself in view, and they thought they heard all the bells therein to ring, to welcome them thereto. But above all, the warm and joyful thoughts that they had about their own dwelling there, with such company, and that for ever and ever. Oh, by what tongue or pen can their glorious joy be expressed! And thus they came up to the gate.

Now, when they were come up to the gate, there was written over it in letters of gold, "Blessed are they that do his commandments, that they may have right to the tree of life, and may enter in through the gates into the city."

Then I saw in my dream, that the Shining Men bid them call at the gate; the which, when they did, some looked from above over the gate, to wit, Enoch, Moses, and Elijah, etc., to whom it was said, These pilgrims are come from the City of Destruction, for the love that they bear to the King of this place; and then the pilgrims gave in unto them each man his certificate, which they had received in the beginning; those, therefore, were carried in to the King, who, when he had read them, said, Where are the men? To whom it was answered, They are standing without the gate. The King then commanded to open the gate, "That the righteous nation," said he, "which keepeth the truth, may enter in."

Now I saw in my dream that these two men went in at the gate: and lo, as they entered, they were transfigured, and they had raiment put on that shone like gold. There were also that met them with harps and crowns, and gave them to them —the harps to praise withal, and the crowns in token of honor. Then I heard in my dream that all the bells in the city rang again for joy, and that it was said unto them, "*Enter ye into the joy of your Lord.*" I also heard the men themselves, that they sang with a loud voice, saying, "*Blessing and honor, and glory, and power, be unto Him that sitteth upon the throne, and unto the Lamb, for ever and ever.*"

Now, just as the gates were opened to let in the men, I looked in after them, and, behold, the City shone like the sun; the streets also were paved with gold, and in them walked many men, with crowns on their heads, palms in their hands, and golden harps to sing praises withal.

There were also of them that had wings, and they answered

one another without intermission, saying, "Holy, holy, holy is the Lord." And after that they shut up the gates; which, when I had seen, I wished myself among them.

Now while I was gazing upon all these things, I turned my head to look back, and saw Ignorance come up to the river side; but he soon got over, and that without half that difficulty which the other two men met with. For it happened that there was then in that place, one Vain-hope, a ferryman, that with his boat helped him over; so he, as the other I saw, did ascend the hill, to come up to the gate, only he came alone; neither did any man meet him with the least encouragement. When he was come up to the gate, he looked up to the writing that was above, and then began to knock, supposing that entrance should have been quickly administered to him; but he was asked by the men that looked over the top of the gate, Whence came you? and what would you have? He answered, I have eat and drank in the presence of the King, and he has taught in our streets. Then they asked him for his certificate, that they might go in and show it to the King; so he fumbled in his bosom for one, and found none. Then said they, Have you none? But the man answered never a word. So they told the King, but he would not come down to see him, but commanded the two Shining Ones that conducted Christian and Hopeful to the City, to go out and take Ignorance, and bind him hand and foot, and have him away. Then they took him up, and carried him through the air, to the door that I saw in the side of the hill, and put him in there. Then I saw that there was a way to hell, even from the gates of heaven, as well as from the City of Destruction! So I awoke, and behold it was a dream.

FOR DISCUSSION

1. In view of the fact that Bunyan started writing this allegory in prison, what place might the Den signify? How would you interpret the expression "the wilderness of this world" in the opening line?

2. What is the "burden" that causes Christian's distress? Why does he want to escape from the city? What book do you think made him weep and cry out?
3. What is revealed about Evangelist and Christian by their conversation? What directions does Evangelist give Christian? In seeking his own salvation, is Christian justified in leaving his wife and children behind in the City of Destruction? Defend your answer.
4. Bunyan gives the name of The Enchanted Ground to that period of indulgence in the soul's journey when backsliding is a particularly dangerous possibility. Consult a good dictionary, as well as Isaiah 62:4, for the origin and significance of the name *Beulah.* Notice how Bunyan uses quotations from Isaiah.
5. What explanation can you offer for the pilgrims' inability to look upon the city of "pure gold" at this point in their journey? What do Christian and his companion Hopeful learn from the two men in shining raiment? Why is crossing the river such a harrowing experience for Christian? How does Hopeful try to help Christian? What restores Christian's courage? What might the river represent?
6. How are the pilgrims to spend eternity when they reach "the holy place"? Discuss the concept of heaven that Bunyan expresses here in the light of the kind of life that he and his fellow believers lead on this earth. Tell why the Celestial City does, or does not, meet the pilgrims' expectations.
7. Some critics have pointed out that in *The Pilgrim's Progress* Bunyan emphasizes Faith and Hope, but rarely mentions Charity. On the basis of your reading, do you think that charity—or love—is lacking in this work which characterizes Puritan culture? Discuss.

FOR COMPOSITION

1. Describe in your own words Christian's passage through the river, the cause and effect of his fear, and the help given him by Hopeful.
2. Write a report, to be read to the class, on another episode from *The Pilgrim's Progress* such as the one about Vanity Fair, Doubting Castle, or the Enchanted Ground. In your report tell what happened in the episode and indicate what the various characters and actions were intended to represent.

Jonathan Swift

"Style?" Jonathan Swift snorted; "Here's a fine pother about nothing; proper words in proper places make a true definition of a style." Yet for most writers prior to the eighteenth century, putting "proper words in proper places" was not an accomplished skill; and English prose was often heavy-handed and involved. The conciseness that Swift achieved had few precedents and is still envied for its "concentrated force and perfect clarity."

In *Gulliver's Travels,* Swift was so successful in achieving a simple, clear style that children have instinctively claimed the first part as their own. Because of this, older readers may overlook what a complex, adult, and amusing work *Gulliver's Travels* actually is. One critic has written:

> It is, of course, a satire on four aspects of man: the physical, the political, the intellectual, and the moral. The last three are inseparable, and when Swift writes of one he always has in view the others. It is also a brilliant parody of travel literature; and it is at once science fiction and a witty parody of science fiction. It expresses savage indignation at the follies, vices, and stupidities of men, and everywhere implicit in the book as a whole is an awareness of man's tragic insufficiency. But at the same time it is a great comic masterpiece, a fact that solemn and too-sensitive readers often miss.*

*Samuel Holt Monk, "The Pride of Lemuel Gulliver." *The Sewanee Review* (Winter, 1955), p. 48.

from Gulliver's Travels

The book known as *Gulliver's Travels* was originally published as *Travels into Several Remote Nations of the World* (in four parts) and was supposedly written by one Lemuel Gulliver. The name Gulliver, never used in the actual text, appeared on the title page as "first surgeon and then captain of several ships." The first voyage (Part I) took Gulliver to Lilliput, the land of pygmies; the second voyage (Part II), to Brobdingnag, the land of giants. Gulliver's third voyage (Part III) brought him to Laputa and nearby places, where he visited an absurd academy of science and a land where some unfortunates never die. His fourth voyage (Part IV) introduced him to the Houyhnhnms, a wonderful race of horses whose advanced culture and superior intelligence made men, called Yahoos, appear filthy, disgusting animals. In the following excerpt from the first voyage, Gulliver has just been taken prisoner by the tiny Lilliputians, who are treating him kindly; for to kill him, they reason, would be to risk causing an epidemic from the stench of his huge carcass.

from A VOYAGE TO LILLIPUT

CHAPTER THREE. *The Author diverts the Emperor and his nobility of both sexes, in a very uncommon manner. The diversions of the court of Lilliput described. The Author hath his liberty granted him upon certain conditions.*

My gentleness and good behaviour had gained so far on the Emperor and his court, and indeed upon the army and people in general, that I began to conceive hopes of getting my liberty in a short time. I took all possible methods to cultivate this favourable disposition. The natives came by degrees to be less apprehensive of any danger from me. I would sometimes lie down, and let five or six of them dance on my hand. And at last the boys and girls would venture to come and play at hide and seek in my hair. I had now made a good progress in understanding and speaking their language. The Emperor had a mind one day to entertain me with several of the country shows, wherein they exceed all nations I have known, both for dexterity and magnificence. I was diverted with none so much as that of the rope-dancers, performed upon a slender white thread, extended about two foot, and twelve inches from the ground. Upon which I shall desire liberty, with the reader's patience, to enlarge a little.

This diversion is only practised by those persons who are candidates for great employments and high favour at court. They were trained in this art from their youth, and are not always of noble birth, or liberal education. When a great office is vacant either by death or disgrace (which often happens) five or six of those candidates petition the Emperor to entertain his Majesty and the court with a dance on the rope; and whoever jumps the highest without falling, succeeds in the office. Very often the chief ministers themselves are commanded to show their skill, and to convince the Emperor that they have not lost their faculty. Flimnap, the Treasurer, is allowed to cut a caper on the straight rope, at least an inch higher than any other lord in the whole empire. I have seen him do the summerset several times together upon a trencher fixed on the rope, which is no thicker than a common packthread in England. My friend Reldresal, principal Secretary for Private Affairs, is, in my opinion, if I am not partial, the second after the Treasurer; the rest of the great officers are much upon a par.

These diversions are often attended with fatal accidents, whereof great numbers are on record. I myself have seen two or three candidates break a limb. But the danger is much greater when the ministers themselves are commanded to show their dexterity: for by contending to excel themselves and their fellows, they strain so far, that there is hardly one of them who hath not received a fall, and some of them two or three. I was assured that a year or two before my arrival, Flimnap would have infallibly broke his neck, if one of the King's cushions, that accidentally lay on the ground, had not weakened the force of his fall.[1]

[1]Eighteenth-century readers recognized in Flimnap a portrait of Sir Robert Walpole, who was appointed in 1715 as chancellor of the exchequer and first lord of the treasury. Reldresal may represent Walpole's successor in 1717. In 1721, through the influence of someone close to the King, Walpole was reinstated as chancellor.

There is likewise another diversion, which is only shown before the Emperor and Empress, and first minister, upon particular occasions. The Emperor lays on a table three fine silken threads of six inches long. One is blue, the other red, and the third green. These threads are proposed as prizes for those persons whom the Emperor hath a mind to distinguish by a peculiar mark of his favour. The ceremony is performed in his Majesty's great chamber of state, where the candidates are to undergo a trial of dexterity very different from the former, and such as I have not observed the least resemblance of in any other country of the old or the new world. The Emperor holds a stick in his hands, both ends parallel to the horizon, while the candidates, advancing one by one, sometimes leap over the stick, sometimes creep under it backwards and forwards several times, according as the stick is advanced or depressed. Sometimes the Emperor holds one end of the stick, and his first minister the other; sometimes the minister has it entirely to himself. Whoever performs his part with most agility, and holds out the longest in *leaping* and *creeping*, is rewarded with the blue-coloured silk; the red is given to the next, and the green to the third, which they all wear girt twice round about the middle; and you see few great persons about this court who are not adorned with one of these girdles.

The horses of the army, and those of the royal stables, having been daily led before me, were no longer shy, but would come up to my very feet without starting. The riders would leap them over my hand as I held it on the ground, and one of the Emperor's huntsmen, upon a large courser, took my foot, shoe and all; which was indeed a prodigious leap. I had the good fortune to divert the Emperor one day, after a very extraordinary manner. I desired he would order several sticks of two foot high, and the thickness of an ordinary cane, to be brought me; whereupon his Majesty commanded the master of his woods to give directions accordingly; and the next morning six woodmen arrived with as many carriages, drawn by eight horses to each. I took nine of these sticks, and fixing them firmly in the ground in a quadrangular figure, two foot and a half square, I took four other sticks, and tied them parallel at each corner, about two foot from the ground; then

I fastened my handkerchief to the nine sticks that stood erect, and extended it on all sides till it was as tight as the top of a drum; and the four parallel sticks rising about five inches higher than the handkerchief served as ledges on each side. When I had finished my work, I desired the Emperor to let a troop of his best horse, twenty-four in number, come and exercise upon this plain. His Majesty approved of the proposal, and I took them up one by one in my hands, ready mounted and armed, with the proper officers to exercise them. As soon as they got into order, they divided into two parties, performed mock skirmishes, discharged blunt arrows, drew their swords, fled and pursued, attacked and retired; and in short discovered the best military discipline I ever beheld. The parallel sticks secured them and their horses from falling over the stage; and the Emperor was so much delighted, that he ordered this entertainment to be repeated several days; and once was pleased to be lifted up and give the word of command; and, with great difficulty, persuaded even the Empress herself to let me hold her in her close chair, within two yards of the stage, from whence she was able to take a full view of the whole performance. It was my good fortune that no ill accident happened in these entertainments; only once a fiery horse that belonged to one of the captains, pawing with his hoof struck a hole in my handkerchief, and his foot slipping, he overthrew his rider and himself; but I immediately relieved them both; for covering the hole with one hand, I set down the troop with the other, in the same manner as I took them up. The horse that fell was strained in the left shoulder, but the rider got no hurt, and I repaired my handkerchief as well as I could: however, I would not trust to the strength of it any more in such dangerous enterprises.

About two or three days before I was set at liberty, as I was entertaining the court with these kinds of feats, there arrived an express to inform his Majesty that some of his subjects riding near the place where I was first taken up, had seen a great black substance lying on the ground, very oddly shaped, extending its edges round as wide as his Majesty's bedchamber, and rising up in the middle as high as a man: that it was no living creature, as they at first apprehended, for it lay on the grass without motion, and some of them had walked round it several times: that by mounting upon each other's shoulders, they had got to the top, which was flat and even; and stamping upon it they found it was hollow within: that they humbly conceived it might be something belonging to the Man-Mountain, and if his Majesty pleased, they would undertake to bring it with only five horses. I presently knew what they meant, and was glad at heart to receive this intelligence. It seems, upon my first reaching the shore after our shipwreck, I was in such confusion, that before I came to the place where I went to sleep, my hat, which I had fastened with a string to my head while I was rowing, and had stuck on all the time I was swimming, fell off after I came to land, the string, as I conjecture, breaking by some accident which I never observed, but thought my hat had been lost at sea. I entreated his Imperial Majesty to give orders it might be brought to me as soon as possible, describing to him the use and the nature of it: and the next day the waggoners arrived with it, but not in a very good condition; they had bored two holes in the brim, within an inch and half of the edge, and fastened two hooks in the holes; these hooks were tied by a long cord to the harness, and thus my hat was dragged along for above half an English mile: but the ground in that country being extremely smooth and level, it received less damage than I expected. . . .

I had sent so many memorials and petitions for my liberty, that his Majesty at length mentioned the matter, first in the cabinet, and then in a full council; where it was opposed by none, except Skyresh Bolgolam, who was pleased, without any provocation, to be my mortal enemy. But it was carried against him by the whole board, and confirmed by the Emperor. That minister was *Galbet*, or Admiral of the Realm, very much in his master's confidence, and a person well versed in affairs, but of a morose and sour complexion. However, he was at length persuaded to comply; but prevailed that the articles and conditions upon which I should be set free, and to which I must swear, should be drawn up by himself. These articles were brought to me by Skyresh Bolgolam in person, attended by two under-secretaries, and several persons of distinction. After they were read, I was demanded to swear to the performance of them; first in the manner of my own country, and afterwards in the method prescribed by their laws; which was to hold my right foot in my left hand, to place the middle finger of my right hand on the crown of my head, and my thumb on the tip of my right ear. But because the reader may perhaps be curious to have some idea of the style and manner of expression peculiar to that people, as well as to know the articles upon which I recovered my liberty, I have made a translation of the whole instrument word for word, as near as I was able; which I here offer to the public.

GOLBASTO MOMAREN EVLAME GURDILO SHEFIN MULLY ULLY GUE, most mighty Emperor of Lilliput, delight and terror of the universe, whose dominions extend five thousand *blustrugs* (about twelve miles in circumference) to the extremities of the globe; monarch of all monarchs, taller than the sons of men; whose feet press down to the centre, and whose head strikes against the sun; at whose nod the princes of the earth shake their knees; pleasant as the spring, comfortable as the summer, fruitful as autumn, dreadful as winter. His most sublime Majesty proposeth to the Man-Mountain, lately arrived at our celestial dominions, the following articles, which by a solemn oath he shall be obliged to perform.

First, The Man-Mountain shall not depart from our dominions, without our licence under our great seal.

Secondly, He shall not presume to come into our metropolis, without our express order; at which time the inhabitants shall have two hours' warning to keep within their doors.

Thirdly, The said Man-Mountain shall confine his walks to our principal high roads, and not offer to walk or lie down in a meadow or field of corn.

Fourthly, As he walks the said roads, he shall take the utmost care not to trample upon the bodies of any of our loving subjects, their horses, or carriages; nor take any of our said subjects into his hands, without their own consent.

Fifthly, If an express requires extraordinary dispatch, the Man-Mountain shall be obliged to carry in his pocket the messenger and horse a six days' journey once in every moon, and return the said messenger back (if so required) safe to our Imperial Presence.

Sixthly, He shall be our ally against our enemies in the Island of Blefuscu, and do his utmost to destroy their fleet, which is now preparing to invade us.

Seventhly, That the said Man-Mountain shall, at his times of leisure, be aiding and assisting to our workmen, in helping to raise certain great stones, towards covering the wall of the principal park, and our other royal buildings.

Eighthly, That the said Man-Mountain shall, in two moons' time, deliver in an exact survey of the circumference of our dominions by a computation of his own paces round the coast.

Lastly, That upon his solemn oath to observe all the above articles, the said Man-Mountain shall have a daily allowance of meat and drink sufficient for the support of 1728 of our subjects; with free access to our Royal Person, and other marks of our favour. Given at our Palace at Belfaborac the twelfth day of the ninety-first moon of our reign.

I swore and subscribed to these articles with great cheerfulness and content, although some of them were not so honourable as I could have wished; which proceeded wholly from the malice of Skyresh Bolgolam the High Admiral; whereupon my chains were immediately unlocked, and I was at full liberty; the Emperor himself, in person, did me the honour to be by at the whole ceremony. I made my acknowledgments by prostrating myself at his Majesty's feet: but he commanded me to rise; and after many gracious expressions, which, to avoid the censure of vanity, I shall not repeat, he added, that he hoped I should prove a useful servant, and well deserve all the favours he had already conferred upon me, or might do for the future.

The reader may please to observe, that in the last article for the recovery of my liberty the Emperor stipulates to allow me a quantity of meat and drink sufficient for the support of 1728 Lilliputians. Some time after, asking a friend at court how they came to fix on that determinate number, he told me that his Majesty's mathematicians, having taken the height of my body by the help of a quadrant, and finding it to exceed theirs in the proportion of twelve to one, they concluded from the similarity of their bodies, that mine must contain at last 1728 of theirs, and consequently would require as much food as was necessary to support that number of Lilliputians. By which the reader may conceive an idea of the ingenuity of that people, as well as the prudent and exact economy of so great a prince.

CHAPTER FOUR. *Mildendo, the metropolis of Lilliput, described, together with the Emperor's palace. A conversation between the Author and a principal Secretary, concerning the affairs of that empire: the Author's offers to serve the Emperor in his wars.*

The first request I made after I had obtained my liberty, was, that I might have licence to see Mildendo, the metropolis; which the Emperor easily granted me, but with a special charge to do no hurt either to the inhabitants or their houses. The people had notice by proclamation of my design to visit the town. The wall which encompassed it is two foot and an half high, and at least eleven inches broad, so that a coach and horses may be driven very safely round it; and it is flanked with strong towers at ten foot distance. I stept over the great Western Gate, and passed very gently, and sideling through the two principal streets, only in my short waistcoat, for fear of damaging the roofs and eaves of the house with the skirts of my coat. I walked with the utmost circumspection, to avoid treading on any stragglers, who might remain in the streets, although the orders were very strict, that all people should keep in their houses at their own peril. The garret windows and tops of houses were so crowded with spectators, that I thought in all my travels I had not seen a more populous place. The city is an exact square, each side of the wall being five hundred foot long. The two great streets, which run across and divide it into four quarters, are five foot wide. The lanes and alleys, which I could not enter, but only viewed them as I passed, are from twelve to eighteen inches. The town is capable of holding five hundred thousand souls. The houses are from three to five stories. The shops and markets well provided.

The Emperor's palace is in the centre of the city, where the two great streets meet. It is enclosed by a wall of two foot high, and twenty foot distant from the buildings. I had his Majesty's permission to step over this wall; and the space being so wide between that and the palace, I could easily view it on every side. The outward court is a square of forty foot, and includes two other courts: in the inmost are the royal apartments, which I was very desirous to see, but found it extremely difficult; for the great gates, from one square into another, were but eighteen inches high and seven inches wide. Now the buildings of the outer court were at least five foot high, and it was impossible for me to stride over them without infinite damage to the pile, though the walls were strongly built of hewn stone, and four inches thick. At the same time the Emperor had a great desire that I should see the magnificence of his palace; but this I was not able to do till three days after, which I spent in cutting down with my knife some of the largest trees in the royal park, about an hundred yards distant from the city. Of these trees I made two stools, each about three foot high, and strong enough to bear my weight. The people having received notice a second time, I went again through the city to the palace, with my two stools in my hands. When I came to the side of the outer court, I stood upon one stool, and took the other in my hand: this I lifted over the roof, and gently set it down on the space between the first and second court, which was eight foot wide. I then stept over the buildings very conveniently from one stool to the other, and drew up the first after me with a hooked stick. By this contrivance I got into the inmost court; and lying down upon my side, I applied my face to the windows of the middle stories, which were left open on purpose, and discovered the most splendid apartments that can be imagined. There I saw the Empress, and the young Princes, in their several lodgings, with their chief attendants about them. Her

Imperial Majesty was pleased to smile very graciously upon me, and gave me out of the window her hand to kiss.

But I shall not anticipate the reader with farther descriptions of this kind, because I reserve them for a greater work, which is now almost ready for the press; containing a general description of this empire, from its first erection, through a long series of princes, with a particular account of their wars and politics, laws, learning, and religion, their plants and animals, their peculiar manners and customs, with other matters very curious and useful; my chief design at present being only to relate such events and transactions as happened to the public, or to myself, during a residence of about nine months in that empire.

One morning, about a fortnight after I had obtained my liberty, Reldresal, principal Secretary (as they style him) of Private Affairs, came to my house attended only by one servant. He ordered his coach to wait at a distance, and desired I would give him an hour's audience; which I readily consented to, on account of his quality and personal merits, as well as the many good offices he had done me during my solicitations at court. I offered to lie down, that he might the more conveniently reach my ear; but he chose rather to let me hold him in my hand during our conversation. He began with compliments on my liberty; said he might pretend to some merit in it; but, however, added, that if it had not been for the present situation of things at court, perhaps I might not have obtained it so soon. "For," said he, "as flourishing a condition as we may appear to be in to foreigners, we labour under two mighty evils; a violent faction at home, and the danger of an invasion by a most potent enemy from abroad. As to the first, you are to understand, that for above seventy moons past, there have been two struggling parties in this empire, under the names of *Tramecksan* and *Slamecksan*, from the high and low heels on their shoes, by which they distinguish themselves.[2]

[2]The High Heels represent the Tories or conservatives who favored older and more traditional and formal religious worship, or a "high church" service. The Whigs (represented by the Low Heels), who were more liberal, advocated liberalizing the forms of worship, or a "low church" service. While George I favored the Whigs (led by Walpole), the Prince of Wales, heir to the throne, vacillated between the two parties.

"It is alleged indeed, that the high heels are most agreeable to our ancient constitution: but however this be, his Majesty hath determined to make use of only low heels in the administration of the government, and all offices in the gift of the Crown; as you cannot but observe; and particularly, that his Majesty's Imperial heels are lower at least by a *drurr* than any of his court; (*drurr* is a measure about the fourteenth part of an inch). The animosities between these two parties run so high, that they will neither eat nor drink, nor talk with each other. We compute the *Tramecksan*, or High-Heels, to exceed us in number; but the power is wholly on our side. We apprehend his Imperial Highness, the Heir to the Crown, to have some tendency towards the High-Heels; at least we can plainly discover one of his heels higher than the other, which gives him a hobble in his gait. Now, in the midst of these intestine disquiets, we are threatened with an invasion from the Island of Blefuscu,[3] which is the other great empire of the universe, almost as large and powerful as this of his Majesty. For as to what we have heard you affirm, that there are other kingdoms and states in the world, inhabited by human creatures as large as yourself, our philosophers are in much doubt; and would rather conjecture that you dropped from the moon, or one of the stars; because it is certain, that an hundred mortals of your bulk would, in a short time, destroy all the fruits and cattle of his Majesty's dominions. Besides, our histories of six thousand moons make no mention of any other regions, than the two great empires of Lilliput and Blefuscu. Which two mighty powers have, as I was going to tell you, been engaged in a most obstinate war for six and thirty moons past. It began upon the following occasion. It is allowed on all hands, that the primitive way of breaking eggs before we eat them, was upon the larger end: but his present Majesty's grandfather, while he was a boy, going to eat an egg, and breaking it according to the ancient practice, happened to cut one of his fingers. Whereupon the Emperor his father published an edict, commanding all his subjects, upon great penalties, to break the smaller end of their eggs. The people so highly resented this law, that our histories tell us there have

[3]Blefuscu represents France.

been six rebellions raised on that account; wherein one Emperor lost his life, and another his crown. These civil commotions were constantly fomented by the monarchs of Blefuscu; and when they were quelled, the exiles always fled for refuge to that empire. It is computed, that eleven thousand persons have, at several times, suffered death, rather than submit to break their eggs at the smaller end. Many hundred large volumes have been published upon this controversy: but the books of the Big-Endians have been long forbidden, and the whole party rendered incapable by law of holding employments.[4] During the course of these troubles, the Emperors of Blefuscu did frequently expostulate by their ambassadors, accusing us of making a schism in religion, by offending against a fundamental doctrine of our great prophet Lustrog, in the fifty-fourth chapter of the *Brundecral* (which is their Alcoran). This, however, is thought to be a mere strain upon the text: for the words are these; *That all true believers shall break their eggs at the convenient end:* and which is the convenient end, seems, in my humble opinion, to be left to every man's conscience, or at least in the power of the chief magistrate to determine. Now the Big-Endian exiles have found so much credit in the Emperor of Blefuscu's court, and so much private assistance and encouragement from their party here at home, that a bloody war hath been carried on between the two empires for six and thirty moons with various success; during which time we have lost forty capital ships, and a much greater number of smaller vessels, together with thirty thousand of our best seamen and soldiers; and the damage received by the enemy is reckoned to be somewhat greater than ours. However, they have now equipped a numerous fleet, and are just preparing to make a descent upon us; and his Imperial Majesty, placing great confidence in your valour and strength, hath commanded me to lay this account of his affairs before you."

I desired the Secretary to present my humble duty to the

[4]Roman Catholics, especially in France, are symbolized by the Big-Endians. Protestantism as practiced in England is symbolized by the Little-Endians. Roman Catholics were greatly restricted in Swift's England and could neither hold public office nor attend the public universities.

Emperor, and to let him know, that I thought it would not become me, who was a foreigner, to interfere with parties; but I was ready, with the hazard of my life, to defend his person and state against all invaders.

CHAPTER FIVE. *The Author, by an extraordinary stratagem, prevents an invasion. A high title of honour is conferred upon him. . . .*

The Empire of Blefuscu is an island situated to the north-north-east side of Lilliput, from whence it is parted only by a channel of eight hundred yards wide. I had not yet seen it, and upon this notice of an intended invasion, I avoided appearing on that side of the coast, for fear of being discovered by some of the enemy's ships, who had received no intelligence of me, all intercourse between the two empires having been strictly forbidden during the war, upon pain of death, and an embargo laid by our Emperor upon all vessels whatsoever. I communicated to his Majesty a project I had formed of seizing the enemy's whole fleet: which, as our scouts assured us, lay at anchor in the harbour ready to sail with the first fair wind. I consulted the most experienced seamen, upon the depth of the channel, which they had often plumbed; who told me, that in the middle at high-water it was seventy *glumgluffs* deep, which is about six foot of European measure; and the rest of it fifty *glumgluffs* at most. I walked to the north-east coast over against Blefuscu; where, lying down behind a hillock, I took out my small pocket perspective-glass, and viewed the enemy's fleet at anchor, consisting of about fifty men of war, and a great number of transports: I then came back to my house, and gave order (for which I had a warrant) for a great quantity of the strongest cable and bars of iron. The cable was about as thick as packthread, and the bars of the length and size of a knitting-needle. I trebled the cable to make it stronger, and for the same reason I twisted three of the iron bars together, binding the extremities into a hook. Having thus fixed fifty hooks to as many cables, I went back to the north-east coast, and putting off my coat, shoes, and stockings, walked into the sea in my leathern jerkin, about half an hour before high water. I waded with what haste I could, and swam in the middle about thirty yards till I felt ground; I arrived at the fleet in less than half an hour. The enemy was so frighted when they saw me, that they leaped out of their ships, and swam to shore, where there could not be fewer than thirty thousand souls. I then took my tackling, and fastening a hook to the hole at the prow of each, I tied all the cords together at the end. While I was thus employed, the enemy discharged several thousand arrows, many of which stuck in my hands and face; and besides the excessive smart, gave me much disturbance in my work. My greatest apprehension was for mine eyes, which I should have infallibly lost, if I had not suddenly thought of an expedient. I kept among other little necessaries a pair of spectacles in a private pocket, which, as I observed before, had escaped the Emperor's searchers. These I took out and fastened as strongly as I could upon my nose, and thus armed went on boldly with my work in spite of the enemy's arrows, many of which stuck against the glasses of my spectacles, but without any other effect, further than a little to discompose them. I had now fastened all the hooks, and taking the knot in my hand, began to pull; but not a ship would stir, for they were all too fast held by their anchors, so that the boldest part of my enterprise remained. I therefore let go the cord, and leaving the hooks fixed to the ships, I resolutely cut with my knife the cables that fastened the anchors, receiving above two hundred shots in my face and hands; then I took up the knotted end of the cables to which my hooks were tied, and with great ease drew fifty of the enemy's largest men-of-war after me.

The Blefuscudians, who had not the least imagination of what I intended, were at first confounded with astonishment. They had seen me cut the cables, and thought my design was only to let the ships run a-drift, or fall foul on each other: but when they perceived the whole fleet moving in order, and saw me pulling at the end, they set up such a scream of grief and despair, that it is almost impossible to describe or conceive. When I had got out of danger, I stopt awhile to pick out the arrows that stuck in my hands and face, and rubbed on some of the same ointment that was given me at my first arrival, as I have formerly mentioned. I then took off my spectacles, and waiting about an hour, till the tide was a little fallen, I waded through the middle with my cargo, and arrived safe at the royal port of Lilliput.

The Emperor and his whole court stood on the shore expecting the issue of this great adventure. They saw the ships move forward in a large half-moon, but could not discern me, who was up to my breast in water. When I advanced to the middle of the channel, they were yet in more pain, because I was under water to my neck. The Emperor concluded me to be drowned, and that the enemy's fleet was approaching in a hostile manner: but he was soon eased of his fears; for the channel growing shallower every step I made, I came in a short time within hearing, and holding up the end of the cable by which the fleet was fastened, I cried in a loud voice, "*Long live the most puissant Emperor of Lilliput!*" This great prince received me at my landing with all possible encomiums, and created me a *Nardac* upon the spot, which is the highest title of honour among them. . . .

FOR DISCUSSION

1. What satiric effects does Swift achieve by portraying Gulliver as a humble commoner anxious to please the seven-inch-tall king and his court? Who is the primary object of satire in such a situation?
2. When he describes the rope-dancers, what does Swift suggest about the character, qualifications, and activities of those who win high positions at court? Do you think Swift intended a double meaning when he spoke of "fatal accidents" and "breaking a limb" at rope-dancing?
3. What kind of honors might Swift be satirizing through the different colored threads? What do the courtiers seem to resemble when they leap over a stick the Emperor holds for them? What does the description of the military maneuvers on Gulliver's handkerchief suggest about such displays in general?
4. Through the articles to which Gulliver must submit for his free-

dom, what does Swift imply about laws of the land? about a monarch's view of his subjects? about a monarch's view of himself and of his kingdom?

5. What does Swift imply about the reputed magnificence of London through his descriptions of Mildendo, the Lilliputian capital? What does he suggest about the immense and impressive royal palaces of England?
6. Does the fact that Swift was a Tory explain any phrases in his description of the High Heels and the Low Heels? What does he suggest about such factionalism in general?
7. What does the Lilliputian explanation for Gulliver's existence imply about the wisdom and objectivity of philosophers? about the extent to which wishful thinking dictates philosophical ideas?
8. What does Swift seem to think about controversies over church dogma? How appropriate a symbol for such fighting is the egg-controversy? What particular church doctrines might the eggs represent? What does the "scriptural" reference to eggs suggest about the bases for such controversies?

FOR COMPOSITION

1. Write an essay analyzing Swift's irony in the selection you have read. Does more than one kind or level of irony appear here?
2. The prominent British critic F. R. Leavis asserted that the moral implication of Swift's satiric technique was "the self-defeat of life." Either attack or defend Leavis's judgment, using this selection for your evidence.
3. Write a research paper on English court politics between 1715 and 1725 (*Gulliver's Travels* appeared in 1727). Then relate your discoveries to Swift's satire. You may wish to concentrate on one figure such as Walpole or the King.

THE FLOWERING OF THE ENGLISH NOVEL

A study of English literature would not be complete without a sampling of the great English novels, for the novel has been the dominant type of popular literature in the past two centuries. Rising as a literary form in the eighteenth century, the novel derives in part from medieval romances, chivalric epics, realistic rogue stories (see Glossary), moral tales, fables, and Elizabethan drama. But the novel differs from other forms in its comprehensiveness: it is a long prose narrative involving a number of characters and incidents. Its central interest may be a particular character, a social problem, a mode of behavior, or an adventure. To express such interests, however, it employs a wider range of episodes than its sister arts.

The English novel as we recognize it today first emerged in 1719 with the publication of *Robinson Crusoe*, generally considered the earliest English novel of incident. Daniel Defoe, a clever journalist, often supplemented his news stories with imaginary details if original material was lacking. He imagined *The Surprising Adventures of Robinson Crusoe* out of the story of Alexander Selkirk, a sailor who had lived for many years as a castaway on a small Pacific Island. The succession of adventures in this lively book is held together largely because they happened to one person. It was Samuel Richardson who first devised a continuous narrative impelled along its course by a single motive.

Samuel Richardson, a London printer, was asked by a publisher to write a series of letters to serve as models for the correspondence and behavior of people in the lower walks of life, especially for young girls obliged to go into service. He began the letters as those of a young serving girl to her parents, telling the story of her temptation by her master, her resistance, and her final triumph in marrying him. But he became so interested in the girl's story that he put aside his original task and, retaining the epistolary form, wrote *Pamela*, *or Virtue Rewarded* in 1740. He followed this in 1748 with his greatest novel, *Clarissa,* in which he revealed an astonishing ability to understand and describe in detail the feelings and thoughts of a young woman. Richardson's contribution to the development of the novel was the dramatic presentation of events through a series of letters, and the analysis of human emotions and motivation in prose story form. The careful attention to the minute impulses of the heart prepared the foundation for later novels of sentiment.

HENRY FIELDING—playwright, law student, police magistrate, and free-lance writer—was appalled by what he saw as the sentimentality, narrow vision, and shallow ethics of *Pamela.* He began a burlesque of it, in which he subjected Joseph Andrews, supposedly a brother of Pamela, to the same temptations from his mistress that Pamela had suffered from her master. Joseph, too, resists but is turned out of doors and has to make his way back home. As Fielding portrayed the rough English life of post roads, inns, and country houses, he abandoned his original satirical purpose, and *Joseph Andrews* (1742) became a novel of adventures in high and low life, mock-heroic in style and language.

Fielding's masterpiece is *Tom Jones* (1749), the story of a foundling who has been turned out of his guardian's home through the machinations of a jealous nephew. Tom's travels to London, his wayside adventures, his romance with the daughter of a country squire, the final discovery of his true identity, and the exposure of his opponent's villainy all unravel with numerous complications. The outstanding quality of the protagonist is that he is an ordinary man; in modern terms, he is something of an anti-hero. Tom is memorable for his abounding physical vigor, high spirits, and indifference to moral codes. Perhaps the chief fault in his character is this lack of prudence. Fielding's achievement was to extend the form of the novel by writing a comic epic: the action is long and complicated, the many characters represent all classes of society and all manner of men, and the tone is ironic and satiric. Fielding's novels are devoted to the exposure of the ridiculousness, affectations, and hypocrisy in human nature.

Although JANE AUSTEN lived when the tide of Romanticism

was at the flood, she was not a Romantic writer. Her good sense, clarity, irony, and detachment recall the neoclassical period whose traditions lingered in the country parishes and provincial towns she knew. Focusing her attention on social relationships, she wrote about the small world of the country gentry, among whom few dramatic incidents occurred. Her extraordinarily truthful picture of life and her perceptive knowledge of human nature universalized these experiences. Miss Austen may be considered a pivotal figure in the development of the novel: eighteenth-century in values, nineteenth-century in form. Her six published novels remain the most outstanding examples of the novel of manners.

Pride and Prejudice (1813) shows Jane Austen's knowledge of Fielding. The dramatic brilliance of this work derives from the wonderfully ironic and revealing dialogue of the characters. At this method of characterization Jane Austen was a master. She ranks among the major English novelists today for the organic unity of her works: their careful design, the balance of part to whole, and the direction of the whole to the elucidation of the basic moral theme.

It is not difficult to understand why few novels were produced by nineteenth-century Romantic writers, who, preferring lyric bursts of mood and feeling, shied away from narratives in general and realistic narratives in particular. The imagination of a Romantic would have felt cramped by the journalistic, true-to-life approach of Defoe and Fielding and by the sort of boisterous story that appealed to their readers. "Fit audience though few" was the ideal of the pure Romantic spirit—and who fitter (or fewer) than the discriminating lovers of poetry? So the novel languished, and verse flourished.

The chief exceptions to this situation were CHARLOTTE BRONTË and her sister Emily, who wrote with the impulsive fire of poets. Though they both published their novels in 1847 in the middle of the Victorian period, Charlotte's *Jane Eyre* and Emily's *Wuthering Heights* are Romantic in spirit. The characters of these novels are great and passionate, and the events take place against traditionally Gothic settings—windswept moors, brooding manors, rugged hills, and driving rain.

No novel gives a more vivid impression of Romantic feeling than *Wuthering Heights;* but *Jane Eyre* may have a greater appeal for some, since the story is told through the eyes of an oppressed young heroine. The novels of both sisters are studies in loneliness. Instead of employing the conventional, idealized heroine, Charlotte Brontë in *Jane Eyre* chose a quiet, plain young woman with a fiercely independent spirit and strong personal integrity. Jane's feelings are strong; she is true to them; and the book is an excellent example of the English Romantic novel.

WILLIAM MAKEPEACE THACKERAY picked up the thread of the novel of manners from Jane Austen but wove his pattern upon a much larger loom in order to present a panorama of Victorian society. In *Vanity Fair* (1847-1848), Thackeray, himself from the upper class, satirized the affectations of high society. The title of the work recalls Bunyan's *The Pilgrim's Progress,* in which a town called Vanity is continually holding fairs. Thackeray used the idea of Vanity to depict mankind's weakness and folly. A realist and a moralist, Thackeray was concerned with people who had reverence for nothing but material prosperity. He was interested in famous events and persons only for their effects on the affairs of ordinary men. Thackeray's tendency to divide his characters into good and bad and to administer poetic justice to each reflects the uncompromising view of the Victorian age toward moral issues.

CHARLES DICKENS saw life most often from the point of view of the poor and oppressed of a great city. He voiced a popular distrust of governmental methods and a hatred of organized authority. He attacked the workhouses in *Oliver Twist* (1838), chancery courts in *Bleak House* (1853), and debtors' prisons in *Little Dorrit* (1857). He knew at firsthand the despair and deprivation of poverty. At the age of ten he was working long hours and spending his Sundays with his family in prison, where his father was confined for debt.

Part of Dickens' achievement as a novelist was in creating unforgettable characters, some of whose names have become tag-names for the characteristics they represented: Micawber for irresponsibility, Uriah Heep for false humility, Pecksniff for hypocrisy. But he was first and last a storyteller, an entertainer, and his vast public appreciated his wonderfully melodramatic plots and techniques: the disguised lover, the long-lost heir, mistaken identity, and the supposed dead returning in the nick of time. The twists and turns of the narrative, the stretching and padding sometimes criticized today, were perhaps unavoidable results of serial publication and meeting printers' deadlines. Dickens wrung the last possible tear from sentimental situations, especially those in which children are victims of society. Oliver Twist, Little Nell, David Copperfield, and Florence Dombey stand out in celestial innocence and goodness in contrast to the evil creatures whose persecutions they suffer until Dickens rescues them.

Of all his qualities, however, none has endeared Dickens to the reading public more than his exuberant sense of humor. Few writers have cared for people so deeply as Dickens; few have laughed so uproariously at them. And nowhere is the laughter greater than in his first success, the *Pickwick Papers.*

The great eighteenth- and nineteenth-century novelists established certain "principles" which seemed absolute and essential to the novel form: the novel was an imaginative form of fiction, longer than a short story and wider in scope; its effects were not immediate but cumulative; it was more expansive, inclusive, and diverse than a poem but lacked the compactness of poetry; its story moved chronologically; it reflected human experience and was as true to life as the writer's perception and vision would allow.

It was left for early twentieth-century novelists, such as James Joyce and Virginia Woolf to put aside certain of these assumptions by ignoring chronology and plot in the ordinary sense, and writing from a new concept about the nature of time. The younger experimentalists also strove to perfect new techniques, while writers such as D. H. Lawrence, using the older narrative forms, strove to establish new mores and beliefs about age-old taboos. Before one can appreciate the experiments of these innovators, however, he must understand what they rejected. Surely no more pleasurable learning is possible than that one receives by reading the ever-fresh works of Fielding, Miss Austen, Dickens, Thackeray, and the Brontë sisters.

Henry Fielding

Most of the moralists from his time to ours have disliked Henry Fielding's novels. His contemporary Samuel Johnson thought Fielding "a blockhead" and "a barren rascal" for penning such boisterous and ribald tales. Those twentieth-century critics who feel art should offer constructive criticism of society's shortcomings have also objected to Fielding's work. One can, of course find in *Tom Jones* an honest portrayal of the flaws and foibles in Fielding's world. But such foibles are never treated with righteous indignation or moral scorn. Fielding is the most tolerant of writers. He recognizes and faces evil unflinchingly, but he always maintains a moral balance through laughter. In *Tom Jones,* Fielding's wit, urbanity, education, natural elegance, and stylistic grace are given full rein. The result is an episodic novel (strongly influenced by *Don Quixote*) in which people appear no better than they are, though their humanity continues to delight modern readers.

from Tom Jones

In *Tom Jones,* a just and honest, though somewhat shortsighted, country magistrate, Mr. Allworthy, returns from an extended visit to London and finds a tiny baby in his bed. He resolves to rear the boy as his own son, even after circumstantial evidence indicates that the child is the illegitimate offspring of a schoolmaster and a servant-girl. Though alarmingly prone to get into trouble, Tom Jones soon proves a favorite in the neighborhood for his handsome face, winning manners, and high spirits. One of his playmates is Sophia Western, the lovely and virtuous daughter of a profane squire living nearby, who is being reared by her once socially prominent aunt, Mrs. Western. Another companion is young Master Blifil, snivelling son of Allworthy's sister and heir to the Allworthy fortune. Tom's acquaintances also include Thwackum, his sadistic tutor; Molly Seagrim, handsome daughter of Allworthy's gamekeeper; and Parson Supple, the gluttonous curate of the parish.

Thwackum and Blifil ally themselves against Tom and spy on his amorous adventures with Molly, for which Tom soundly beats them. Soon, however, Tom decides that he truly loves Sophia Western, though he has no hope of winning her father's permission to marry her. When Squire Western learns that Tom's affection is returned by Sophia, and when Tom's past conduct is deliberately misrepresented to Allworthy by Blifil and Thwackum, the unfortunate young man is sent away from his benefactor's home. Tom thus begins the long series of misadventures which culminate in his gradually maturing and finally gaining Sophia as his wife.

Chapter Seven

A PICTURE OF FORMAL COURTSHIP IN MINIATURE, AS IT ALWAYS OUGHT TO BE DRAWN, AND A SCENE OF A TENDERER KIND PAINTED AT FULL LENGTH

It was well remarked by one (and perhaps by more) that misfortunes do not come single. This wise maxim was now verified by Sophia, who was not only disappointed of seeing the man she loved, but had the vexation of being obliged to dress herself out, in order to receive a visit from the man she hated.

That afternoon Mr. Western, for the first time, acquainted his daughter with his intention; telling her, he knew very well that she had heard it before from her aunt. Sophia looked very grave upon this, nor could she prevent a few pearls from stealing into her eyes. "Come, come," says Western, "none of your maidenish airs; I know all; I assure you sister hath told me all."

"Is it possible," says Sophia, "that my aunt can have betrayed me already?"—"Ay, ay," says Western; "betrayed you! ay. Why, you betrayed yourself yesterday at dinner. You showed your fancy very plainly, I think. But you young girls never know what you would be at. So you cry because I am going to marry you to the man you are in love with! Your mother, I remembered, whimpered and whined just in the same manner; but it was all over within twenty-four hours after we were married: Mr. Blifil is a brisk young man, and will soon put an end to your squeamishness. Come, cheer up, cheer up; I expect un every minute."

Sophia was now convinced that her aunt had behaved honourably to her: and she determined to go through that disagreeable afternoon with as much resolution as possible, and without giving the least suspicion in the world to her father.

Mr. Blifil soon arrived; and Mr. Western soon after withdrawing, left the young couple together.

Here a long silence of near a quarter of an hour ensued; for the gentleman who was to begin the conversation had all the unbecoming modesty which consists in bashfulness. He often attempted to speak, and as often suppressed his words just at the very point of utterance. At last out they broke in a torrent of far-fetched and high-strained compliments, which were answered on her side by downcast looks, half bows, and civil monosyllables. Blifil, from his inexperience in the ways of women, and from his conceit of himself, took this behaviour for a modest assent to his courtship; and when, to shorten a scene which she could no longer support, Sophia rose up and left the room, he imputed that, too, merely to bashfulness, and comforted himself that he should soon have enough of her company.

He was indeed perfectly well satisfied with his prospect of success; for as to that entire and absolute possession of the heart of his mistress which romantic lovers require, the very idea of it never entered his head. Her fortune and her person were the sole objects of his wishes, of which he made no doubt soon to obtain the absolute property; as Mr. Western's mind was so earnestly bent on the match; and as he well knew the strict obedience which Sophia was always ready to pay to her father's will, and the greater still which her father would exact, if there was occasion. This authority, therefore, together with the charms which he fancied in his own person and conversation, could not fail, he thought, of succeeding with a young lady whose inclinations were, he doubted not, entirely disengaged.

Of Jones he certainly had not even the least jealousy; and I have often thought it wonderful that he had not. Perhaps he imagined the character which Jones bore all over the country (how justly, let the reader determine), of being one of the wildest fellows in England, might render him odious to a lady of the most exemplary modesty. Perhaps his suspicions be laid asleep by the behaviour of Sophia, and of Jones himself, when they were all in company together. Lastly, and indeed principally, he was well assured there was not another Self in the case. He fancied that he knew Jones to the bottom, and had in reality a great contempt for his understanding, for not being more attached to his own interest. He had no apprehension that Jones was in love with Sophia; and as for any lucrative motives, he imagined they would sway very little with so silly a fellow. Blifil, moreover, thought the affair of Molly Seagrim still went on, and indeed believed it would end in marriage: for Jones really loved him from his childhood, and had kept no secret from him, till his behaviour on the sickness of Mr. Allworthy had entirely alienated his heart;[1] and it was by means of the quarrel which had

[1] . . . *alienated his heart:* Though cautioned that Allworthy should not be upset, Blifil announced the death of Allworthy's sister to the ailing man.

ensued on this occasion, and which was not yet reconciled, that Mr. Blifil knew nothing of the alteration which had happened in the affection which Jones had formerly borne towards Molly.

From these reasons, therefore, Mr. Blifil saw no bar to his success with Sophia. He concluded her behaviour was like that of all other young ladies on a first visit from a lover, and it had indeed entirely answered his expectations.

Mr. Western took care to waylay the lover at his exit from his mistress. He found him so elevated with his success, so enamoured with his daughter, and so satisfied with her reception of him, that the old gentleman began to caper and dance about his hall, and by many other antic actions to express the extravagance of his joy; for he had not the least command over any of his passions; and that which had at any time the ascendant in his mind hurried him to the wildest excesses.

As soon as Blifil was departed, which was not till after many hearty kisses and embraces bestowed on him by Western, the good squire went instantly in quest of his daughter, whom he no sooner found than he poured forth the most extravagant raptures, bidding her choose what clothes and jewels she pleased; and declaring that he had no other use for fortune but to make her happy. He then caressed her again and again with the utmost profusion of fondness, called her by the most endearing names, and protested she was his only joy on earth.

Sophia perceiving her father in this fit of affection, which she did not absolutely know the reason of (for fits of fondness were not unusual to him, though this was rather more violent than ordinary), thought she should never have a better opportunity of disclosing herself than at present, as far at least as regarded Mr. Blifil; and she too well foresaw the necessity which she should soon be under of coming to a full explanation. After having thanked the squire, therefore, for all his professions of kindness, she added, with a look full of inexpressible softness, "And is it possible my papa can be so good to place all his joy in his Sophy's happiness?" which Western having confirmed by a great oath and a kiss; she then laid hold of his hand, and, falling on her knees, after many warm and passionate declarations of affection and duty, she begged him "not to make her the most miserable creature on earth by forcing her to marry a man whom she detested. This I entreat of you, dear sir," said she, "for your sake, as well as my own, since you are so very kind to tell me your happiness depends on mine."—"How! what!" says Western, staring wildly.—"Oh! sir," continued she, "not only your poor Sophy's happiness; her very life, her being, depends upon your granting her request. I cannot live with Mr. Blifil. To force me into this marriage would be killing me."—"You can't live with Mr. Blifil?" says Western.—"No, upon my soul I can't," answered Sophia.—"Then die and be d—d," cries he, spurning her from him.—"Oh! sir," cries Sophia, catching hold of the skirt of his coat, "take pity on me, I beseech you. Don't look and say such cruel—Can you be unmoved while you see your Sophy in this dreadful condition? Can the best of fathers break my heart? Will he kill me by the most painful, cruel, lingering death?"—"Pooh! pooh!" cries the squire; "all stuff and nonsense; all maidenish tricks. Kill you, indeed! Will marriage kill you?"—"Oh! sir," answered Sophia, "such a marriage is worse than death. He is not even indifferent; I hate and detest him."—"If you detest un never so much," cries Western, "you shall ha'un." This he bound by an oath too shocking to repeat; and after many violent asseverations, concluded in these words: "I am resolved upon the match, and unless you consent to it I will not give you a groat, not a single farthing; no, though I saw you expiring with famine in the street, I would not relieve you with a morsel of bread. This is my fixed resolution, and so I leave you to consider on it." He then broke from her with such violence, that her face dashed against the floor; and he burst directly out of the room, leaving poor Sophia prostrate on the ground.

When Western came into the hall, he there found Jones; who seeing his friend looking wild, pale, and almost breathless, could not forbear inquiring the reason of all these melancholy appearances. Upon which the squire immediately acquainted him with the whole matter, concluding with bitter denunciations against Sophia, and very pathetic lamentations of the misery of all fathers who are so unfortunate to have daughters.

Jones, to whom all the resolutions which had been taken in favour of Blifil were yet a secret, was at first almost struck dead with this relation; but recovering his spirits a little, mere despair, as he afterwards said, inspired him to mention a matter to Mr. Western, which seemed to require more impudence than a human forehead was ever gifted with. He desired leave to go to Sophia, that he might endeavour to obtain her concurrence with her father's inclinations.

If the squire had been as quicksighted as he was remarkable for the contrary, passion might at present very well have blinded him. He thanked Jones for offering to undertake the office, and said, "Go, go, prithee, try what canst do," and then swore many execrable[2] oaths that he would turn her out of doors unless she consented to the match.

Chapter Eight

THE MEETING BETWEEN JONES AND SOPHIA

Jones departed instantly in quest of Sophia, whom he found just risen from the ground, where her father had left her, with the tears trickling from her eyes, and the blood running from her lips. He presently ran to her, and with a voice full at once of tenderness and terror, cried, "O my Sophia, what means this dreadful sight?" She looked softly at him for a moment before she spoke, and then said, "Mr. Jones, for Heaven's sake how came you here? Leave me, I beseech you, this moment."—"Do not," says he, "impose so harsh a command upon me—my heart bleeds faster than those lips. O Sophia, how easily could I drain my veins to preserve one drop of that dear blood."—"I have too many obligations to you already," answered she, "for sure you

[2]*execrable:* detestable

meant them such." Here she looked at him tenderly almost a minute, and then bursting into an agony, cried, "Oh, Mr. Jones, why did you save my life? my death would have been happier for us both."—"Happier for us both!" cried he. "Could racks or wheels kill me so painfully as Sophia's—I cannot bear the dreadful sound. Do I live but for her?" Both his voice and looks were full of inexpressible tenderness when he spoke these words; and at the same time he laid gently hold on her hand, which she did not withdraw from him; to say the truth, she hardly knew what she did or suffered. A few moments now passed in silence between these lovers, while his eyes were eagerly fixed on Sophia, and hers declining towards the ground: at last she recovered strength enough to desire him again to leave her, for that her certain ruin would be the consequence of their being found together; adding, "Oh, Mr. Jones, you know not, you know not what hath passed this cruel afternoon."—"I know all, my Sophia," answered he; "your cruel father hath told me all, and he himself hath sent me hither to you."—"My father sent you to me!" replied she: "sure you dream."—"Would to Heaven," cries he, "it was but a dream! Oh, Sophia, your father hath sent me to you to be an advocate for my odious rival, to solicit you in his favour. I took any means to get access to you. O speak to me, Sophia! comfort my bleeding heart. Sure no one ever loved, ever doted like me. Do not unkindly withhold this dear, this soft, this gentle hand—one moment, perhaps, tears you for ever from me—nothing less than this cruel occasion could, I believe, have ever conquered the respect and awe with which you have inspired me." She stood a moment silent, and covered with confusion; then lifting up her eyes gently towards him, she cried, "What would Mr. Jones have me say?"—"O do but promise," cried he, "that you never will give yourself to Blifil."—"Name not," answered she, "the detested sound. Be assured I never will give him what is in my power to withhold from him."—"Now then," cries he, "while you are so perfectly kind, go a little farther, and add that I may hope."—"Alas!" says she, "Mr. Jones, whither will you drive me? What hope have I to bestow? You know my father's intentions."—"But I know," answered he, "your compliance with them cannot be compelled."— "What," says she, "must be the dreadful consequence of my disobedience? My own ruin is my least concern. I cannot bear the thoughts of being the cause of my father's misery." —"He is himself the cause," cries Jones, "by exacting a power over you which Nature hath not given him. Think on the misery which I am to suffer if I am to lose you, and see on which side pity will turn the balance."—"Think of it!" replied she: "can you imagine I do not feel the ruin which I must bring on you, should I comply with your desire? It is that thought which gives me resolution to bid you fly from me for ever, and avoid your own destruction."—"I fear no destruction," cries he, "but the loss of Sophia. If you would save me from the most bitter agonies, recall that cruel sentence. Indeed, I can never part with you, indeed I cannot."

The lovers now stood both silent and trembling, Sophia being unable to withdraw her hand from Jones, and he almost as unable to hold it; when the scene, which I believe some of my readers will think had lasted long enough, was interrupted by one of so different a nature, that we shall reserve the relation of it for a different chapter.

Chapter Nine

BEING OF A MUCH MORE TEMPESTUOUS KIND THAN THE FORMER

Before we proceed with what now happened to our lovers, it may be proper to recount what had passed in the hall during their tender interview.

Soon after Jones had left Mr. Western in the manner above-mentioned, his sister came to him, and was presently informed of all that had passed between her brother and Sophia relating to Blifil.

This behaviour in her niece the good lady construed to be an absolute breach of the condition on which she had engaged to keep her love for Mr. Jones a secret. She considered herself, therefore, at full liberty to reveal all she knew to the squire, which she immediately did in the most explicit terms, and without any ceremony or preface.

The idea of a marriage between Jones and his daughter had never once entered into the squire's head, either in the warmest minutes of his affection towards that young man, or from suspicion, or on any other occasion. He did indeed consider a parity[3] of fortune and circumstances to be physically as necessary an ingredient in marriage as difference of sexes, or any other essential; and had no more apprehension of his daughter's falling in love with a poor man than with any animal of a different species.

He became, therefore, like one thunderstruck at his sister's relation. He was, at first, incapable of making any answer, having been almost deprived of his breath by the violence of the surprise. This, however, soon returned, and, as is usual in other cases after an intermission, with redoubled force and fury.

The first use he made of the power of speech, after his recovery from the sudden effects of his astonishment, was to discharge a round volley of oaths and imprecations.[4] After which he proceeded hastily to the apartment where he expected to find the lovers, and murmured, or rather indeed roared forth, intentions of revenge every step he went.

As when two doves, or two wood-pigeons, or as when Strephon and Phyllis[5] (for that comes nearest to the mark) are retired into some pleasant solitary grove, to enjoy the delightful conversation of Love, that bashful boy, who cannot speak in public, and is never a good companion to more than two at a time; here, while every object is serene, should hoarse thunder burst suddenly through the shattered clouds, and rumbling roll along the sky, the frightened maid starts from the mossy bank or verdant turf, the pale livery of death succeeds the red regimentals in which Love had before dressed her cheeks, fear shakes her whole frame, and her lover scarce supports her trembling, tottering limbs.

[3] *parity:* equality
[4] *imprecations:* curses
[5] *Strephon and Phyllis:* conventional names for the lovers in pastoral works

Or as when two gentlemen, strangers to the wondrous wit of the place, are cracking a bottle together at some inn or tavern at Salisbury, if the great Dowdy, who acts the part of a madman as well as some of his setters-on do that of a fool, should rattle his chains, and dreadfully hum forth the grumbling catch along the gallery; the frighted strangers stand aghast; scared at the horrid sound, they seek some place of shelter from the approaching danger; and if the well-barred windows did admit their exit, would venture their necks to escape the threatening fury now coming upon them.

So trembled poor Sophia, so turned she pale at the noise of her father, who, in a voice most dreadful to hear, came on swearing, cursing, and vowing the destruction of Jones. To say the truth, I believe the youth himself would, from some prudent considerations, have preferred another place of abode at this time, had his terror on Sophia's account given him liberty to reflect a moment on what any otherways concerned himself, than as his love made him partake whatever affected her.

And now the squire, having burst open the door, beheld an object which instantly suspended all his fury against Jones; this was the ghastly appearance of Sophia, who had fainted away in her lover's arms. This tragical sight Mr. Western no sooner beheld than all his rage forsook him; he roared for help with his utmost violence; ran first to his daughter, then back to the door calling for water, and then back again to Sophia, never considering in whose arms she then was, nor perhaps once recollecting that there was such a person in the world as Jones; for indeed I believe the present circumstances of his daughter were now the sole consideration which employed his thoughts.

Mrs. Western and a great number of servants soon came to the assistance of Sophia with water, cordials, and everything necessary on those occasions. These were applied with such success, that Sophia in a very few minutes began to recover, and all the symptoms of life to return. Upon which she was presently led off by her own maid and Mrs. Western: nor did that good lady depart without leaving some wholesome admonitions with her brother on the dreadful effects of his passion, or, as she pleased to call it, madness.

The squire, perhaps, did not understand this good advice, as it was delivered in obscure hints, shrugs, and notes of admiration: at least, if he did understand it, he profited very little by it; for no sooner was he cured of his immediate fears for his daughter, than he relapsed into his former frenzy, which must have produced an immediate battle with Jones, had not Parson Supple, who was a very strong man, been present, and by mere force restrained the squire from acts of hostility.

The moment Sophia was departed, Jones advanced in a very suppliant manner to Mr. Western, whom the parson held in his arms, and begged him to be pacified; for that, while he continued in such a passion, it would be impossible to give him any satisfaction.

"I wull have satisfaction o' thee," answered the squire; "so doff thy clothes. *At unt* half a man, and I'll lick thee as well as wast ever licked in thy life." He then bespattered the youth with abundance of that language which passes between country gentlemen who embrace opposite sides of the question.

To all such wit, Jones very calmly answered, "Sir, this usage may perhaps cancel every other obligation you have conferred on me; but there is one you can never cancel; nor will I be provoked by your abuse to lift my hand against the father of Sophia."

At these words the squire grew still more outrageous than before; so that the parson begged Jones to retire; saying, "You behold, sir, how he waxeth wroth at your abode here; therefore let me pray you not to tarry any longer. His anger is too much kindled for you to commune with him at present. You had better, therefore, conclude your visit, and refer what matters you have to urge in your behalf to some other opportunity."

Jones accepted this advice with thanks, and immediately departed. The squire now regained the liberty of his hands and so much temper as to express some satisfaction in the restraint which had been laid upon him; declaring that he should certainly have beat his brains out; and adding, "It would have vexed one confoundedly to have been hanged for such a rascal."

The parson now began to triumph in the success of his

peace-making endeavours, and proceeded to read a lecture against anger, which might perhaps rather have tended to raise than to quiet that passion in some hasty minds. This lecture he enriched with many valuable quotations from the ancients, particularly from Seneca;[6] who hath indeed so well handled this passion, that none but a very angry man can read him without great pleasure and profit. The doctor concluded this harangue with the famous story of Alexander and Clitus;[7] but as I find that entered in my commonplace under title Drunkenness, I shall not insert it here.

The squire took no notice of this story, nor perhaps of anything he said; for he interrupted him before he had finished, by calling for a tankard of beer; observing (which is perhaps as true as any observation on this fever of the mind) that anger makes a man dry.

No sooner had the squire swallowed a large draught than he renewed the discourse on Jones, and declared a resolution of going the next morning early to acquaint Mr. Allworthy. His friend would have dissuaded him from this, from the mere motive of good-nature; but his dissuasion had no other effect than to produce a large volley of oaths and curses, which greatly shocked the pious ears of Supple; but he did not dare to remonstrate against a privilege which the squire claimed as a freeborn Englishman. To say truth, the parson submitted to please his palate at the squire's table, at the expense of suffering now and then this violence to his ears. He contented himself with thinking he did not promote this evil practice, and that the squire would not swear an oath the less if he never entered within his gates. However, though he was not guilty of ill manners by rebuking a gentleman in his own house, he paid him off obliquely in the pulpit: which had not, indeed, the good effect of working a reformation in the squire himself; yet it so far operated on his conscience, that he put the laws very severely in execution against

[6]*Seneca:* Roman writer of bloody revenge plays

[7]*Alexander and Clitus:* Clitus was a general and close friend of Alexander the Great. He taunted Alexander during a banquet, and the drunken Alexander promptly killed him with a javelin. Alexander's grief for his friend was subsequently inconsolable.

others, and the magistrate was the only person in the parish who could swear with impunity.

Chapter Ten

IN WHICH MR. WESTERN VISITS MR. ALLWORTHY

Mr. Allworthy was now retired from breakfast with his nephew, well satisfied with the report of the young gentleman's successful visit to Sophia (for he greatly desired the match, more on account of the young lady's character than of her riches), when Mr. Western broke abruptly in upon them, and without any ceremony began as follows:—

"There, you have done a fine piece of work truly! You have brought up your boy to a fine purpose; not that I believe you have had any hand in it neither, that is, as a man may say, designedly: but there is a fine kettle-of-fish made on't up at our house."—"What can be the matter, Mr. Western?" said Allworthy.—"O, matter enow of all conscience: my daughter hath fallen in love with your boy, that's all; but I won't ge her a hapeny, not the twentieth part of a brass varden. I always thought what would come o' breeding up a scoundrel like a gentleman, and letting un come about to vok's houses. It's well vor un I could not get at un: I'd a lick'd un; I'd a spoil'd his caterwauling; I'd a taught the son of a hound to meddle with meat for his master. He sha'n't ever have a morsel of meat of mine, or a varden to buy it; if she will ha un, one smock shall be her portion. I'd sooner ge my esteate to the zinking fund, that it may be sent to Hanover to corrupt our nation with."—"I am heartily sorry," cries Allworthy.—"Pox o' your sorrow," says Western; "it will do me abundance of good when I have lost my only child, my poor Sophy, that was the joy of my heart, and all the hope and comfort of my age; but I am resolved I will turn her out o' doors; she shall beg, and starve, and rot in the streets. Not one hapeny, not a hapeny shall she ever hae o' mine. The son of a hound was always good at finding a hare sitting, an be rotted to'n: I little thought what puss he was looking after; but it shall be the worst he ever vound in his life. She shall be no better than carrion: the skin o'er is all he shall ha, and zu may tell un."—"I am in amazement," cries Allworthy, "at what you tell me, after what passed between my nephew and the young lady no longer ago than yesterday."—"Yes, sir," answered Western, "it was after what passed between your nephew and she that the whole matter came out. Mr. Blifil there was no sooner gone that he came lurching about the house. Little did I think when I used to love him for a sportsman that he was all the while a poaching after my daughter."—"Why, truly," says Allworthy, "I could wish you had not given him so many opportunities with her; and you will do me the justice to acknowledge that I have always been averse to his staying so much at your house, though I own I had no suspicion of this kind."—"Why, zounds," cries Western, "who could have thought it? What the devil had she to do wi'n? He did not come there a-courting to her; he came there a-hunting with me."—"But was it possible," says Allworthy, "that you should never discern any symptoms of love between them, when you have seen them so often together?"—"Never in my life, as I hope to be saved," cries Western: "I never so much as zeed him kiss her in all my life; and so far from courting her, he used rather to be more silent when she was in company than at any other time; and as for the girl, she was always less civil to'n than to any young man that came to the house. As to that matter, I am not more easy to be deceived than another; I would not have you think I am, neighbour." Allworthy could scarce refrain laughter at this; but he resolved to do a violence to himself; for he perfectly well knew mankind, and had too much good-breeding and good-nature to offend the squire in his present circumstances. He then asked Western what he would have him do upon this occasion. To which the other answered, "That he would have him keep the rascal away from his house, and that he would go and lock up the wench; for he was resolved to make her marry Mr. Blifil in spite of her teeth." He then shook Blifil by the hand, and swore he would have no other son-in-law. Presently after which he took his leave; saying his house was in such disorder that it was necessary for him to make haste home, to take care his daughter did not give him the slip.

When Allworthy and Blifil were again left together, a long silence ensued between them; all which interval the young gentleman filled up with sighs, which proceeded partly from disappointment, but more from hatred; for the success of Jones was much more grievous to him than the loss of Sophia.

At length his uncle asked him what he was determined to do, and he answered in the following words: – "Alas! sir, can it be a question what step a lover will take, when reason and passion point different ways? I am afraid it is too certain he will, in that dilemma, always follow the latter. Reason dictates to me, to quit all thoughts of a woman who places her affections on another; my passion bids me hope she may in time change her inclinations in my favour. Here, however, I conceive an objection may be raised, which, if it could not fully be answered, would totally deter me from any further pursuit. I mean the injustice of endeavouring to supplant another in a heart of which he seems already in possession; but the determined resolution of Mr. Western shows that, in this case, I shall, by so doing, promote the happiness of every party; not only that of the parent, who will thus be preserved from the highest degree of misery, but of both the others, who must be undone by this match. The lady, I am sure, will be undone in every sense; for, besides the loss of most part of her own fortune, she will be not only married to a beggar, but the little fortune which her father cannot withhold from her will be squandered on that wench with whom I know he yet converses. Nay, that is a trifle; for I know him to be one of the worst men in the world; for had my dear uncle known what I have hitherto endeavoured to conceal, he must have long since abandoned so profligate a wretch." – "How!" said Allworthy; "hath he done anything worse than I already know? Tell me, I beseech you?" – "No," replied Blifil; "it is now past, and perhaps he may have repented of it." – "I command you, on your duty," said Allworthy, "to tell me what you mean." – "You know, sir," says Blifil, "I never disobeyed you; but I am sorry I mentioned it, since it may now look like revenge, whereas, I thank Heaven, no such motive ever entered my heart; and if you oblige me to discover it, I must be his petitioner to you for your forgiveness."—"I will have no conditions," answered Allworthy; "I think I have shown tenderness enough towards him, and more perhaps than you ought to thank me for."—"More, indeed, I fear, than he deserves," cries Blifil; "for in the very day of your utmost danger, when myself and all the family were in tears, he filled the house with riot and debauchery. He drank, and sung, and roared; and when I gave him a gentle hint of the indecency of his actions, he fell into a violent passion, swore many oaths, called me rascal, and struck me."—"How!" cries Allworthy; "did he dare to strike you?"—"I am sure," cries Blifil, "I have forgiven him that long ago. I wish I could so easily forget his ingratitude to the best of benefactors; and yet even that I hope you will forgive him, since he must have certainly been possessed with the devil: for that very evening, as Mr. Thwackum and myself were taking the air in the fields, and exulting in the good symptoms which then first began to discover themselves, we unluckily saw him engaged with a wench in a manner not fit to be mentioned. Mr. Thwackum, with more boldness than prudence, advanced to rebuke him, when (I am sorry to say it) he fell upon the worthy man, and beat him so outrageously that I wish he may have yet recovered the bruises. Nor was I without my share of the effects of his malice, while I endeavoured to protect my tutor; but that I have long forgiven; nay, I prevailed with Mr. Thwackum to forgive him too, and not to inform you of a secret which I feared might be fatal to him. And now, sir, since I have unadvisedly dropped a hint of this matter, and your commands have obliged me to discover the whole, let me intercede with you for him."—"O child!" said Allworthy, "I know not whether I should blame or applaud your goodness, in concealing such villainy a moment: but where is Mr. Thwackum? Not that I want any confirmation of what you say; but I will examine all the evidence of this matter, to justify to the world the example I am resolved to make of such a monster."

Thwackum was now sent for, and presently appeared. He corroborated every circumstance which the other had deposed; nay, he produced the record upon his breast, where the handwriting of Mr. Jones remained very legible in black and blue. He concluded with declaring to Mr. Allworthy, that he should have long since informed him of this matter, had not Mr. Blifil, by the most earnest interpositions, prevented him. "He is," says he, "an excellent youth: though such forgiveness of enemies is carrying the matter too far."

In reality, Blifil had taken some pains to prevail with the parson, and to prevent the discovery at that time; for which he had many reasons. He knew that the minds of men are apt to be softened and relaxed from their usual severity by sickness. Besides, he imagined that if the story was told when the fact was so recent, and the physician about the house, who might have unravelled the real truth, he should never be able to give it the malicious turn which he intended. Again, he resolved to hoard up this business till the indiscretion of Jones should afford some additional complaints; for he thought the joint weight of many facts falling upon him together would be the most likely to crush him; and he watched, therefore, some such opportunity as that with which Fortune had now kindly presented him. Lastly, by prevailing with Thwackum to conceal the matter for a time, he knew he should confirm an opinion of his friendship to Jones, which he had greatly laboured to establish in Mr. Allworthy.

Chapter Eleven

A SHORT CHAPTER; BUT WHICH CONTAINS SUFFICIENT MATTER TO AFFECT THE GOOD-NATURED READER

It was Mr. Allworthy's custom never to punish any one, not even to turn away a servant, in a passion. He resolved, therefore, to delay passing sentence on Jones till the afternoon.

The poor young man attended at dinner, as usual; but his heart was too much loaded to suffer him to eat. His grief, too, was a good deal aggravated by the unkind looks of Mr. Allworthy; whence he concluded that Western had discovered the whole affair between him and Sophia; but as to Mr. Blifil's story, he had not the least apprehension; for of much the greater part he was entirely innocent; and for the residue, as he had forgiven and forgotten it himself, so he suspected no remembrance on the other side. When dinner was over, and the servants departed, Mr. Allworthy began to harangue. He set forth, in a long speech, the many iniquities of which Jones had been guilty, particularly those which this day had brought to light; and concluded by telling him, "That unless he could clear himself of the charge, he was resolved to banish him from his sight for ever."

Many disadvantages attended poor Jones in making his defence; nay, indeed, he hardly knew his accusation; for as Mr. Allworthy, in recounting the drunkenness, etc., while he lay ill, out of modesty sunk everything that related particularly to himself, which indeed principally constituted the crime, Jones could not deny the charge. His heart was, besides, almost broken already; and his spirits were so sunk, that he could say nothing for himself; but acknowledged the whole, and, like a criminal in despair, threw himself upon mercy; concluding, "That though he must own himself guilty of many follies and inadvertencies, he hoped he had done nothing to deserve what would be to him the greatest punishment in the world."

Allworthy answered, That he had forgiven him too often already, in compassion to his youth, and in hopes of his amendment: that he now found he was an abandoned reprobate, and such as it would be criminal in any one to support and encourage. "Nay," said Mr. Allworthy to him, "your audacious attempt to steal away the young lady calls upon me to justify my own character in punishing you. The world who have already censured the regard I have shown for you may think, with some colour at least of justice, that I connive at so base and barbarous an action—an action of which you must have known my abhorrence; and which, had you had any concern for my ease and honour, as well as for my friendship, you would never have thought of undertaking. Fie upon it, young man! indeed there is scarce any punishment equal to your crimes, and I can scarce think myself justifiable in what I am now going to bestow on you. However, as I have educated you like a child of my own, I will not turn you naked into the world. When you open this paper, therefore, you will find something which may enable you, with industry, to get an honest livelihood; but if you employ it to worse purposes, I shall not think myself obliged to supply you farther, being resolved, from this day forward, to converse no more with you on any account. I cannot avoid saying, there is no part of your conduct which I resent more than your ill-treatment of that good young man (meaning Blifil) who hath behaved with so much tenderness and honour towards you."

These last words were a dose almost too bitter to be swallowed. A flood of tears now gushed from the eyes of Jones, and every faculty of speech and motion seemed to have deserted him. It was some time before he was able to obey Allworthy's peremptory commands of departing; which he at length did, having first kissed his hands with a passion difficult to be affected, and as difficult to be described.

The reader must be very weak, if, when he considers the light in which Jones then appeared to Mr. Allworthy, he should blame the rigour of his sentence. And yet all the neighbourhood, either from this weakness, or from some worse motive, condemned this justice and severity as the highest cruelty. Nay, the very persons who had before censured the good man for the kindness and tenderness shown to a scoundrel (his own, according to the general opinion), now cried out as loudly against turning his own child out of doors. The women especially were unanimous in taking the part of Jones, and raised more stories on the occasion than I have room, in this chapter, to set down.

One thing must not be omitted, that, in their censures on this occasion, none ever mentioned the sum contained in the paper which Allworthy gave Jones, which was no less than five hundred pounds; but all agreed that he was sent away penniless, and some said naked, from the house of his inhuman father.

FOR DISCUSSION

1. Characterize Squire Western and Sophia. To what extent are they individualized and to what extent are they stereotypes? What is the literary effect of Western's speaking in dialect?
2. How does Fielding satirize contemporary romances in his description of Sophia's speech and conduct? What clichés does he deliberately include for satiric effect? What details are exaggerated to make such romances appear absurd? What details satirize conventional love scenes? What kind of young man does Fielding suggest actually appeals to dewy-eyed heroines?
3. What is the narrator of *Tom Jones* like? Does he reveal a personality of his own? What is his attitude toward characters and events? Why does he occasionally pretend to be stupid? What passages are excessively flowery, inflated, and pretentious? What comic effects does Fielding achieve by such deliberately bad prose?
4. Describe the satire directed against the English clergy at the end of Chapter 9. Of what does Fielding accuse churchmen?
5. Describe Tom Jones. How does Fielding make him a likeable hero?

FOR COMPOSITION

1. Write an essay discussing the elements in the scenes between Sophia and her father or between Squire Western and Allworthy which reveal Fielding's training as a playwright.
2. Explain how the speeches of Squire Western and Blifil reveal the characters, outlooks, and habits of each. You may wish to emphasize Western's use of hunting terms and Blifil's sanctimoniousness.

Jane Austen

Jane Austen described her novels as "the little bit (two inches wide) of ivory on which I work with so fine a brush, as produces little effect after much labor." Such a comment suggests the ironic understatement typical of Miss Austen's style. While it is true that she chose to describe a limited range of subjects, it is certainly not true that her efforts produced little effect. Her studies of the provincial lives led by eighteenth-century England's landed gentry are so acutely perceptive, so full of wit and wisdom, and so elegantly phrased, that Miss Austen is the writer who the great Victorian critic Thomas Macaulay felt most deserved to be ranked with Shakespeare. George Saintsbury, a leading English critic, listed Elizabeth Bennet, the heroine of *Pride and Prejudice*, among his favorite characters in fiction. About Jane Austen, Saintsbury observes, "She is the mother of the English nineteenth-century novel, as Scott is the father of it."

from Pride and Prejudice

Chapter One

It is a truth universally acknowledged, that a single man in possession of a good fortune must be in want of a wife.

However little known the feelings or views of such a man may be on his first entering a neighborhood, this truth is so well fixed in the minds of the surrounding families that he is considered as the rightful property of some one or other of their daughters.

"My dear Mr. Bennet," said his lady to him one day, "have you heard that Netherfield Park is let at last?"

Mr. Bennet replied that he had not.

"But it is," returned she; "for Mrs. Long has just been here, and she told me all about it."

Mr. Bennet made no answer.

"Do not you want to know who has taken it?" cried his wife impatiently.

"*You* want to tell me, and I have no objection to hearing it."

This was invitation enough.

"Why, my dear, you must know, Mrs. Long says that Netherfield is taken by a young man of large fortune from the north of England; that he came down on Monday in a chaise-and-four to see the place, and was so much delighted with it that he agreed with Mr. Morris immediately; that he is to take possession before Michaelmas, and some of his servants are to be in the house by the end of next week."

"What is his name?"

"Bingley."

"Is he married or single?"

"Oh! single, my dear, to be sure! A single man of large fortune; four or five thousand a year. What a fine thing for our girls!"

"How so? how can it affect them?"

"My dear Mr. Bennet," replied his wife, "how can you be so tiresome! you must know that I am thinking of his marrying one of them."

"Is that his design in settling here?"

"Design! nonsense, how can you talk so! But it is very likely that he *may* fall in love with one of them, and therefore you must visit him as soon as he comes."

"I see no occasion for that. You and the girls may go, or you may send them by themselves, which perhaps will be still better, for as you are as handsome as any of them, Mr. Bingley might like you the best of the party."

"My dear, you flatter me. I certainly *have* had my share of beauty, but I do not pretend to be anything extraordinary now. When a woman has five grown-up daughters, she ought to give over thinking of her own beauty."

"In such cases, a woman has not often much beauty to think of."

"But, my dear, you must indeed go and see Mr. Bingley when he comes into the neighborhood."

"It is more than I engage for, I assure you."

"But consider your daughters. Only think what an establishment it would be for one of them. Sir William and Lady Lucas are determined to go, merely on that account, for in general, you know, they visit no newcomers. Indeed you must go, for it will be impossible for *us* to visit him if you do not."

"You are over-scrupulous,[1] surely. I dare say Mr. Bingley will be very glad to see you; and I will send a few lines by you to assure him of my hearty consent to his marrying whichever he chooses of the girls: though I must throw in a good word for my little Lizzy."

"I desire you will do no such thing. Lizzy is not a bit better than the others; and I am sure she is not half so handsome as Jane, nor half so good-humored as Lydia. But you are always giving *her* the preference."

"They have none of them much to recommend them," replied he; "they are all silly and ignorant, like other girls: but Lizzy has something more of quickness[2] than her sisters."

"Mr. Bennet, how can you abuse your own children in such a way! You take delight in vexing me. You have no compassion on my poor nerves."

"You mistake me, my dear. I have a high respect for your nerves. They are my old friends. I have heard you mention them with consideration these twenty years at least."

"Ah! you do not know what I suffer."

"But I hope you will get over it, and live to see many young men of four thousand a year come into the neighborhood."

"It will be no use to us, if twenty such should come, since you will not visit them."

"Depend upon it, my dear, that when there are twenty, I will visit them all."

Mr. Bennet was so odd a mixture of quick parts, sarcastic humor, reserve, and caprice,[3] that the experience of three-and-twenty years had been insufficient to make his wife understand his character. *Her* mind was less difficult to develop. She was a woman of mean[4] understanding, little information, and uncertain temper. When she was discontented, she fancied

[1]*over-scrupulous:* too careful and exacting
[2]*quickness:* alertness; intelligence
[3]*caprice:* whim; sudden change of mind without apparent cause
[4]*mean:* inferior

herself nervous. The business of her life was to get her daughters married; its solace was visiting and news.

Chapter Two

Mr. Bennet was among the earliest of those who waited on Mr. Bingley. He had always intended to visit him, though to the last always assuring his wife that he should not go; and till the evening after the visit was paid she had no knowledge of it. It was then disclosed in the following manner:—Observing his second daughter employed in trimming a hat, he suddenly addressed her with,

"I hope Mr. Bingley will like it, Lizzy."

"We are not in a way to know *what* Mr. Bingley likes," said her mother resentfully, "since we are not to visit."

"But you forget, mamma," said Elizabeth, "that we shall meet him at the assemblies,[5] and that Mrs. Long has promised to introduce him."

"I do not believe Mrs. Long will do any such thing. She has two nieces of her own. She is a selfish, hypocritical woman, and I have no opinion of her."

"No more have I," said Mr. Bennet; "and I am glad to find that you do not depend on her serving you."

Mrs. Bennet deigned not to make any reply, but unable to contain herself, began scolding one of her daughters.

"Don't keep coughing so, Kitty, for Heaven's sake! Have a little compassion on my nerves. You tear them to pieces."

"Kitty has no discretion in her coughs," said her father; "she times them ill."

"I do not cough for my own amusement," replied Kitty fretfully. "When is your next ball to be, Lizzy?"

"To-morrow fortnight."[6]

"Aye, so it is," cried her mother, "and Mrs. Long does not

[5]*assemblies:* dances or public balls
[6]*fortnight:* two weeks

come back till the day before; so it will be impossible for her to introduce him, for she will not know him herself."

"Then, my dear, you may have the advantage of your friend, and introduce Mr. Bingley to *her*."

"Impossible, Mr. Bennet, impossible, when I am not acquainted with him myself; how can you be so teasing?"

"I honor your circumspection.[7] A fortnight's acquaintance is certainly very little. One cannot know what a man really is by the end of a fortnight. But if *we* do not venture somebody else will; and after all, Mrs. Long and her nieces must stand their chance; and, therefore, as she will think it an act of kindness, if you decline the office, I will take it on myself."

The girls stared at their father. Mrs. Bennet said only, "Nonsense, nonsense!"

"What can be the meaning of that emphatic exclamation?" cried he. "Do you consider the forms of introduction, and the stress that is laid on them, as nonsense? I cannot quite agree with you *there*. What say you, Mary? for you are a young lady of deep reflection, I know, and read great books and make extracts."

Mary wished to say something very sensible, but knew not how.

"While Mary is adjusting her ideas," he continued, "let us return to Mr. Bingley."

"I am sick of Mr. Bingley," cried his wife.

"I am sorry to hear *that*; but why did not you tell me so before? If I had known as much this morning I certainly would not have called on him. It is very unlucky; but as I have actually paid the visit, we cannot escape the acquaintance now."

The astonishment of the ladies was just what he wished; that of Mrs. Bennet perhaps surpassing the rest; though, when the first tumult of joy was over, she began to declare that it was what she had expected all the while.

"How good it was in you, my dear Mr. Bennet! But I knew I should persuade you at last. I was sure you loved your girls too well to neglect such an acquaintance. Well, how pleased

[7]*circumspection:* caution; prudence

I am! and it is such a good joke, too, that you should have gone this morning and never said a word about it till now."

"Now, Kitty, you may cough as much as you choose," said Mr. Bennet; and, as he spoke, he left the room, fatigued with the raptures of his wife.

"What an excellent father you have, girls!" said she, when the door was shut. "I do not know how you will ever make him amends for his kindness; or me either, for that matter. At our time of life it is not so pleasant, I can tell you, to be making new acquaintance every day; but for your sakes, we would do anything. Lydia, my love, though you *are* the youngest, I dare say Mr. Bingley will dance with you at the next ball."

"Oh!" said Lydia stoutly, "I am not afraid; for though I *am* the youngest, I'm the tallest."

The rest of the evening was spent on conjecturing[8] how soon he would return Mr. Bennet's visit, and determining when they should ask him to dinner.

Chapter Three

Not all that Mrs. Bennet, however, with the assistance of her five daughters, could ask on the subject, was sufficient to draw from her husband any satisfactory description of Mr. Bingley. They attacked him in various ways—with barefaced questions, ingenious[9] suppositions, and distant surmises; but he eluded the skill of them all, and they were at last obliged to accept the second-hand intelligence[10] of their neighbor, Lady Lucas. Her report was highly favorable. Sir William had been delighted with him. He was quite young, wonderfully handsome, extremely agreeable, and, to crown the whole, he meant to be at the next assembly with a large party. Nothing could be more delightful! To be fond of dancing was a

[8]*conjecturing:* guessing
[9]*ingenious:* clever
[10]*intelligence:* information; news

certain step towards falling in love; and very lively hopes for Mr. Bingley's heart were entertained.

"If I can but see one of my daughters happily settled at Netherfield," said Mrs. Bennet to her husband, "and all the others equally well married, I shall have nothing to wish for."

In a few days Mr. Bingley returned Mr. Bennet's visit, and sat about ten minutes with him in his library. He had entertained hopes of being admitted to a sight of the young ladies, of whose beauty he had heard much; but he saw only the father. The ladies were somewhat more fortunate, for they had the advantage of ascertaining from an upper window that he wore a blue coat, and rode a black horse.

An invitation to dinner was soon afterwards dispatched; and already had Mrs. Bennet planned the courses that were to do credit to her housekeeping, when an answer arrived which deferred it all. Mr. Bingley was obliged to be in town the following day, and, consequently, unable to accept the honor of their invitation, &c. Mrs. Bennet was quite disconcerted. She could not imagine what business he could have in town so soon after his arrival in Hertfordshire; and she began to fear that he might be always flying about from one place to another, and never settled at Netherfield as he ought to be. Lady Lucas quieted her fears a little by starting the idea of his being gone to London only to get a large party for the ball; and a report soon followed, that Mr. Bingley was to bring twelve ladies and seven gentlemen with him to the assembly. The girls grieved over such a number of ladies, but were comforted the day before the ball by hearing, that instead of twelve he had brought only six with him from London,—his five sisters and a cousin. And when the party entered the assembly room it consisted only of five altogether,—Mr. Bingley, his two sisters, the husband of the eldest, and another young man.

Mr. Bingley was good-looking and gentlemanlike; he had a pleasant countenance, and easy, unaffected manners. His sisters were fine women, with an air of decided fashion. His brother-in-law, Mr. Hurst, merely looked the gentleman; but his friend Mr. Darcy soon drew the attention of the room by his fine, tall person, handsome features, noble mien,[11] and the report which was in general circulation within five minutes after his entrance, of his having ten thousand a year. The gentlemen pronounced him to be a fine figure of a man, the ladies declared he was much handsomer than Mr. Bingley, and he was looked at with great admiration for about half the evening, till his manners gave a disgust which turned the tide of his popularity; for he was discovered to be proud; to be above his company, and above being pleased; and not all his large estate in Derbyshire could then save him from having a most forbidding, disagreeable countenance, and being unworthy to be compared with his friend.

Mr. Bingley had soon made himself acquainted with all the principal people in the room; he was lively and unreserved, danced every dance, was angry that the ball closed so early, and talked of giving one himself at Netherfield. Such amiable qualities must speak for themselves. What a contrast between him and his friend! Mr. Darcy danced only once with Mrs. Hurst and once with Miss Bingley, declined being introduced to any other lady, and spent the rest of the evening in walking about the room, speaking occasionally to one of his own party. His character was decided. He was the proudest, most disagreeable man in the world, and everybody hoped that he would never come there again. Amongst the most violent against him was Mrs. Bennet, whose dislike of his general behavior was sharpened into particular resentment by his having slighted one of her daughters.

Elizabeth Bennet had been obliged, by the scarcity of gentlemen, to sit down for two dances; and during part of that time, Mr. Darcy had been standing near enough for her to overhear a conversation between him and Mr. Bingley, who came from the dance for a few minutes, to press his friend to join in.

"Come, Darcy," said he, "I must have you dance. I hate to see you standing about by yourself in this stupid manner. You had much better dance."

[11]*mien:* bearing

"I certainly shall not. You know how I detest it, unless I am particularly acquainted with my partner. At such an assembly as this it would be insupportable. Your sisters are engaged, and there is not another woman in the room whom it would not be a punishment to me to stand up with."

"I would not be so fastidious[12] as you are," cried Bingley, "for a kingdom! Upon my honor, I never met with so many pleasant girls in my life as I have this evening; and there are several of them you see uncommonly pretty."

"*You* are dancing with the only handsome girl in the room," said Mr. Darcy, looking at the eldest Miss Bennet.

"Oh! she is the most beautiful creature I ever beheld! But there is one of her sisters sitting down just behind you, who is very pretty, and I dare say very agreeable. Do let me ask my partner to introduce you."

"Which do you mean?" and turning round he looked for a moment at Elizabeth, till catching her eye, he withdrew his own and coldly said, "She is tolerable, but not handsome enough to tempt *me;* and I am in no humor at present to give consequence to young ladies who are slighted by other men. You had better return to your partner and enjoy her smiles, for you are wasting your time with me."

Mr. Bingley followed his advice. Mr. Darcy walked off; and Elizabeth remained with no very cordial feelings toward him. She told the story, however, with great spirit among her friends; for she had a lively, playful disposition, which delighted in anything ridiculous.

The evening altogether passed off pleasantly to the whole family. Mrs. Bennet had seen her eldest daughter much admired by the Netherfield party. Mr. Bingley had danced with her twice, and she had been distinguished by his sisters. Jane was as much gratified by this as her mother could be, though in a quieter way. Elizabeth felt Jane's pleasure. Mary had heard herself mentioned to Miss Bingley as the most accomplished girl in the neighborhood; and Catherine and Lydia had been fortunate enough to be never without partners, which was all that they had learnt to care for at a ball.

[12]*fastidious:* hard to please; critical

They returned, therefore, in good spirits to Longbourn, the village where they lived, and of which they were the principal inhabitants. They found Mr. Bennet still up. With a book he was regardless of time; and on the present occasion he had a good deal of curiosity as to the event of an evening which had raised such splendid expectations. He had rather hoped that all his wife's views on the stranger would be disappointed; but he soon found that he had a very different story to hear.

"Oh! my dear Mr. Bennet," as she entered the room, "we have had a most delightful evening, a most excellent ball. I wish you had been there. Jane was so admired, nothing could be like it. Everybody said how well she looked; and Mr. Bingley thought her quite beautiful, and danced with her twice! Only think of *that,* my dear; he actually danced with her twice! and she was the only creature in the room that he asked a second time. First of all, he asked Miss Lucas. I was so vexed to see him stand up[13] with her! but, however, he did not admire her at all; indeed, nobody can, you know; and he seemed quite struck with Jane as she was going down the dance. So he inquired who she was, and got introduced, and asked her for the two next. Then the two third he danced with Miss King, and the two fourth with Maria Lucas, and the two fifth with Jane again, and the two sixth with Lizzy and the Boulanger."

"If he had had any compassion for *me,*" cried her husband impatiently, "he would not have danced half so much! For God's sake, say no more of his partners. O that he had sprained his ankle in the first dance!"

"Oh! my dear," continued Mrs. Bennet, "I am quite delighted with him. He is so excessively handsome! and his sisters are charming women. I never in my life saw anything more elegant than their dresses. I dare say the lace upon Mrs. Hurst's gown—"

Here she was interrupted again. Mr. Bennet protested against any description of finery. She was therefore obliged to seek another branch of the subject, and related, with much

[13]*stand up:* dance

bitterness of spirit and some exaggeration, the shocking rudeness of Mr. Darcy.

"But I can assure you," she added, "that Lizzy does not lose much by not suiting *his* fancy; for he is a most disagreeable, horrid man, not at all worth pleasing. So high and so conceited that there was no enduring him! He walked here, and he walked there, fancying himself so very great! Not handsome enough to dance with! I wish you had been there, my dear, to have given him one of your set-downs. I quite detest the man."

Chapter Four

When Jane and Elizabeth were alone, the former, who had been cautious in her praise of Mr. Bingley before, expressed to her sister how very much she admired him.

"He is just what a young man ought to be," said she, "sensible, good-humored, lively; and I never saw such happy manners!—so much ease, with such perfect good-breeding!"

"He is also handsome," replied Elizabeth; "which a young man ought likewise to be, if he possibly can. His character is thereby complete."

"I was very much flattered by his asking me to dance a second time. I did not expect such a compliment."

"Did not you? *I* did for you. But that is one great difference between us. Compliments always take *you* by surprise, and *me* never. What could be more natural than his asking you again? He could not help seeing that you were about five times as pretty as every other woman in the room. No thanks to his gallantry for that. Well, he certainly is very agreeable, and I give you leave to like him. You have liked many a stupider person."

"Dear Lizzy!"

"Oh! you are a great deal too apt, you know, to like people in general. You never see a fault in anybody. All the world are good and agreeable in your eyes. I never heard you speak ill of a human being in my life."

"I would wish not to be hasty in censuring[14] any one; but I always speak what I think."

"I know you do; and it is *that* which makes the wonder. With *your* good sense, to be so honestly blind to the follies and nonsense of others! Affectation of candor is common enough—one meets it everywhere. But to be candid without ostentation[15] or design—to take the good of everybody's character and make it still better, and say nothing of the bad—belongs to you alone. And so you like this man's sisters, too, do you? Their manners are not equal to his."

"Certainly not—at first. But they are very pleasing women when you converse with them. Miss Bingley is to live with her brother, and keep his house; and I am much mistaken if we shall not find a very charming neighbor in her."

Elizabeth listened in silence, but was not convinced; their behavior at the assembly had not been calculated to please in general; and with more quickness of observation and less pliancy of temper than her sister, and with a judgment too unassailed by any attention to herself, she was very little disposed to approve them. They were in fact very fine ladies; not deficient in good humor when they were pleased, nor in the power of being agreeable when they chose it, but proud and conceited. They were rather handsome, had been educated in one of the first private seminaries in town, had a fortune of twenty thousand pounds, were in the habit of spending more than they ought, and of associating with people of rank, and were therefore in every respect entitled to think well of themselves, and meanly of others. They were of a respectable family in the north of England; a circumstance more deeply impressed on their memories than that their brother's fortune and their own had been acquired by trade.

Mr. Bingley inherited property to the amount of nearly an hundred thousand pounds from his father, who had intended to purchase an estate, but did not live to do it. Mr. Bingley intended it likewise, and sometimes made choice of his county; but as he was now provided with a good house and

[14]*censuring:* disapproving, finding fault with
[15]*ostentation:* display intended to impress others

the liberty of a manor, it was doubtful to many of those who best knew the easiness of his temper, whether he might not spend the remainder of his days at Netherfield, and leave the next generation to purchase.

His sisters were very anxious for his having an estate of his own; but, though he was now established only as a tenant, Miss Bingley was by no means unwilling to preside at his table—nor was Mrs. Hurst, who had married a man of more fashion than fortune, less disposed to consider his house as her home when it suited her. Mr. Bingley had not been of age two years, when he was tempted by an accidental recommendation to look at Netherfield House. He did look at it, and into it for half-an-hour—was pleased with the situation and the principal rooms, satisfied with what the owner said in praise, and took it immediately.

Between him and Darcy there was a very steady friendship, in spite of great opposition of character. Bingley was endeared to Darcy by the easiness, openness, and ductility[16] of his temper, though no disposition could offer a greater contrast to his own, and though with his own he never appeared dissatisfied. On the strength of Darcy's regard, Bingley had the firmest reliance, and of his judgment the highest opinion. In understanding, Darcy was the superior. Bingley was by no means deficient, but Darcy was clever. He was at the same time haughty, reserved, and fastidious, and his manners, though well-bred, were not inviting. In that respect his friend had greatly the advantage. Bingley was sure of being liked wherever he appeared, Darcy was continually giving offense.

The manner in which they spoke of the Meryton assembly was sufficiently characteristic. Bingley had never met with pleasanter people or prettier girls in his life; everybody had been most kind and attentive to him; there had been no formality, no stiffness; he had soon felt acquainted with all the room; and as to Miss Bennet, he could not conceive an angel more beautiful. Darcy, on the contrary, had seen a collection of people in whom there was little beauty and no fashion, for none of whom he had felt the smallest interest, and from

[16]*ductility:* easiness to manage

none received either attention or pleasure. Miss Bennet he acknowledged to be pretty, but she smiled too much.

Mrs. Hurst and her sister allowed it to be so – but still they admired her and liked her, and pronounced her to be a sweet girl, and one whom they should not object to know more of. Miss Bennet was therefore established as a sweet girl, and their brother felt authorized by such commendation to think of her as he chose.

Chapter Five

Within a short walk of Longbourn lived a family with whom the Bennets were particularly intimate. Sir William Lucas had been formerly in trade in Meryton, where he had made a tolerable fortune, and risen to the honor of knighthood by an address to the king, during his mayoralty. The distinction had perhaps been felt too strongly. It had given him a disgust to his business, and to his residence in a small market town; and, quitting them both, he had removed with his family to a house about a mile from Meryton, denominated from that period Lucas Lodge, where he could think with pleasure of his own importance, and, unshackled by business, occupy himself solely in being civil to all the world. For, though elated by his rank, it did not render him supercilious;[17] on the contrary, he was all attention to everybody. By nature inoffensive, friendly, and obliging, his presentation at St. James's had made him courteous.

Lady Lucas was a very good kind of woman, not too clever to be a valuable neighbor to Mrs. Bennet. They had several children. The eldest of them, a sensible, intelligent young woman, about twenty-seven, was Elizabeth's intimate friend.

That the Miss Lucases and the Miss Bennets should meet to talk over a ball was absolutely necessary; and the morning after the assembly brought the former to Longbourn to hear and to communicate.

"*You* began the evening well, Charlotte," said Mrs. Bennet

[17]*supercilious:* haughty; disdainful

with civil self-command to Miss Lucas. "*You* were Mr. Bingley's first choice."

"Yes; but he seemed to like his second better."

"Oh! you mean Jane, I suppose, because he danced with her twice. To be sure that *did* seem as if he admired her—indeed I rather believe he *did*—I heard something about it—but I hardly know what—something about Mr. Robinson."

"Perhaps you mean what I overheard between him and Mr. Robinson; did not I mention it to you? Mr. Robinson's asking him how he liked our Meryton assemblies, and whether he did not think there were a great many pretty women in the room, and *which* he thought the prettiest? and his answering immediately to the last question—'Oh! the eldest Miss Bennet, beyond a doubt; there cannot be two opinions on that point.'"

"Upon my word!—Well, that was very decided indeed—that does seem as if—but, however, it may all come to nothing, you know."

"*My* overhearings were more to the purpose than *yours*, Eliza," said Charlotte. "Mr. Darcy is not so well worth listening to as his friend, is he?—Poor Eliza!— to be only just *tolerable.*"

"I beg you would not put it into Lizzy's head to be vexed by his ill-treatment, for he is such a disagreeable man, that it would be quite a misfortune to be liked by him. Mrs. Long told me last night that he had sat close to her for half-an-hour without once opening his lips.

"Are you quite sure, ma'am?—is not there a little mistake?" said Jane. "I certainly saw Mr. Darcy speaking to her."

"Aye—because she asked him at last how he liked Netherfield, and he could not help answering her; but she said he seemed very angry at being spoke to."

"Miss Bingley told me," said Jane, "that he never speaks much, unless among his intimate acquaintance. With *them* he is remarkably agreeable."

"I do not believe a word of it, my dear. If he had been so very agreeable, he would have talked to Mrs. Long. But I can guess how it was; everybody says that he is eat up with pride, and I dare say he had heard somehow that Mrs. Long does not keep a carriage, and had come to the ball in a hack chaise."

"I do not mind his not talking to Mrs. Long," said Miss Lucas, "but I wish he had danced with Eliza."

"Another time, Lizzy," said her mother, "I would not dance with *him*, if I were you."

"I believe, ma'am, I may safely promise you *never* to dance with him."

"His pride," said Miss Lucas, "does not offend *me* so much as pride often does, because there is an excuse for it. One cannot wonder that so very fine a young man, with family, fortune, everything in his favor, should think highly of himself. If I may so express it, he has a *right* to be proud."

"That is very true," replied Elizabeth, "and I could easily forgive *his* pride, if he had not mortified *mine.*"

"Pride," observed Mary, who piqued[18] herself upon the solidity of her reflections, "is a very common failing, I believe. By all that I have read, I am convinced that it is very common indeed; that human nature is particularly prone to it, and that there are very few of us who do not cherish a feeling of self-complacency on the score of some quality or the other, real or imaginary. Vanity and pride are different things, though the words are often used synonymously. A person may be proud without being vain. Pride relates more to our opinion of ourselves, vanity to what we would have others think of us."

"If I were as rich as Mr. Darcy," cried a young Lucas, who came with his sisters, "I should not care how proud I was. I would keep a pack of foxhounds, and drink a bottle of wine every day."

"Then you would drink a great deal more than you ought," said Mrs. Bennet; "and if I were to see you at it I should take away your bottle directly."

The boy protested that she should not; she continued to declare that she would, and the argument ended only with the visit.

[18]*piqued:* prided herself

FOR DISCUSSION

1. What tone does the opening sentence establish? What does this sentence tell you about the narrator? What attitude toward marriage and personal relations does the second sentence imply? How would you describe a group which shares such attitudes?
2. How would you characterize the relationship between Mr. and Mrs. Bennet? What kind of person is each? By what different methods are their characters revealed? What is the relationship between parents and daughters in this family?
3. Jane Austen has been praised for her realistic portrayal of the life she knew. What do you learn here of the late eighteenth century's idea of the perfect gentleman? the perfect lady? attitudes toward tradesmen? toward property and inheritance? What kind of manners were identified with "true gentility"?
4. Describe Elizabeth Bennet. How does she seem to differ from the conventional young lady of the time? How does she differ from Miss Lucas?
5. What different kinds of humor do you find in these opening chapters? What creates or provides the humor? How would you describe Jane Austen's humor?

FOR COMPOSITION

1. Judging from this selection, describe what it was like to be a young lady in the late eighteenth century. Describe such a lady's probable interests, opinions, attitudes, habits, hobbies, and expectations.
2. Write an essay describing the social rules or conventions of eighteenth-century England, basing your generalizations on this selection.

Charles Dickens

On March 31, 1836, the first installment of the *Pickwick Papers* by Charles Dickens appeared, and the career of one of the great English novelists was brilliantly launched. The *Pickwick Papers* was ostensibly the "faithful record of the perambulations, perils, travels, adventures, and sporting transactions" of the members of the Pickwick Club, founded by Mr. Samuel Pickwick and counting as its members the Messrs. Tracy Tupman, Augustus Snodgrass, and Nathaniel Winkle. However, as Dickens went on writing installment after installment, the book soared beyond its original intention. As his biographer Edgar Johnson says, "a glorious surge of creative affirmation lifts the *Pickwick Papers* high into the radiant light of the sun and makes it a joyful masterpiece."*

As he was to do in his later novels, Dickens created a gallery of remarkable and unforgettable characters, among the best of them Mr. Pickwick, the kindly, benevolent idealist, and Sam Weller, servant and "philosopher." Dickens' capacity for including hilarious incidents and his excellent storytelling techniques are much in evidence in the *Pickwick Papers*, and can be seen in the episode that follows.

from Pickwick Papers

Chapter Nineteen

A pleasant day, with an unpleasant termination

The birds, who, happily for their own peace of mind and personal comfort, were in blissful ignorance of the preparations which had been making to astonish them on the first of September, hailed it, no doubt, as one of the pleasant-

*Edgar Johnson, *Charles Dickens, His Tragedy and Triumph*, Volume I (New York: Simon and Shuster, 1952), p. 143.

est mornings they had seen that season. Many a young partridge who strutted complacently among the stubble, with all the finicking, coxcombry[1] of youth, and many an older one who watched his levity[2] out of his little round eye, with the contemptuous air of a bird of wisdom and experience, alike unconscious of their approaching doom, basked in the fresh morning air with lively and blithesome feelings, and a few hours afterwards were laid low upon the earth. But we grow affecting[3]—let us proceed.

In plain commonplace matter of fact, then, it was a fine morning—so fine that you would scarcely have believed that the few months of an English summer had yet flown by. Hedges, fields, and trees, hill and moorland, presented to the eye their ever-varying shades of deep rich green; scarce a leaf had fallen; scarce a sprinkle of yellow mingled with the hues of summer warned you that autumn had begun. The sky was cloudless; the sun shone out bright and warm; the songs of birds and hum of myriads of summer insects filled the air; and the cottage gardens, crowded with flowers of every rich and beautiful tint, sparkled in the heavy dew like beds of glittering jewels. Everything bore the stamp of summer, and none of its beautiful colours had yet faded from the dye.

Such was the morning when an open carriage, in which were three Pickwickians (Mr. Snodgrass having preferred to remain at home), Mr. Wardle, and Mr. Trundle, with Sam Weller on the box beside the driver, pulled up by a gate at the roadside, before which stood a tall, raw-boned gamekeeper and a half booted, leather-leggined boy, each bearing a bag of capacious dimensions, and accompanied by a brace of pointers.[4]

"I say," whispered Mr. Winkle to Wardle as the man let down the steps, "they don't suppose we're going to kill game enough to fill those bags, do they?"

"Fill them!" exclaimed old Wardle. "Bless you, yes! You

[1]*coxcombry:* strutting or vain behavior
[2]*levity:* lighthearted mood
[3]*affecting:* affected or pretentious
[4]*brace of pointers:* pair of birddogs

shall fill one, and I the other; and when we've done with them, the pockets of our shooting-jackets will hold as much more."

Mr. Winkle dismounted without saying anything in reply to this observation; but he thought within himself that if the party remained in the open air until he had filled one of the bags, they stood a considerable chance of catching colds in their heads.

"Hi, Juno, lass—hi, old girl; down, Daph, down," said Wardle, caressing the dogs. "Sir Geoffrey still in Scotland, of course, Martin?"

The tall gamekeeper replied in the affirmative and looked with some surprise from Mr. Winkle, who was holding his gun as if he wished his coat-pocket to save him the trouble of pulling the trigger, to Mr. Tupman who was holding his as if he were afraid of it—as there is no earthly reason to doubt he really was.

"My friends are not much in the way of this sort of thing yet, Martin," said Wardle, noticing the look. "Live and learn, you know. They'll be good shots one of these days. I beg my friend Winkle's pardon, though; he has had some practice."

Mr. Winkle smiled feebly over his blue neckerchief in acknowledgement of the compliment, and got himself so mysteriously entangled with his gun, in his modest confusion, that if the piece had been loaded, he must inevitably have shot himself dead upon the spot.

"You mustn't handle your piece in that 'ere way when you come to have the charge in it, sir," said the tall gamekeeper gruffly, "or I'm damned if you won't make cold meat of some of us."

Mr. Winkle, thus admonished, abruptly altered its position, and in so doing contrived to bring the barrel into pretty sharp contact with Mr. Weller's head.

"Hallo!" said Sam, picking up his hat, which had been knocked off, and rubbing his temple. "Hallo, sir! If you comes it this vay, you'll fill one o' them bags, and something to spare, at one fire."

Here the leather-leggined boy laughed very heartily and

then tried to look as if it was somebody else, whereat Mr. Winkle frowned majestically.

"Where did you tell the boy to meet us with the snack, Martin?" inquired Wardle.

"Side of One-Tree Hill at twelve o'clock, sir."

"That's not Sir Geoffrey's land, is it?"

"No, sir; but it's close by it. It's Captain Boldwig's land; but there'll be nobody to interrupt us, and there's a fine bit of turf there."

"Very well," said old Wardle. "Now the sooner we're off, the better. Will you join us at twelve, then, Pickwick?"

Mr. Pickwick was particularly desirous to view the sport, the more especially as he was rather anxious in respect of Mr. Winkle's life and limbs. On so inviting a morning, too, it was very tantalizing to turn back and leave his friends to enjoy themselves. It was, therefore, with a very rueful air that he replied, "Why, I suppose I must."

"An't the gentleman a shot, sir?" inquired the long game-keeper.

"No," replied Wardle, "and he's lame besides."

"I should very much like to go," said Mr. Pickwick, "very much."

There was a short pause of commiseration.[5]

"There's a barrow t'other side the hedge," said the boy. "If the gentleman's servant would wheel along the paths, he could keep nigh us, and we could lift it over the stiles and that."

"The wery thing," said Mr. Weller, who was a party interested, inasmuch as he ardently longed to see the sport. "The wery thing. Well said, smallcheek; I'll have it out in a minute."

But here a difficulty arose. The long gamekeeper resolutely protested against the introduction into a shooting-party of a gentleman in a barrow, as a gross violation of all established rules and precedents.

It was a great objection, but not an insurmountable one. The gamekeeper having been coaxed and fed, and having,

[5]*commiseration:* condolence or sympathy

moreover, eased his mind by "punching" the head of the inventive youth who had first suggested the use of the machine, Mr. Pickwick was placed in it, and off the party set; Wardle and the long gamekeeper leading the way, and Mr. Pickwick in the barrow, propelled by Sam, bringing up the rear.

"Stop, Sam," said Mr. Pickwick when they had got half across the first field.

"What's the matter now?" said Wardle.

"I won't suffer this barrow to be moved another step," said Mr. Pickwick resolutely, "unless Winkle carries that gun of his in a different manner."

"How *am* I to carry it?" said the wretched Winkle.

"Carry it with the muzzle to the ground," replied Mr. Pickwick.

"It's so unsportsman-like," reasoned Winkle.

"I don't care whether it's unsportsman-like or not," replied Mr. Pickwick; "I am not going to be shot in a wheelbarrow, for the sake of appearances, to please anybody."

"I know the gentleman'll put that 'ere charge into somebody afore he's done," growled the long man.

"Well, well—I don't mind," said poor Winkle, turning his gun-stock uppermost; "there."

"Anythin' for a quiet life," said Mr. Weller; and on they went again.

"Stop!" said Mr. Pickwick after they had gone a few yards further.

"What now?" said Wardle.

"That gun of Tupman's is not safe; I know it isn't," said Mr. Pickwick.

"Eh? What! Not safe?" said Mr. Tupman in a tone of great alarm.

"Not as you are carrying it," said Mr. Pickwick. "I am very sorry to make any further objection, but I cannot consent to go on unless you carry it as Winkle does his."

"I think you had better, sir," said the long gamekeeper, "or you're quite as likely to lodge the charge in yourself as in anything else."

Mr. Tupman, with the most obliging haste, placed his

piece in the position required, and the party moved on again; the two amateurs marching with reversed arms, like a couple of privates at a royal funeral.

The dogs suddenly came to a dead stop, and the party, advancing stealthily a single pace, stopped too.

"What's the matter with the dogs' legs?" whispered Mr. Winkle. "How queer they're standing."

"Hush, can't you?" replied Wardle softly. "Don't you see they're making a point?"

"Making a point!" said Mr. Winkle, staring about him as if he expected to discover some particular beauty in the landscape which the sagacious animals were calling special attention to. "Making a point! What are they pointing at?"

"Keep your eyes open," said Wardle, not heeding the question in the excitement of the moment. "Now, then."

There was a sharp whirring noise that made Mr. Winkle start back as if he had been shot himself. Bang, bang, went a couple of guns—the smoke swept quickly away over the field and curled into the air.

"Where are they?" said Mr. Winkle in a state of the highest excitement, turning round and round in all directions. "Where are they? Tell me when to fire. Where are they—where are they?"

"Where are they?" said Wardle, taking up a brace of birds which the dogs had deposited at his feet. "Why, here they are."

"No, no; I mean the others," said the bewildered Winkle.

"Far enough off by this time," replied Wardle, coolly reloading his gun.

"We shall very likely be up with another covey in five minutes," said the long gamekeeper. "If the gentleman begins to fire now, perhaps he'll just get the shot out of the barrel by the time they rise."

"Ha! Ha! Ha!" roared Mr. Weller.

"Sam," said Mr. Pickwick, compassionating his follower's confusion and embarrassment.

"Sir."

"Don't laugh."

"Certainly not, sir." So, by way of indemnification,[6] Mr. Weller contorted his features from behind the wheelbarrow, for the exclusive amusement of the boy with the leggings, who thereupon burst into a boisterous laugh, and was summarily cuffed by the long gamekeeper, who wanted a pretext for turning round, to hide his own merriment.

"Bravo, old fellow!" said Wardle to Mr. Tupman. "You fired that time, at all events."

"Oh, yes," replied Mr. Tupman with conscious pride. "I let it off."

"Well done. You'll hit something next time if you look sharp. Very easy, ain't it?"

"Yes, it's very easy," said Mr. Tupman. "How it hurts one's shoulder, though. It nearly knocked me backwards. I had no idea these small fire-arms kicked so."

"Ah," said the old gentleman, smiling, "you'll get used to it in time. Now, then—all ready—all right with the barrow there?"

"All right, sir," replied Mr. Weller.

"Come along, then."

"Hold hard, sir," said Sam, raising the barrow.

"Aye, aye," replied Mr. Pickwick; and on they went, as briskly as need be.

"Keep that barrow back now," cried Wardle when it had been hoisted over a stile into another field and Mr. Pickwick had been deposited in it once more.

"All right, sir," replied Mr. Weller, pausing.

"Now, Winkle," said the old gentleman, "follow me softly, and don't be too late this time."

"Never fear," said Mr. Winkle. "Are they pointing?"

"No, no; not now. Quietly now, quietly." On they crept, and very quietly they would have advanced if Mr. Winkle, in the performance of some very intricate evolutions with his gun, had not accidentally fired, at the most critical moment, over the boy's head, exactly in the very spot where the tall man's brain would have been had he been there instead.

[6]*indemnification:* compensation

"Why, what on earth did you do that for?" said old Wardle as the birds flew unharmed away.

"I never saw such a gun in my life," replied poor Mr. Winkle, looking at the lock, as if that would do any good. "It goes off of its own accord. It *will* do it."

"Will do it!" echoed Wardle with something of irritation in his manner. "I wish it would kill something of its own accord."

"It'll do that afore long, sir," observed the tall man in a low, prophetic voice.

"What do you mean by that observation, sir?" inquired Mr. Winkle angrily.

"Never mind, sir, never mind," replied the long gamekeeper; "I've no family myself, sir; and this here boy's mother will get something handsome from Sir Geoffrey if he's killed on his land. Load again, sir, load again."

"Take away his gun," cried Mr. Pickwick from the barrow, horror-stricken at the long man's dark insinuations. "Take away his gun, do you hear, somebody?"

Nobody, however, volunteered to obey the command; and Mr. Winkle, after darting a rebellious glance at Mr. Pickwick, reloaded his gun and proceeded onwards with the rest.

We are bound, on the authority of Mr. Pickwick, to state that Mr. Tupman's mode of proceeding evinced far more of prudence and deliberation than that adopted by Mr. Winkle. Still, this by no means detracts from the great authority of the latter gentleman on all matters connected with the field; because, as Mr. Pickwick beautifully observes, it has somehow or other happened, from time immemorial, that many of the best and ablest philosophers who have been perfect lights of science in matters of theory have been wholly unable to reduce them to practice.

Mr. Tupman's process, like many of our most sublime discoveries, was extremely simple. With the quickness and penetration of a man of genius, he had at once observed that the two great points to be attained were—first, to discharge his piece without injury to himself, and secondly, to do so without danger to the bystanders; obviously the best thing to do, after surmounting the difficulty of firing at all, was to shut his eyes firmly and fire into the air.

On one occasion, after performing this feat, Mr. Tupman, on opening his eyes, beheld a plump partridge in the act of falling wounded to the ground. He was on the point of congratulating Mr. Wardle on his invariable success when that gentleman advanced towards him and grasped him warmly by the hand.

"Tupman," said the old gentleman, "you singled out that particular bird?"

"No," said Mr. Tupman, "no."

"You did," said Wardle. "I saw you do it—I observed you pick him out—I noticed you as you raised your piece to take aim; and I will say this, that the best shot in existence could not have done it more beautifully. You are an older hand at this than I thought you, Tupman, you have been out before."

It was in vain for Mr. Tupman to protest, with a smile of self-denial, that he never had. The very smile was taken as evidence to the contrary; and from that time forth his reputation was established. It is not the only reputation that has been acquired as easily, nor are such fortunate circumstances confined to partridge-shooting.

Meanwhile, Mr. Winkle flashed and blazed and smoked away, without producing any material results worth of being noted down; sometimes expending his charge in mid-air, and at others sending it skimming along so near the surface of the ground as to place the lives of the two dogs on a rather uncertain and precarious tenure. As a display of fancy shooting, it was extremely varied and curious; as an exhibition of firing with any precise object, it was, upon the whole, perhaps a failure. It is an established axiom that "Every bullet has its billet." If it apply in an equal degree to shot, those of Mr. Winkle were unfortunate foundlings deprived of their natural rights, cast loose upon the world, and billeted[7] nowhere.

"Well," said Wardle, walking up to the side of the barrow

[7]*billeted:* housed

and wiping the streams of perspiration from his jolly red face, "smoking day, isn't it?"

"It is, indeed," replied Mr. Pickwick. "The sun is tremendously hot, even to me. I don't know how you must feel it."

"Why," said the old gentleman, "pretty hot. It's past twelve, though. You see that green hill there?"

"Certainly."

"That's the place where we are to lunch; and by Jove, there's the boy with the basket, punctual as clockwork!"

"So he is," said Mr. Pickwick, brightening up. "Good boy, that. I'll give him a shilling presently. Now, then, Sam, wheel away."

"Hold on, sir," said Mr. Weller, invigorated with the prospect of refreshments. "Out of the vay, young leathers. If, you walley my precious life, don't upset me, as the gen'lm'n said to the driver when they was a-carryin' him to Tyburn." And quickening his pace to a sharp run, Mr. Weller wheeled his master nimbly to the green hill, shot him dexterously out by the very side of the basket, and proceeded to unpack it with the utmost dispatch.

"Weal-pie," said Mr. Weller, soliloquizing as he arranged the eatables on the grass. "Wery good thing is weal-pie when you know the lady as made it, and is quite sure it an't kittens; and arter all, though, where's the odds when they're so like weal that the wery piemen themselves don't know the difference?"

"Don't they, Sam?" said Mr. Pickwick.

"Not they, sir," replied Mr. Weller, touching his hat. "I lodged in the same house vith a pieman once, sir, and a wery nice man he was—reg'lar clever chap, too—make pies out o' anything, he could. 'What a number o' cats you keep, Mr. Brooks,' says I when I'd got intimate with him. 'Ah,' says he, 'I do—a good many,' says he. 'You must be wery fond o' cats,' says I. 'Other people is,' says he, a-winkin' at me; 'they an't in season till the winter, though,' says he. 'Not in season!' says I. 'No,' says he, 'fruits is in, cats is out.' 'Why, what do you mean?' says I. 'Mean?' says he. 'That I'll never be a party to the combination o' the butchers, to keep up the prices o' meat,' says he. 'Mr. Weller,' says he, a-squeezing my hand wery hard and vispering in my ear, 'don't mention this here again—but it's the seasonin' as does it. They're all made o' them noble animals,' says he, a-pointin' to a wery nice little tabby kitten, 'and I seasons 'em for beef-steak, weal, or kidney, 'cording to the demand. And more than that,' says he, 'I can make a weal a beef-steak, or a beef-steak a kidney, or any one on 'em a mutton, at a minute's notice, just as the market changes and appetites wary!'"

"He must have been a very ingenious young man, that, Sam," said Mr. Pickwick with a slight shudder.

"Just was, sir," replied Mr. Weller, continuing his occupation of emptying the basket, "and the pies was beautiful. Tongue; well, that's a wery good thing when it an't a woman's. Bread—knuckle o' ham, reg'lar pictur—cold beef in slices, wery good. What's in them stone jars, young touch-and-go?"

"Beer in this one," replied the boy, taking from his shoulder a couple of large stone bottles fastened together by a leathern strap, "cold punch in t'other."

"And a wery good notion of a lunch it is, take it altogether," said Mr. Weller, surveying his arrangement of the repast with great satisfaction. "Now, gen'lm'n 'fall on,' as the English said to the French when they fixed bagginets."

It needed no second invitation to induce the party to yield full justice to the meal; and as little pressing did it require to induce Mr. Weller, the long gamekeeper, and the two boys to station themselves on the grass, at a little distance, and do good execution upon a decent proportion of the viands. An old oak afforded a pleasant shelter to the group, and a rich prospect of arable[8] and meadow land, intersected with luxuriant hedges and richly ornamented with wood, lay spread out below them.

"This is delightful—thoroughly delightful!" said Mr. Pickwick, the skin of whose expressive countenance was rapidly peeling off with exposure to the sun.

"So it is, so it is, old fellow," replied Wardle. "Come—a glass of punch!"

"With great pleasure," said Mr. Pickwick, the satisfaction

[8]*arable:* easily plowed

of whose countenance, after drinking it, bore testimony to the sincerity of the reply.

"Good," said Mr. Pickwick, smacking his lips. "Very good. I'll take another. Cool, very cool. Come, gentlemen," continued Mr. Pickwick, still retaining his hold upon the jar, "a toast. Our friends at Dingley Dell."

The toast was drunk with loud acclamations.

"I'll tell you what I shall do to get up my shooting again," said Mr. Winkle, who was eating bread and ham with a pocket-knife. "I'll put a stuffed partridge on the top of a post and practise at it, beginning at a short distance and lengthening it by degrees. I understand it's capital practice."

"I know a gen'lm'n, sir," said Mr. Weller, "as did that and begun at two yards; but he never tried it on agin; for he blowed the bird right clean away at the first fire, and nobody ever seed a feather on him arterwards."

"Sam," said Mr. Pickwick.

"Sir," replied Mr. Weller.

"Have the goodness to reserve your anecdotes till they are called for."

"Cert'nly, sir."

Here Mr. Weller winked the eye which was not concealed by the beer-can he was raising to his lips, with such exquisiteness that the two boys went into spontaneous convulsions, and even the long man condescended to smile.

"Well, that certainly is most capital cold punch," said Mr. Pickwick, looking earnestly at the stone bottle; "and the day is extremely warm, and – Tupman, my dear friend, a glass of punch?"

"With the greatest delight," replied Mr. Tupman; and having drunk that glass, Mr. Pickwick took another, just to see whether there was any orange peel in the punch, because orange peel always disagreed with him; and finding that there was not, Mr. Pickwick took another glass to the health of their absent friend, and then felt himself imperatively called upon to propose another in honour of the punch-compounder, unknown.

This constant succession of glasses produced considerable effect upon Mr. Pickwick; his countenance beamed with the most sunny smiles, laughter played around his lips, and good-humoured merriment twinkled in his eye. Yielding by degrees to the influence of the exciting liquid, rendered more so by the heat, Mr. Pickwick expressed a strong desire to recollect a song which he had heard in his infancy, and the attempt proving abortive,[9] sought to stimulate his memory with more glasses of punch, which appeared to have quite a contrary effect; for, from forgetting the words of the song, he began to forget how to articulate any words at all; and finally, after rising to his legs to address the company in an eloquent speech, he fell into the barrow, and fast asleep, simultaneously.

The basket having been repacked, and it being found perfectly impossible to awaken Mr. Pickwick from his torpor, some discussion took place whether it would be better for Mr. Weller to wheel his master back again or to leave him where he was until they should all be ready to return. The latter course was at length decided on; and as the further expedition was not to exceed an hour's duration, and as Mr. Weller begged very hard to be one of the party, it was determined to leave Mr. Pickwick asleep in the barrow and to call for him on their return. So away they went, leaving Mr. Pickwick snoring most comfortably in the shade.

That Mr. Pickwick would have continued to snore in the shade until his friends came back or, in default thereof, until the shades of evening had fallen on the landscape, there appears no reasonable cause to doubt, always supposing that he had been suffered to remain there in peace. But he was *not* suffered to remain there in peace. And this was what prevented him.

Captain Boldwig was a little fierce man in a stiff black neckerchief and blue surtout, who, when he did condescend to walk about his property, did it in company with a thick rattan stick with a brass ferrule,[10] and a gardener and sub-gardener with meek faces, to whom (the gardeners, not the stick) Captain Boldwig gave his orders with all due grandeur and ferocity—for Captain Boldwig's wife's sister had married

[9] *abortive:* incomplete or short-lived
[10] *ferrule:* the metal cap which protects the end of a cane

a marquis, and the captain's house was a villa, and his land "grounds," and it was all very high, and mighty, and great.

Mr. Pickwick had not been asleep half an hour when little Captain Boldwig, followed by the two gardeners, came striding along as fast as his size and importance would let him; and when he came near the oak-tree, Captain Boldwig paused and drew a long breath, and looked at the prospect as if he thought the prospect ought to be highly gratified at having him to take notice of it; and then he struck the ground emphatically with his stick and summoned the head gardener.

"Hunt," said Captain Boldwig.

"Yes, sir," said the gardener.

"Roll this place to-morrow morning—do you hear, Hunt?"

"Yes, sir."

"And take care that you keep me this place in good order—do you hear, Hunt?"

"Yes, sir."

"And remind me to have a board done about trespassers and spring-guns and all that sort of thing, to keep the common people out. Do you hear, Hunt? Do you hear?"

"I'll not forget it, sir."

"I beg your pardon, sir," said the other man, advancing, with his hand to his hat.

"Well, Wilkins, what's the matter with *you?*" said Captain Boldwig.

"I beg your pardon, sir—but I think there have been trespassers here to-day."

"Ha!" said the captain, scowling around him.

"Yes, sir—they have been dining here, I think, sir."

"Why, confound their audacity, so they have," said Captain Boldwig as the crumbs and fragments that were strewn upon the grass met his eye. "They have actually been devouring their food here. I wish I had the vagabonds here!" said the captain, clenching the thick stick.

"I wish I had the vagabonds here," said the captain wrathfully.

"Beg your pardon, sir," said Wilkins, "but—"

"But what? Eh?" roared the captain; and following the timid glance of Wilkins, his eyes encountered the wheelbarrow and Mr. Pickwick.

"Who are you, you rascal?" said the captain, administering several pokes to Mr. Pickwick's body with the thick stick. "What's your name?"

"Cold punch," murmured Mr. Pickwick as he sunk to sleep again.

"What?" demanded Captain Boldwig.

No reply.

"What did he say his name was?" asked the captain.

"Punch, I think, sir," replied Wilkins.

"That's his impudence, that's his confounded impudence," said Captain Boldwig. "He's only feigning to be asleep now," said the captain in a high passion. "He's drunk; he's a drunken plebeian.[11] Wheel him away, Wilkins, wheel him away directly."

"Where shall I wheel him to, sir?" inquired Wilkins with great timidity.

"Wheel him to the devil," replied Captain Boldwig.

"Very well, sir," said Wilkins.

"Stay," said the captain.

Wilkins stopped accordingly.

"Wheel him," said the captain, "wheel him to the Pound; and let us see whether he calls himself Punch when he comes to himself. He shall not bully me, he shall not bully me. Wheel him away."

Away Mr. Pickwick was wheeled in compliance with this imperious mandate;[12] and the great Captain Boldwig swelling with indignation, proceeded on his walk.

Inexpressible was the astonishment of the little party when they returned to find that Mr. Pickwick had disappeared and taken the wheelbarrow with him. It was the most mysterious and unaccountable thing that was ever heard of. For a lame man to have got upon his legs without any previous notice, and walked off, would have been most extraordinary; but when it came to his wheeling a heavy barrow before him, by way of amusement, it grew positively miraculous. They searched every nook and corner round, together and separately; they shouted, whistled, laughed, called—and all with the same result. Mr. Pickwick was not to be found. After some

[11]*plebeian:* vulgar or common person
[12]*imperious mandate:* high-handed ruling

hours of fruitless search, they arrived at the unwelcome conclusion that they must go home without him.

Meanwhile Mr. Pickwick had been wheeled to the Pound and safely deposited therein, fast asleep in the wheelbarrow, to the immeasurable delight and satisfaction not only of all the boys in the village but three-fourths of the whole population, who had gathered round in expectation of his waking. If their most intense gratification had been excited by seeing him wheeled in, how many hundredfold was their joy increased when, after a few indistinct cries of "Sam!" he sat up in the barrow and gazed with indescribable astonishment on the faces before him.

A general shout was of course the signal of his having woke up; and his involuntary inquiry of "What's the matter?" occasioned another, louder than the first, if possible.

"Here's a game!" roared the populace.

"Where am I?" exclaimed Mr. Pickwick.

"In the Pound," replied the mob.

"How came I here? What was I doing? Where was I brought from?"

"Boldwig! Captain Boldwig!" was the only reply.

"Let me out," cried Mr. Pickwick. "Where's my servant? Where are my friends?"

"You an't got no friends. Hurrah!" Then there came a turnip, then a potato, and then an egg—with a few other little tokens of the playful disposition of the many-headed.

How long this scene might have lasted or how much Mr. Pickwick might have suffered, no one can tell, had not a carriage, which was driving swiftly by, suddenly pulled up, from whence there descended old Wardle and Sam Weller, the former of whom, in far less time than it takes to write it if not to read it, had made his way to Mr. Pickwick's side and placed him in the vehicle, just as the latter had concluded the third and last round of a single combat with the town-beadle.[13]

"Run to the Justice's!" cried a dozen voices.

"Ah, run avay," said Mr. Weller, jumping up on the box. "Give my compliments—Mr. Veller's compliments to the

[13]*town-beadle:* the officer responsible for keeping order

Justice, and tell him I've spiled his beadle, and that if he'll svear in a new 'un, I'll come back again tomorrow and spile him. Drive on, old feller."

"I'll give directions for the commencement of an action for false imprisonment against this Captain Boldwig, directly I get to London," said Mr. Pickwick as soon as the carriage turned out of the town.

"We were trespassing, it seems," said Wardle.

"I don't care," said Mr. Pickwick, "I'll bring the action."

"No, you won't," said Wardle.

"I will, by—" But as there was a humorous expression in Wardle's face, Mr. Pickwick checked himself and said: "Why not?"

"Because," said old Wardle, half-bursting with laughter, "because they might turn round on some of us and say we had taken too much cold punch."

Do what he would, a smile would come into Mr. Pickwick's face; the smile extended into a laugh; the laugh into a roar; the roar became general. So, to keep up their good humour, they stopped at the first roadside tavern they came to and ordered a glass of brandy and water all round, with a magnum[14] of extra strength for Mr. Samuel Weller.

[14]*magnum:* two-quart bottle

FOR DISCUSSION

1. When the Pickwickians, city dwellers all, take themselves into the English countryside for a sporting holiday, they invariably find themselves in farcical situations. Find examples in this section to prove that Pickwickians in the country are not Pickwickians at their best. Discuss aspects of the author's "deadpan" style that contribute to the humor of the situations he describes.
2. It has been said that Sam Weller is the "eternal disillusioned realist." Find examples in this selection that support this statement. What do you think of Sam Weller?
3. What kind of person is Mr. Pickwick? Use details from the chap-

ter to support your opinion. What does his ultimate reaction to his humiliation reveal about him?

4. Dickens is a realist in his love for the tangible details of this world. Point out sentences to support this.
5. How does Dickens deal with the pompous behavior of Captain Boldwig? What reasons does Dickens give for the captain's behaving as he does? What is Dickens' opinion of such a person? How does he make his opinion clear?

FOR COMPOSITION

1. Be the "tall gamekeeper" for a moment and write the thoughts that would occur to you as you accompany Mr. Pickwick and his friends on a day's shoot. (Imitate his manner of speaking as you have him "talk" to himself.)
2. Read through the selection again, noting particularly the narrator's comments. In a brief essay, characterize the narrator. How does he view what he describes? What is his opinion of Mr. Pickwick and company?

William Makepeace Thackeray

Vanity Fair is a long, often rambling, ironic and satiric novel that provides a sharp and at the same time panoramic view of the upper levels of English society during the pre-Victorian period. Thackeray designed his book to be a revelation of the social mores, greed, cunning, social climbing (and falling), cruelty, and vindictiveness that characterized the people of that world. He concentrated on the aristocracy's struggles to hold onto exclusive social positions and on the rising, wealthy merchant class which was struggling just as hard to join or replace them. Among the characters is one of a different class—Rebecca Sharp, the daughter of a performer and an artist, too poor to count herself among the middle class but too bright, attractive, and ambitious to want less than that held by the highest levels of society.

Thackeray pictured this harsh and unhappy world through individuals who represented the landed aristocracy, the rural gentry, the city businessmen, the military, the colonials, and the hangers-on. His examination of these people is precise, perceptive, honest, witty, but not cruel. The urbane Thackeray, himself a member of genteel society, did not advocate reform; he satirized and moralized, but his tone was not vicious; occasionally it was sad, sometimes tragic, often amused, and usually disdainful. His exploration of snobbery's evils is a principal element in *Vanity Fair,* although he himself was often accused of being a snob.

Thackeray saw his people as puppets, manipulated by the world they lived in, willing to sacrifice all worthy values for false but popular ones; he saw himself as a puppet-master who could exhibit these people as they were. He is ever-present in the novel; he comments on the happenings; he converses with his readers and interprets for them. He is the experienced and disillusioned observer who opens the doors on Vanity Fair and shows all of the false loyalties, the driving ambitions, the power of the expedient, the facades, the intrigues among the people who participate in the fair. An indication of Thackeray's attitude toward these people is the fact that he borrowed his title from Bunyan's *Pilgrim's Progress* and that he himself described his book as "A Novel without a Hero." Perhaps he felt that nobody in the world he described was capable of heroism. Nevertheless, Becky Sharp, in all her vivid reality, continues to live; and one remembers her long after the plot of *Vanity Fair* is, perhaps, forgotten.

from Vanity Fair

After graduating from a girl's school, the sentimental Amelia Sedley invites her scheming but attractive friend Becky Sharp to visit the Sedley family. Here Becky meets Joseph Sedley, Amelia's fat bachelor brother, with whom she tries to flirt. Joseph, however, returns to his military post in India, and Becky has no choice but to begin her service as governess in the family of Sir Pitt Crawley.

Becky soon ingratiates herself with Sir Pitt, but also with his dashing younger son Rawdon, and with Rawdon's doting and wealthy aunt. Growing sick, the aunt insists that Becky serve as her London nurse. Here Becky stays until Sir Pitt appears and proposes marriage. The chagrined Becky is forced to admit that she is already married secretly to Captain Rawdon Crawley. Both the aunt and Sir Pitt angrily withdraw their financial support from the couple.

Meanwhile Amelia has also met personal reverses. When her father loses his fortune, her future father-in-law insists that his son, George Osborne, break his engagement to penniless Amelia. George is willing to comply, but Amelia's true and steadfast friend, Captain Dobbin, persuades George to marry Amelia rather than break her heart. The young Osbornes, as well as the Rawdon Crawleys, are honeymooning in Brighton when Dobbin brings word that Napoleon has landed from Elba and that the English army has been ordered to the Continent. All three men—Crawley, Osborne, and Dobbin—must leave for duty; so the two young couples and Dobbin move to Brussels. Jos Sedley, now a civilian, is also there, as is Mrs. O'Dowd, the wife of Major O'Dowd, a gallant professional soldier.

As the men await the call to arms, their social life in Brussels is active and glittering. The English officers and their wives while away the time by attending parties and balls. Becky soon becomes the center of attention among the officers, and finally even Amelia's husband falls before her charms. During a ball given the night before the Battle of Waterloo begins, Becky flirts outrageously with George, who follows her around all night and leaves his wife miserable and alone. He even passes a note to Becky apparently asking her to meet him. This she is not able to do, because the next morning, the men are called away to battle, and the English and French armies meet in combat. The following chapter describes events in Brussels as the fierce fighting continues.

Chapter Thirty-Three

IN WHICH JOS TAKES FLIGHT, AND THE WAR IS BROUGHT TO A CLOSE

We of peaceful London City have never beheld—and please God never shall witness—such a scene of hurry and alarm, as that which Brussels presented. Crowds rushed to the Namur gate, from which direction the noise proceeded, and many rode along the level *chaussée*,[1] to be in advance of any intelligence from the army. Each man asked his neighbour for news; and even great English lords and ladies condescended to speak to persons whom they did not know. The friends of the French went abroad, wild with excitement, and prophesying the triumph of their emperor. The merchants closed their shops, and came out to swell the general chorus of alarm and clamour. Women rushed to the churches, and crowded the chapels, and knelt and prayed on the flags and steps. The dull sound of the cannon went on rolling, rolling. Presently carriages with travellers began to leave the town, galloping away by the Ghent barrier. The prophecies of the French partisans began to pass for facts. "He has cut the armies in two," it was said. "He is marching straight on

[1]*chaussée:* a paved road

Brussels. He will overpower the English, and be here to-night." "He will overpower the English," shrieked Isidor to his master, "and will be here to-night." The man bounded in and out from the lodgings to the street, always returning with some fresh particulars of disaster. Jos's face grew paler and paler. Alarm began to take entire possession of the stout civilian. All the champagne he drank brought no courage to him. Before sunset he was worked up to such a pitch of nervousness as gratified his friend Isidor to behold, who now counted surely upon the spoils of the owner of the laced coat.

The women were away all this time. After hearing the firing for a moment, the stout major's wife bethought her of her friend in the next chamber, and ran in to watch, and if possible to console, Amelia. The idea that she had that helpless and gentle creature to protect, gave additional strength to the natural courage of the honest Irish-woman. She passed five hours by her friend's side, sometimes in remonstrance, sometimes talking cheerfully, oftener in silence, and terrified mental supplication. "I never let go her hand once," said the stout lady afterwards, "until after sunset, when the firing was over." Pauline, the *bonne*,[2] was on her knees at church hard by, praying for *son homme à elle*.[3]

When the noise of the cannonading was over, Mrs. O'Dowd issued out of Amelia's room into the parlour adjoining, where Jos sat with two emptied flasks, and courage entirely gone. Once or twice he had ventured into his sister's bedroom, looking very much alarmed, and as if he would say something. But the major's wife kept her place, and he went away without disburthening[4] himself of his speech. He was ashamed to tell her that he wanted to fly.

But when she made her appearance in the dining-room, where he sat in the twilight in the cheerless company of his empty champagne-bottles, he began to open his mind to her.

"Mrs. O'Dowd," he said, "hadn't you better get Amelia ready."

"Are you going to take her out a walk?" said the major's lady; "sure she's too weak to stir."

[2]*bonne:* maid
[3]*son homme à elle:* her boyfriend
[4]*disburthening:* unburdening

"I—I've ordered the carriage," he said, "and—and post-horses; Isidor is gone for them," Jos continued.

"What do you want with driving to-night?" answered the lady. "Isn't she better on her bed? I've just got her to lie down."

"Get her up," said Jos, "she must get up, I say," and he stamped his foot energetically. "I say the horses are ordered—yes, the horses are ordered. It's all over, and—"

"And what?" asked Mrs. O'Dowd.

"I'm off for Ghent," Jos answered. "Everybody is going; there's a place for you! We shall start in half an hour."

The major's wife looked at him with infinite scorn. "I don't move till O'Dowd gives me the route," said she. "You may go if you like, Mr. Sedley; but, faith, Amelia and I stop here."

"She *shall* go," said Jos, with another stamp of his foot. Mrs. O'Dowd put herself with arms akimbo before the bed-room door.

"Is it her mother you're going to take her to?" she said; "or do you want to go to mamma yourself, Mr. Sedley? Good marning—a pleasant journey to ye, sir. *Bon voyage,*[5] as they say, and take my counsel, and shave off them moustachios, or they'll bring you into mischief."

"D—n!" yelled out Jos, wild with fear, rage, and mortification; and Isidor came in at this juncture, swearing in his turn. *"Pas de chevaux; sacrebleu!"*[6] hissed out the furious domestic. All the horses were gone. Jos was not the only man in Brussels seized with panic that day.

But Jos's fears, great and cruel as they were already, were destined to increase to an almost frantic pitch before the night was over. It has been mentioned how Pauline, the *bonne,* had *son homme à elle,* also in the ranks of the army that had gone out to meet the Emperor Napoleon. This lover was a native of Brussels, and a Belgian hussar.[7] The troops of his nation signalized themselves in this war for anything but courage, and young Van Cutsum, Pauline's admirer, was too good a soldier to disobey his colonel's orders to run away. Whilst in garrison at Brussels young Regulus (he had been

[5]*Bon voyage:* Have a good trip
[6]*Pas de chevaux; sacrebleu!:* No horses; good heavens!
[7]*hussar:* cavalryman known for his impressive uniform

born in the revolutionary times) found his great comfort, and passed almost all his leisure moments in Pauline's kitchen; and it was with pockets and holsters crammed full of good things from her larder, that he had taken leave of his weeping sweetheart, to proceed upon the campaign a few days before.

As far as his regiment was concerned, this campaign was over now. They had formed a part of the division under the command of his sovereign apparent, the Prince of Orange, and as respected length of swords and moustachios, and the richness of uniform and equipments, Regulus and his comrades looked to be as gallant a body of men as ever trumpets sounded for.

When Ney[8] dashed upon the advance of the allied troops, carrying one position after the other, until the arrival of the great body of the British army from Brussels changed the aspect of the combat of Quatre Bras, the squadrons among which Regulus rode showed the greatest activity in retreating before the French, and were dislodged from one post and another which they occupied with perfect alacrity on their part. Their movements were only checked by the advance of the British in their rear. Thus forced to halt, the enemy's cavalry (whose bloodthirsty obstinacy cannot be too severely reprehended) had at length an opportunity of coming to close quarters with the brave Belgians before them; who preferred to encounter the British rather than the French, and at once turning tail, rode through the English regiments that were behind them, and scattered in all directions. The regiment, in fact, did not exist any more. It was nowhere. It had no head-quarters. Regulus found himself galloping many miles from the field of action, entirely alone; and whither should he fly for refuge so naturally as to that kitchen and those faithful arms in which Pauline had so often welcomed him?

At some ten o'clock the clinking of a sabre might have been heard up the stair of the house where the Osbornes occupied a story in the Continental fashion. A knock might have been heard at the kitchen door; and poor Pauline, come back from church, fainted almost with terror as she opened it

[8]*Ney:* Marshal of the French army

and saw before her her haggard hussar. He looked as pale as the midnight dragoon who came to disturb Leonora. Pauline would have screamed, but that her cry would have called her masters, and discovered her friend. She stifled her scream, then, and leading her hero into the kitchen, gave him beer, and the choice bits from the dinner, which Jos had not had the heart to taste. The hussar showed he was no ghost by the prodigious quantity of flesh and beer which he devoured—and during the mouthfuls he told his tale of disaster.

His regiment had performed prodigies of courage, and had withstood for a while the onset of the whole French army. But they were overwhelmed at last, as was the whole British army by this time. Ney destroyed each regiment as it came up. The Belgians in vain interposed to prevent the butchery of the English. The Brunswickers[9] were routed and had fled—their duke was killed. It was a general débâcle.[10] He sought to drown his sorrow for the defeat in floods of beer.

Isidor, who had come into the kitchen, heard the conversation and rushed out to inform his master. "It is all over," he shrieked to Jos. "Milor[11] duke is a prisoner; the Duke of Brunswick is killed; the British army is in full flight; there is only one man escaped, and he is in the kitchen now—come and hear him." So Jos tottered into that apartment where Regulus still sat on the kitchen-table, and clung fast to his flagon of beer. In the best French which he could muster, and which was in sooth of a very ungrammatical sort, Jos besought the hussar to tell his tale. The disasters deepened as Regulus spoke. He was the only man of his regiment not slain on the field. He had seen the Duke of Brunswick fall, the black hussars fly, the Écossais pounded down by the cannon.

"And the—th?" gasped Jos.

"Cut in pieces," said the hussar—upon which Pauline crying out, "Oh, my mistress, *ma bonne petite dame,*"[12] went off fairly into hysterics, and filled the house with her screams.

[9]*Brunswickers:* forces of the Duke of Brunswick who were allied with the British against Napoleon

[10]*débâcle:* terrible collapse or failure

[11]*Milor:* My lord

[12]*ma bonne petite dame:* my good little mistress

Wild with terror, Mr. Sedley knew not how or where to seek for safety. He rushed from the kitchen back to the sitting-room, and cast an appealing look at Amelia's door, which Mrs. O'Dowd had closed and locked in his face; but he remembered how scornfully the latter had received him, and after pausing and listening for a brief space at the door, he left it, and resolved to go into the street, for the first time that day. So, seizing a candle, he looked about for his gold-laced cap, and found it lying in its usual place, on a console-table, in the ante-room, placed before a mirror at which Jos used to coquet,[13] always giving his side-locks a twirl, and his cap the proper cock over his eye, before he went forth to make appearance in public. Such is the force of habit, that even in the midst of his terror he began mechanically to twiddle with his hair, and arrange the cock of his hat. Then he looked amazed at the pale face in the glass before him, and especially at his moustachios, which had attained a rich growth in the course of near seven weeks, since they had come into the world. They *will* mistake me for a military man, thought he, remembering Isidor's warning, as to the massacre with which all the defeated British army was threatened; and staggering back to his bedchamber, he began wildly pulling the bell which summoned his valet.

Isidor answered that summons. Jos had sunk in a chair—he had torn off his neckcloths, and turned down his collars, and was sitting with both his hands lifted to his throat.

"*Coupez-moi*, Isidor," shouted he; "*vite! coupez-moi!*[14]

Isidor thought for a moment he had gone mad, and that he wished his valet to cut his throat.

"*Les moustaches,*" gasped Jos, "*les moustaches—coupy, rasy, vite!*"[15]—his French was of this sort—voluble, as we have said, but not remarkable for grammar.

Isidor swept off the moustachios in no time with the razor, and heard with inexpressible delight his master's orders that

[13]*coquet:* primp

[14]*vite! coupez-moi!:* Joseph says literally, "Quick! Cut me!"

[15]*les moustaches—coupy, rasy, vite:* "The mustaches—cut, shave, quick!" Throughout this section Thackeray satirizes Joseph's inadequate French and his terrible pronunciation.

he should fetch a hat and a plain coat. *"Ne porty ploo—habit militair—bonny—donny à voo, prenny dehors"*[16]—were Jos's words,—the coat and cap were at last his property.

This gift being made, Jos selected a plain black coat and waistcoat from his stock, and put on a large white neckcloth, and a plain beaver. If he could have got a shovel-hat he would have worn it. As it was, you would have fancied he was a flourishing, large parson of the Church of England.

"Venny maintenong,"[17] he continued, *"sweevy—ally—party—dong la roo."*[18] And so having said, he plunged swiftly down the stairs of the house, and passed into the street.

Although Regulus had vowed that he was the only man of his regiment or of the allied army, almost, who had escaped being cut to pieces by Ney, it appeared that his statement was incorrect, and that a good number more of the supposed victims had survived the massacre. Many scores of Regulus's comrades had found their way back to Brussels, and—all agreeing that they had run away—filled the whole town with an idea of the defeat of the allies. The arrival of the French was expected hourly; the panic continued, and preparations for flight went on everywhere. No horses! thought Jos, in terror. He made Isidor inquire of scores of persons, whether they had any to lend or sell, and his heart sank within him, at the negative answers returned everywhere. Should he take the journey on foot? Even fear could not render that ponderous body so active.

Almost all the hotels occupied by the English in Brussels face the Parc, and Jos wandered irresolutely about in this quarter, with crowds of other people, oppressed as he was by fear and curiosity. Some families he saw more happy than himself, having discovered a team of horses, and rattling through the streets in retreat; others again there were whose case was like his own, and who could not for any bribes or entreaties procure the necessary means of flight. Amongst these would-be fugitives, Jos remarked the Lady Bareacres

[16]*"Ne porty . . . dehors:"* "I'm not wearing it anymore—military outfit—good—give it to you, I'm taking them off."

[17]*venny maintenong:* come now

[18]*sweevy . . . roo:* follow—go—leave—in the street

and her daughter, who sat in their carriage in the *porte-cochère* of their hotel, all their imperials packed, and the only drawback to whose flight was the same want of motive power which kept Jos stationary.

Rebecca Crawley occupied apartments in this hotel; and had before this period had sundry hostile meetings with the ladies of the Bareacres family. My lady Bareacres cut Mrs. Crawley on the stairs when they met by chance; and in all places where the latter's name was mentioned, spoke perseveringly ill of her neighbour. The countess was shocked at the familiarity of General Tufto with the aide de camp's wife. The Lady Blanche avoided her as if she had been an infectious disease. Only the earl himself kept up a sly occasional acquaintance with her, when out of the jurisdiction of his ladies.

Rebecca had her revenge now upon these insolent enemies. It became known in the hotel that Captain Crawley's horses had been left behind, and when the panic began, Lady Bareacres condescended to send her maid to the captain's wife with her ladyship's compliments, and a desire to know the price of Mrs. Crawley's horses. Mrs. Crawley returned a note with her compliments, and an intimation that it was not her custom to transact bargains with ladies' maids.

This curt reply brought the earl in person to Becky's apartment; but he could get no more success than the first ambassador. "Send a lady's maid to *me!*" Mrs. Crawley cried in great anger; "why didn't my Lady Bareacres tell me to go and saddle the horses! Is it her ladyship that wants to escape, or her ladyship's *femme de chambre?*"[19] And this was all the answer that the earl bore back to his countess.

What will not necessity do? The countess herself actually came to wait upon Mrs. Crawley on the failure of her second envoy. She entreated her to name her own price, she even offered to invite Becky to Bareacres House, if the latter would but give her the means of returning to that residence. Mrs. Crawley sneered at her.

"I don't want to be waited on by bailiffs in livery," she said;

[19]*femme de chambre:* chambermaid

"you will never get back though, most probably—at least not you and your diamonds together. The French will have those. They will be here in two hours, and I shall be half-way to Ghent by that time. I would not sell you my horses, no, not for the two largest diamonds that your ladyship wore at the ball." Lady Bareacres trembled with rage and terror. The diamonds were sewed into her habit, and secreted in my lord's padding and boots. "Woman, the diamonds are at the banker's, and I *will* have the horses," she said. Rebecca laughed in her face. The infuriate countess went below, and sat in her carriage; her maid, her courier and her husband were sent once more through the town, each to look for cattle; and woe betide those who came last! Her ladyship was resolved on departing the very instant the horses arrived from any quarter—with her husband or without him.

Rebecca had the pleasure of seeing her ladyship in the horseless carriage, and keeping her eyes fixed upon her, and bewailing, in the loudest tone of voice, the countess's perplexities. "Not to be able to get horses!" she said, "and to have all those diamonds sewed into the carriage cushions! What a prize it will be for the French when they come!— the carriage and the diamonds I mean; not the lady!" She gave this information to the landlord, to the servants, to the guests, and the innumerable stragglers about the courtyard. Lady Bareacres could have shot her from the carriage-window.

It was while enjoying the humiliation of her enemy that Rebecca caught sight of Jos, who made towards her directly he perceived her.

That altered, frightened, fat face, told his secret well enough. He too wanted to fly, and was on the look-out for the means of escape. "*He* shall buy my horses," thought Rebecca, "and I'll ride the mare."

Jos walked up to his friend, and put the question for the hundredth time during the past hour, "Did she know where horses were to be had?"

"What, *you* fly?" said Rebecca, with a laugh. "I thought you were the champion of all the ladies, Mr. Sedley."

"I—I'm not a military man," gasped he.

"And Amelia?—Who is to protect that poor little sister of

yours?" asked Rebecca. "You surely would not desert her?"

"What good can I do her, suppose—suppose the enemy arrive?" Jos answered. "They'll spare the women; but my man tells me that they have taken an oath to give no quarter to the men—the dastardly cowards."

"Horrid!" cried Rebecca, enjoying his perplexity.

"Besides, I don't want to desert her," cried the brother. "She *shan't* be deserted. There is a seat for her in my carriage, and one for you, dear Mrs. Crawley, if you will come, and if we can get horses—" sighed he—

"I have two to sell," the lady said. Jos could have flung himself into her arms at the news. "Get the carriage, Isidor," he cried; "we've found them—we have found them!"

"My horses never were in harness," added the lady. "Bulfinch would kick the carriage to pieces, if you put him in the traces."

"But he is quiet to ride?" asked the civilian.

"As quiet as a lamb, and as fast as a hare," answered Rebecca.

"Do you think he is up to my weight?" Jos said. He was already on his back, in imagination, without ever so much as a thought for poor Amelia. What person who loved a horse-speculation could resist such a temptation?

In reply, Rebecca asked him to come into her room, whither he followed her quite breathless to conclude the bargain. Jos seldom spent a half-hour in his life which cost him so much money. Rebecca, measuring the value of the goods which she had for sale by Jos's eagerness to purchase, as well as by the scarcity of the article, put upon her horses a price so prodigious as to make even the civilian draw back. She would sell both or neither, she said resolutely. Rawdon had ordered her not to part with them for a price less than that which she specified. Lord Bareacres below would give her the same money—and with all her love and regard for the Sedley family, her dear Mr. Joseph must conceive that poor people must live—nobody, in a word, could be more affectionate, but more firm about the matter of business.

Jos ended by agreeing, as might be supposed of him. The sum he had to give her was so large that he was obliged to ask for time; so large as to be a little fortune to Rebecca, who rapidly calculated that with this sum, and the sale of the residue of Rawdon's effects, and her pension as a widow should he fall, she would now be absolutely independent of the world, and might look her weeds steadily in the face.

Once or twice in the day she certainly had herself thought about flying. But her reason gave her better counsel. "Suppose the French do come," thought Becky, "what can they do to a poor officer's widow? Bah! the times of sacks and sieges are over. We shall be let to go home quietly, or I may live pleasantly abroad with a snug little income."

Meanwhile Jos and Isidor went off to the stables to inspect the newly-purchased cattle. Jos bade his man saddle the horses at once. He would ride away that very night, that very hour. And he left the valet busy in getting the horses ready, and went homewards himself to prepare for his departure. It must be secret. He would go to his chamber by the back entrance. He did not care to face Mrs. O'Dowd and Amelia, and own to them that he was about to run.

By the time Jos's bargain with Rebecca was completed, and his horses had been visited and examined, it was almost morning once more. But though midnight was long passed, there was no rest for the city; the people were up, the lights in the houses flamed, crowds were still about the doors, and the streets were busy. Rumours of various natures went still from mouth to mouth: one report averred that the Prussians had been utterly defeated; another that it was the English who had been attacked and conquered: a third that the latter had held their ground. This last rumour gradually got strength. No Frenchmen had made their appearance. Stragglers had come in from the army bringing reports more and more favourable: at last an aide de camp actually reached Brussels with dispatches for the commandant of the place, who placarded presently through the town an official announcement of the success of the allies at Quatre Bras, and the entire repulse of the French under Ney after a six hours' battle. The aide de camp must have arrived some time while Jos and Rebecca were making their bargain together, or the latter was inspecting his purchase. When he reached his own hotel, he found a score of its numerous inhabitants on the threshold discoursing of the news; there was no doubt as to its truth. And he went up to communicate it to the ladies under his charge. He did not think it was necessary to tell them how he had intended to take leave of them, how he had bought horses, and what a price he had paid for them.

But success or defeat was a minor matter to them, who had only thought for the safety of those they loved. Amelia, at the news of the victory, became still more agitated even than before. She was for going that moment to the army. She besought her brother with tears to conduct her thither. Her doubts and terrors reached their paroxysm; and the poor girl, who for many hours had been plunged into stupor, raved and ran hither and thither in hysteric insanity—a piteous sight. No man writhing in pain on the hard-fought field fifteen miles off, where lay, after their struggles, so many of the brave—no man suffered more keenly than this poor harmless victim of the war. Jos could not bear the sight of her pain. He left his sister in the charge of her stouter female companion, and descended once more to the threshold of the hotel, where everybody still lingered, and talked, and waited for more news.

It grew to be broad daylight as they stood here, and fresh news began to arrive from the war, brought by men who had been actors in the scene. Wagons and long country carts laden with wounded came rolling into the town; ghastly groans came from within them, and haggard faces looked up sadly from out of the straw. Jos Sedley was looking at one of these carriages with a painful curiosity—the moans of the people within were frightful—the wearied horses could hardly pull the cart. "Stop! stop!" a feeble voice cried from the straw, and the carriage stopped opposite Mr. Sedley's hotel.

"It is George, I know it is!" cried Amelia, rushing in a moment to the balcony, with a pallid face and loose flowing hair. It was not George, however, but it was the next best thing: it was news of him.

It was poor Tom Stubble, who had marched out of Brussels so gallantly twenty-four hours before, bearing the colours of the regiment, which he had defended very gallantly upon the field. A French lancer had speared the young ensign in the leg, who fell, still bravely holding to his flag. At the conclusion of the engagement, a place had been found for the poor boy in a cart, and he had been brought back to Brussels.

"Mr. Sedley, Mr. Sedley!" cried the boy, faintly, and Jos came up almost frightened at the appeal. He had not at first distinguished who it was that called him.

Little Tom Stubble held out his hot and feeble hand. "I'm to be taken in here," he said. "Osborne—and—and Dobbin said I was; and you are to give the man two napoleons: my mother will pay you." This young fellow's thoughts, during the long feverish hours passed in the cart, had been wandering to his father's parsonage which he had quitted only a few months before, and he had some times forgotten his pain in that delirium.

The hotel was large, and the people kind, and all the inmates of the cart were taken in and placed on various couches. The young ensign was conveyed upstairs to Osborne's quarters. Amelia and the major's wife had rushed down to him, when the latter had recognized him from the balcony. You may fancy the feelings of these women when they were told that the day was over, and both their husbands were safe; in what mute rapture Amelia fell on her good friend's neck, and embraced her; in what a grateful passion of prayers she fell on her knees, and thanked the Power which had saved her husband.

Our young lady, in her fevered and nervous condition, could have had no more salutary medicine prescribed for her by any physician than that which chance put in her way. She and Mrs. O'Dowd watched incessantly by the wounded lad, whose pains were very severe, and in the duty thus forced upon her, Amelia had not time to brood over her personal anxieties, or to give herself up to her own fears and forebodings after her wont. The young patient told in his simple fashion the events of the day, and the actions of our friends of the gallant —th. They had suffered severely. They had lost very many officers and men. The major's horse had been shot under him as the regiment charged, and they all thought that O'Dowd was gone, and that Dobbin had got his majority, until on their return from the charge to their old ground, the major was discovered seated on Pyramus's carcass, refreshing himself from a case-bottle. It was Captain Osborne that cut down the French lancer who had speared the ensign. Amelia turned so pale at the notion that Mrs. O'Dowd stopped the young ensign in this story. And it was Captain Dobbin who at the end of the day, though wounded himself, took up the lad in his arms and carried him to the surgeon, and thence to the cart which was to bring him back to Brussels. And it was he who promised the driver two louis if he would make his way to Mr. Sedley's hotel in the city; and tell Mrs. Captain Osborne that the action was over, and that her husband was unhurt and well.

"Indeed, but he has a good heart that William Dobbin," Mrs. O'Dowd said, "though he is always laughing at me."

Young Stubble vowed there was not such another officer in the army, and never ceased his praises of the senior captain, his modesty, his kindness, and his admirable coolness in the field. To these parts of the conversation, Amelia lent a very distracted attention: it was only when George was spoken of that she listened, and when he was not mentioned, she thought about him.

In tending her patient, and in thinking of the wonderful escapes of the day before, her second day passed away not too slowly with Amelia. There was only one man in the army for her: and as long as he was well, it must be owned that its movements interested her little. All the reports which Jos brought from the streets fell very vaguely on her ears; though they were sufficient to give that timorous gentleman, and many other people then in Brussels, every disquiet. The French had been repulsed certainly, but it was after a severe and doubtful struggle, and with only a division of the French army. The emperor,[20] with the main body, was away at Ligny, where he had utterly annihilated the Prussians, and was now free to bring his whole force to bear upon the allies. The Duke of Wellington[21] was retreating upon the capital, and a great

[20]*emperor:* Napoleon
[21]*Duke of Wellington:* British general and statesman who defeated Napoleon at Waterloo

battle must be fought under its walls probably, of which the chances were more than doubtful. The Duke of Wellington had but twenty thousand British troops on whom he could rely, for the Germans were raw militia, the Belgians disaffected; and with this handful his Grace had to resist a hundred and fifty thousand men that had broken into Belgium under Napoleon. Under Napoleon! What warrior was there, however famous and skilful, that could fight at odds with him?

Jos thought of all these things, and trembled. So did all the rest of Brussels—where people felt that the fight of the day before was but the prelude to the greater combat which was imminent. One of the armies opposed to the emperor was scattered to the winds already. The few English that could be brought to resist him would perish at their posts, and the conqueror would pass over their bodies into the city. Woe be to those whom he found there! Addresses were prepared, public functionaries assembled and debated secretly, apartments were got ready, and tricoloured banners and triumphal emblems manufactured, to welcome the arrival of his majesty the emperor and king.

The emigration still continued, and wherever families could find means of departure, they fled. When Jos, on the afternoon of the 17th of June, went to Rebecca's hotel, he found that the great Bareacres's carriage had at length rolled away from the *porte-cochère.* The earl had procured a pair of horses somehow, in spite of Mrs. Crawley, and was rolling on the road to Ghent. Louis the Desired was getting ready his portmanteau in that city, too. It seemed as if Misfortune was never tired of worrying into motion that unwieldy exile.

Jos felt that the delay of yesterday had been only a respite, and that his dearly bought horses must of a surety be put into requisition. His agonies were very severe all this day. As long as there was an English army between Brussels and Napoleon, there was no need of immediate flight; but he had his horses brought from their distant stables, to the stables in the courtyard of the hotel where he lived; so that they might be under his own eyes, and beyond the risk of violent abduction. Isidor watched the stable-door constantly, and had the horses saddled, to be ready for the start. He longed intensely for that event.

After the reception of the previous day,[22] Rebecca did not care to come near her dear Amelia. She clipped the bouquet which George had brought her, and gave fresh water to the flowers, and read over the letter which he had sent her. "Poor wretch," she said, twirling round the little bit of paper in her fingers, "how I could crush her with this!—and it is for a thing like this that she must break her heart, forsooth—for a man who is stupid—a coxcomb—and who does not care for her. My poor good Rawdon is worth ten of this creature." And then she fell to thinking what she should do if—if anything happened to poor good Rawdon, and what a great piece of luck it was that he had left his horses behind.

In the course of this day, too, Mrs. Crawley, who saw not without anger the Bareacres party drive off, bethought her of the precaution which the countess had taken, and did a little needlework for her own advantage; she stitched away the major part of her trinkets, bills, and bank-notes about her person, and so prepared, was ready for any event—to fly if she thought fit, or to stay and welcome the conqueror, were he Englishman or Frenchman. And I am not sure that she did not dream that night of becoming a duchess and madame la maréchale, while Rawdon, wrapped in his cloak, and making his bivouac under the rain at Mount St. John, was thinking, with all the force of his heart, about the little wife whom he had left behind him.

The next day was a Sunday. And Mrs Major O'Dowd had the satisfaction of seeing both her patients refreshed in health and spirits by some rest which they had taken during the night. She herself had slept on a great chair in Amelia's room, ready to wait upon her poor friend or the ensign, should either need her nursing. When morning came, this robust woman went back to the house where she and her major had their billet; and here performed an elaborate and splendid toilette, befitting the day. And it is very possible that whilst alone in that chamber, which her husband had inhabited, and where his cap still lay on the pillow, and his cane stood in the corner,

[22]Rebecca had visited Amelia and had been received so coldly and bitterly by her that even Becky was forced to realize the great pain her behavior toward George had caused Amelia.

one prayer at least was sent up to Heaven for the welfare of the brave soldier Michael O'Dowd.

When she returned she brought her Prayer-book with her, and her uncle the dean's famous book of sermons, out of which she never failed to read every Sabbath; not understanding all, haply, not pronouncing many of the words aright, which were long and abstruse—for the dean was a learned man, and loved long Latin words—but with great gravity, vast emphasis, and with tolerable correctness in the main. How often has my Mick listened to these sermons, she thought, and me reading in the cabin of a calm! She proposed to resume this exercise on the present day, with Amelia and the wounded ensign for a congregation. The same service was read on that day in twenty thousand churches at the same hour; and millions of British men and women, on their knees, implored protection of the Father of all.

They did not hear the noise which disturbed our little congregation at Brussels. Much louder than that which had interrupted them two days previously, as Mrs. O'Dowd was reading the service in her best voice, the cannon of Waterloo began to roar.

When Jos heard that dreadful sound, he made up his mind that he would bear this perpetual recurrence of terrors no longer, and would fly at once. He rushed into the sick man's room, where our three friends had paused in their prayers, and further interrupted them by a passionate appeal to Amelia.

"I can't stand it any more, Emmy," he said; "I won't stand it; and you must come with me. I have bought a horse for you—never mind at what price—and you must dress and come with me, and ride behind Isidor."

"God forgive me, Mr. Sedley, but you are no better than a coward," Mrs. O'Dowd said, laying down the book.

"I say come, Amelia," the civilian went on; "never mind what she says; why are we to stop here and be butchered by the Frenchmen?"

"You forget the —th, my boy," said the little Stubble, the wounded hero, from his bed—"and—and you won't leave me, will you, Mrs. O'Dowd?"

"No, my dear fellow," said she, going up and kissing the boy. "No harm shall come to you while *I* stand by. I don't budge till I get the word from Mick. A pretty figure I'd be, wouldn't I, stuck behind that chap on a pillion?"[23]

This image caused the young patient to burst out laughing in his bed, and even made Amelia smile. "I don't ask her," Jos shouted out—"I don't ask that—that Irishwoman, but you, Amelia; once for all, will you come?"

"Without my husband, Joseph?" Amelia said, with a look of wonder, and gave her hand to the major's wife. Jos's patience was exhausted.

"Good-bye, then," he said, shaking his fist in a rage, and slamming the door by which he retreated. And this time he really gave his order for march: and mounted in the courtyard. Mrs. O'Dowd heard the clattering hoofs of the horses as they issued from the gate; and looking on, made many scornful remarks on poor Joseph as he rode down the street with Isidor after him in the laced cap. The horses, which had not been exercised for some days, were lively, and sprang about the street. Jos, a clumsy and timid horseman, did not look to advantage in the saddle. "Look at him, Amelia dear, driving into the parlour window. Such a bull in a china-shop *I* never saw." And presently the pair of riders disappeared at a canter down the street leading in the direction of the Ghent road, Mrs. O'Dowd pursuing them with a fire of sarcasm so long as they were in sight.

All that day from morning until past sunset, the cannon never ceased to roar. It was dark when the cannonading stopped all of a sudden.

All of us have read of what occurred during that interval. The tale is in every Englishman's mouth; and you and I, who were children when the great battle was won and lost, are never tired of hearing and recounting the history of that famous action. Its remembrance rankles still in the bosoms of millions of the countrymen of those brave men who lost the day. They pant for an opportunity of revenging that humiliation; and if a contest, ending in a victory on their part, should

[23]*pillion:* a padded woman's seat attached behind a saddle

ensue, elating them in their turn, and leaving its cursed legacy of hatred and rage behind to us, there is no end to the so-called glory and shame, and to the alternations of successful and unsuccessful murder in which two high-spirited nations might engage. Centuries hence, we Frenchmen and Englishmen might be boasting and killing each other still, carrying out bravely the Devil's code of honour.

All our friends took their share and fought like men in the great field. All day long, whilst the women were praying ten miles away, the lines of the dauntless English infantry were receiving and repelling the furious charges of the French horsemen. Guns which were heard at Brussels were ploughing up their ranks, and comrades falling, and the resolute survivors closing in. Towards evening, the attack of the French, repeated and resisted so bravely, slackened in its fury. They had other foes besides the British to engage, or were preparing for a final onset. It came at last: the columns of the Imperial Guard marched up the hill of St. Jean, at length and at once to sweep the English from the height which they had maintained all day, and spite of all: unscared by the thunder of the artillery, which hurled death from the English line —the dark rolling column pressed on and up the hill. It seemed almost to crest the eminence, when it began to wave and falter. Then it stopped, still facing the shot. Then at last the English troops rushed from the post from which no enemy had been able to dislodge them, and the Guard turned and fled.

No more firing was heard at Brussels—the pursuit rolled miles away. Darkness came down on the field and city: and Amelia was praying for George, who was lying on his face, dead, with a bullet through his heart.

FOR DISCUSSION

1. How does Thackeray convey the confusion and hurry and alarm of Brussels? What is Isidor's role? What is Regulus's role? How does Jos Sedley react to news about the approach of the French?

What opinion do you form of Jos from the information given in this chapter?

2. What do Becky's actions (and motives) in the exchanges with Lady Bareacres and Jos reveal about her? How do her thoughts of her soldier husband differ from Amelia's attitude toward hers? How, from this chapter, would you compare or contrast Becky and Amelia?
3. What view of the British upper class does Thackeray give through the persons of Lady Bareacres and her husband? Do you feel that Becky was justified in her treatment of Lady Bareacres and Sedley? Explain.
4. What is the role of the narrator? Does he simply report or does he interpret actions? What attitudes, if any, does the narrator reveal? How would you describe the narrator?

FOR COMPOSITION

1. Thackeray once wrote that he wanted *Vanity Fair* to indicate that "we are for the most part an abominably foolish and selfish people . . . all eager after vanities." In an essay, tell whether you think he achieved this in the selection you have read and explain your answer in terms of the selection.
2. In a brief essay, describe how the physical details given in this chapter help to establish and sustain the mood of the chapter.

Charlotte Brontë

The fantastic kingdoms and characters she created in her childhood on the Yorkshire moors continued to live in the imagination of Charlotte Brontë and to find expression in her adult fiction. A case in point is her popular novel *Jane Eyre.* Though its settings are the familiar ones of the English countryside, its characters are a curious mixture of those Charlotte first conjured up as a girl, and those she knew in actuality. Rochester's model was a tempestuous, winningly wicked Duke in Charlotte's imaginary kingdom of Angria. Melodramatic events involving Rochester were also developed first in Charlotte's adolescent tales. But Jane is modelled after Charlotte herself—the homely but independent governess who often manages to attract men. (Charlotte refused three offers of marriage before she finally wed.)

The novel itself has been praised for its sense of brooding mystery, its intensity of emotion, its vivid atmosphere, and its sustained suspense. Charlotte Brontë's prose is that of the talented writer who instinctively chooses words which evoke strong sense impressions and rhythms which build strong feelings.

from Jane Eyre

Jane Eyre, a destitute orphan, is hired as a governess in the home of Edward Fairfax Rochester, owner of Thornfield Hall. Though she enjoys her life there and soon admits her attraction toward her employer, she still finds it difficult to explain all the mysteries of Thornfield. A major mystery is the character of Rochester himself, who is gruff and tender, brusque and complimentary by turns. But the mysteries include events as well as personalities. One night Jane hears a strange noise and finds Rochester's bed on fire. During other nights she hears a terrible, maniacal laugh.

Rochester has been paying court to Blanche Ingram, the fashionable daughter of Lady Ingram. One day Rochester brings a whole party of guests, including the Ingrams, to Thornfield. The following selection describes what happens during their stay, after the arrival of another, uninvited, guest—a stranger named Mason.

Chapter Twenty

I had forgotten to draw my curtain, which I usually did; and also to let down my window-blind. The consequence was, that when the moon, which was full and bright (for the night was fine), came in her course to that space in the sky opposite my casement, and looked in at me through the unveiled panes, her glorious gaze roused me. Awakening in the dead of night, I opened my eyes on her disk—silver-white and crystal-clear. It was beautiful, but too solemn: I half rose, and stretched my arm to draw the curtain.

Good God! What a cry!

The night—its silence—its rest, was rent in twain by a savage, a sharp, a shrilly sound that ran from end to end of Thornfield Hall.

My pulse stopped: my heart stood still; my stretched arm was paralysed. The cry died, and was not renewed. Indeed, whatever being uttered that fearful shriek could not soon repeat it: not the widest-winged condor[1] on the Andes could, twice in succession, send out such a yell from the cloud shrouding his eyrie.[2] The thing delivering such utterance must rest ere it could repeat the effort.

It came out of the third story; for it passed overhead. And overhead—yes, in the room just above my chamber-ceiling—I now heard a struggle: a deadly one it seemed from the noise; and a half-smothered voice shouted—

"Help! help! help!" three times rapidly.

"Will no one come?" it cried; and then, while the stagger-

[1]*condor:* a large vulture
[2]*eyrie:* an eagle's or vulture's nest

ing and stamping went on wildly, I distinguished through plank and plaster: –

"Rochester! Rochester! for God's sake, come!"

A chamber-door opened: some one ran, or rushed, along the gallery. Another step stamped on the flooring above and something fell; and there was silence.

I put on some clothes, though horror shook all my limbs: I issued from my apartment. The sleepers were all aroused: ejaculations,[3] terrified murmurs sounded in every room; door after door unclosed; one looked out and another looked out; the gallery filled. Gentlemen and ladies alike had quitted their beds; and "Oh! what is it?"–"Who is hurt?"–"What has happened?"–"Fetch a light!"–"Is it fire?"–"Are there robbers?"–"Where shall we run?" was demanded confusedly on all hands. But for the moonlight they would have been in complete darkness. They ran to and fro; they crowded together: some sobbed, some stumbled: the confusion was inextricable.

"Where the devil is Rochester?" cried Colonel Dent.[4] "I cannot find him in his bed."

"Here! here!" was shouted in return. "Be composed, all of you: I'm coming."

And the door at the end of the gallery opened, and Mr. Rochester advanced with a candle: he had just descended from the upper story. One of the ladies ran to him directly; she seized his arm: it was Miss Ingram.

"What awful event has taken place?" said she. "Speak! let us know the worst at once!"

"But don't pull me down or strangle me," he replied: for the Misses Eshton were clinging about him now; and the two dowagers, in vast white wrappers, were bearing down on him like ships in full sail.

"All's right!–all's right!" he cried, "It's a mere rehearsal of Much Ado About Nothing. Ladies, keep off; or I shall wax dangerous."

[3]*ejaculations:* shouts or emphatic statements

[4]*Colonel Dent:* Dent, Miss Ingram, and the others who appear in the hallway are Rochester's house guests.

And dangerous he looked: his black eyes darted sparks. Calming himself by an effort, he added:—

"A servant has had the nightmare; that is all. She's an excitable, nervous person: she construed her dream into an apparition, or something of that sort, no doubt; and has taken a fit with fright. Now then, I must see you all back into your rooms; for, till the house is settled, she cannot be looked after. Gentlemen, have the goodness to set the ladies the example. Miss Ingram, I am sure you will not fail in evincing superiority to idle terrors. Amy and Louisa, return to your nests like a pair of doves, as you are. Mesdames" (to the dowagers), "you will take cold to a dead certainty, if you stay in this chill gallery any longer."

And so, by dint of alternate coaxing and commanding, he contrived to get them all once more enclosed in their separate dormitories. I did not wait to be ordered back to mine; but retreated unnoticed: as unnoticed as I had left it.

Not, however, to go to bed: on the contrary, I began and dressed myself carefully. The sounds I had heard after the scream, and the words that had been uttered, had probably been heard only by me; for they had proceeded from the room above mine: but they assured me that it was not a servant's dream which had thus struck horror through the house; and that the explanation Mr. Rochester had given was merely an invention framed to pacify his guests. I dressed, then, to be ready for emergencies. When dressed, I sat a long time by the window, looking out over the silent grounds and silvered fields, and waiting for I knew not what. It seemed to me that some event must follow the strange cry, struggle, and call.

No; stillness returned: each murmur and movement ceased gradually, and in about an hour Thornfield Hall was again as hushed as a desert. It seemed that sleep and night had resumed their empire. Meantime the moon declined: she was about to set. Not liking to sit in the cold and darkness, I thought I would lie down on my bed, dressed as I was. I left the window, and moved with little noise across the carpet; as I stooped to take off my shoes, a cautious hand tapped low at the door.

"Am I wanted?" I asked.

"Are you up?" asked the voice I expected to hear, viz,[5] my master's.

"Yes, sir."

"And dressed?"

"Yes."

"Come out, then, quietly."

I obeyed. Mr. Rochester stood in the gallery, holding a light.

"I want you," he said: "come this way: take your time, and make no noise."

My slippers were thin: I could walk the matted floor as softly as a cat. He glided up the gallery and up the stairs, and stopped in the dark, low corridor of the fateful third story: I had followed and stood at his side.

"Have you a sponge in your room?" he asked in a whisper.

"Yes, sir."

"Have you any salts—volatile salts?"

"Yes."

"Go back and fetch both."

I returned, sought the sponge on the wash-stand, the salts in my drawer, and once more retraced my steps. He still waited; he held a key in his hand: approaching one of the small, black doors, he put it in the lock; he paused and addressed me again.

"You don't turn sick at the sight of blood?"

"I think I shall not: I have never been tried yet."

I felt a thrill while I answered him; but no coldness, and no faintness.

"Just give me your hand," he said, "it will not do to risk a fainting fit."

I put my fingers in his. "Warm and steady," was his remark: he turned the key and opened the door.

I saw a room I remembered to have seen before; the day Mrs. Fairfax showed me over the house: it was hung with tapestry; but the tapestry was now looped up in one part, and there was a door apparent, which had then been concealed.

[5]*viz.:* namely

This door was open; a light shone out of the room within: I heard thence a snarling, snatching sound, almost like a dog quarrelling. Mr. Rochester, putting down his candle, said to me, "Wait a minute," and he went forward to the inner apartment. A shout of laughter greeted his entrance; noisy at first, and terminating in Grace Poole's[6] own goblin ha! ha! *She* then was there. He made some sort of arrangement, without speaking: though I heard a low voice address him: he came out and closed the door behind him.

"Here, Jane!" he said; and I walked round to the other side of a large bed, which with its drawn curtains concealed a considerable portion of the chamber. An easy-chair was near the bed-head: a man sat in it, dressed with the exception of his coat; he was still; his head leant back; his eyes were closed. Mr. Rochester held the candle over him; I recognised in his pale and seemingly lifeless face—the stranger, Mason: I saw too that his linen on one side, and one arm, was almost soaked in blood.

"Hold the candle," said Mr. Rochester, and I took it; he fetched a basin of water from the wash-stand: "Hold that," said he. I obeyed. He took the sponge, dipped it in and moistened the corpse-like face: he asked for my smelling-bottle, and applied it to the nostrils. Mr. Mason shortly unclosed his eyes; he groaned. Mr. Rochester opened the shirt of the wounded man, whose arm and shoulder were bandaged: he sponged away blood, trickling fast down.

"Is there immediate danger?" murmured Mr. Mason.

"Pooh! No—a mere scratch. Don't be so overcome, man: bear up! I'll fetch a surgeon for you now, myself: you'll be able to be removed by morning, I hope. Jane," he continued.

"Sir?"

"I shall have to leave you in this room with this gentleman, for an hour, or perhaps two hours; you will sponge the blood as I do when it returns: if he feels faint, you will put the glass of water on that stand to his lips, and your salts to his nose. You will not speak to him on any pretext—and—Richard—it will be at the peril of your life if you speak to her: open

[6]*Grace Poole:* a servant at Thornfield Hall whom Rochester had accused of causing disturbances

your lips—agitate yourself—and I'll not answer for the consequences."

Again the poor man groaned: he looked as if he dared not move: fear, either of death or of something else, appeared almost to paralyse him. Mr. Rochester put the now bloody sponge into my hand, and I proceeded to use it as he had done. He watched me a second, then saying, "Remember!—No conversation," he left the room. I experienced a strange feeling as the key grated in the lock, and the sound of his retreating step ceased to be heard.

Here then I was in the third story, fastened into one of its mystic cells; night around me; a pale and bloody spectacle under my eyes and hands; a murderess hardly separated from me by a single door: yes—that was appalling—the rest I could bear; but I shuddered at the thought of Grace Poole bursting out upon me.

I must keep to my post, however. I must watch this ghastly countenance—these blue, still lips forbidden to unclose—these eyes now shut, now opening, now wandering through the room, now fixing on me, and ever glazed with the dulness of horror. I must dip my hand again and again in the basin of blood and water, and wipe away the trickling gore. I must see the light of the unsnuffed candle wane on my employment; the shadows darken on the wrought, antique tapestry round me, and grow black under the hangings of the vast old bed, and quiver strangely over the doors of a great cabinet opposite—whose front, divided into twelve panels, bore, in grim design, the heads of the twelve apostles, each inclosed in its separate panel as in a frame; while above them at the top rose an ebon crucifix and a dying Christ.

According as the shifting obscurity and flickering gleam hovered here or glanced there, it was now the bearded physician, Luke, that bent his brow; now St. John's long hair that waved; and anon the devilish face of Judas, that grew out of the panel, and seemed gathering life and threatening a revelation of the arch-traitor—of Satan himself—in his subordinate's form.

Amidst all this, I had to listen as well as watch: to listen for the movements of the wild beast or the fiend in yonder side den. But since Mr. Rochester's visit it seemed spell-bound: all the night I heard but three sounds at three long intervals,—a step creak, a momentary renewal of the snarling, canine noise, and a deep human groan.

Then my own thoughts worried me. What crime was this, that lived incarnate[7] in this sequestered[8] mansion, and could neither be expelled nor subdued by the owner?—What mystery, that broke out, now in fire and now in blood, at the deadest hours of night? What creature was it, that, masked in an ordinary woman's face and shape, uttered the voice, now of a mocking demon, and anon of a carrion-seeking bird of prey?

And this man I bent over—this common-place, quiet stranger—how had he become involved in the web of horror? and why had the Fury flown at him? What made him seek this quarter of the house at an untimely season, when he should have been asleep in bed? I had heard Mr. Rochester assign him an apartment below—what brought him here? And why, now, was he so tame under the violence or treachery done him? Why did he so quietly submit to the concealment Mr. Rochester enforced? Why *did* Mr. Rochester enforce this concealment? His guest had been outraged, his own life on a former occasion had been hideously plotted against,[9] and both attempts he smothered in secrecy and sank in oblivion! Lastly, I saw Mr. Mason was submissive to Mr. Rochester; that the impetuous will of the latter held complete sway over the inertness of the former: the few words which had passed between them assured me of this. It was evident that in their former intercourse, the passive disposition of the one had been habitually influenced by the active energy of the other: whence then had arisen Mr. Rochester's dismay when he heard of Mr. Mason's arrival? Why had the mere name of this unresisting individual—whom his word now sufficed to control like a child—fallen on him, a few hours since, as a thunderbolt might fall on an oak?

[7]*incarnate:* embodied in human form
[8]*sequestered:* isolated
[9]*plotted against:* One night before these happenings occurred, Rochester's bedroom was set on fire while he slept; as in the present case, mystery shrouded the event.

Oh! I could not forget his look and his paleness when he whispered: "Jane, I have got a blow – I have got a blow, Jane." I could not forget how the arm had trembled which he rested on my shoulder: and it was no light matter which could thus bow the resolute spirit and thrill the vigorous frame of Fairfax Rochester.

"When will he come? When will he come?" I cried inwardly, as the night lingered and lingered – as my bleeding patient drooped, moaned, sickened: and neither day nor aid arrived. I had, again and again, held the water to Mason's white lips; again and again offered him the stimulating salts: my efforts seemed ineffectual: either bodily or mental suffering, or loss of blood, or all three combined, were fast prostrating his strength. He moaned so, and looked so weak, wild, and lost, I feared he was dying; and I might not even speak to him!

The candle, wasted at last, went out; as it expired, I perceived streaks of grey light edging the window curtains; dawn was then approaching. Presently I heard Pilot bark far below, out of his distant kennel in the court-yard: hope revived. Nor was it unwarranted: in five minutes more the grating key, the yielding lock, warned me my watch was relieved. It could not have lasted more than two hours: many a week seemed shorter.

Mr. Rochester entered, and with him the surgeon he had been to fetch.

"Now, Carter, be on the alert," he said to this last: "I give you but half an hour for dressing the wound, fastening the bandages, getting the patient downstairs and all."

"But is he fit to move, sir?"

"No doubt of it; it is nothing serious: he is nervous, his spirits must be kept up. Come, set to work."

Mr. Rochester drew back the thick curtain, drew up the holland blind, let in all the daylight he could; and I was surprised and cheered to see how far dawn was advanced: what rosy streaks were beginning to brighten the east. Then he approached Mason, whom the surgeon was already handling.

"Now, my good fellow, how are you?" he asked.

"She's done for me, I fear," was the faint reply.

"Not a whit! – courage! This day fortnight you'll hardly

be a pin the worse of it: you've lost a little blood; that's all. Carter, assure him there's no danger."

"I can do that conscientiously," said Carter, who had now undone the bandages; "only I wish I could have got here sooner: he would not have bled so much—but how is this? The flesh on the shoulder is torn as well as cut. This wound was not done with a knife: there have been teeth here?"

"She bit me," he murmured. "She worried me like a tigress, when Rochester got the knife from her."

"You should not have yielded: you should have grappled with her at once," said Mr. Rochester.

"But under such circumstances what could one do?" returned Mason. "Oh, it was frightful!" he added shuddering. "And I did not expect it: she looked so quiet at first."

"I warned you," was his friend's answer; "I said —be on your guard when you go near her. Besides, you might have waited till to-morrow, and had me with you: it was mere folly to attempt the interview to-night, and alone."

"I thought I could have done some good."

"You thought! you thought! Yes; it makes me impatient to hear you: but, however, you have suffered, and are likely to suffer enough for not taking my advice; so I'll say no more. Carter—hurry!—hurry! The sun will soon rise, and I must have him off."

"Directly, sir; the shoulder is just bandaged. I must look to this other wound in the arm: she has had her teeth here too, I think."

"She sucked the blood: she said she'd drain my heart," said Mason.

I saw Mr. Rochester shudder: a singularly marked expression of disgust, horror, hatred, warped his countenance almost to distortion; but he only said:—

"Come, be silent, Richard, and never mind her gibberish: don't repeat it."

"I wish I could forget it," was the answer.

"You will when you are out of the country: when you get back to Spanish Town, you may think of her as dead and buried—or rather, you need not think of her at all."

"Impossible to forget this night!"

"It is not impossible: have some energy, man. You thought you were as dead as a herring two hours since, and you are all alive and talking now. There!—Carter has done with you or nearly so; I'll make you decent in a trice. Jane" (he turned to me for the first time since his re-entrance) "take this key: go down into my bed-room, and walk straight forward into my dressing-room; open the top drawer of the wardrobe and take out a clean shirt and neck-handkerchief: bring them here; and be nimble."

I went; sought the repository he had mentioned, found the articles named, and returned with them.

"Now," said he, "go to the other side of the bed while I order his toilet; but don't leave the room: you may be wanted again."

I retired as directed.

"Was anybody stirring below when you went down, Jane?" inquired Mr. Rochester, presently.

"No, sir; all was very still."

"We shall get you off cannily, Dick; and it will be better, both for your sake, and for that of the poor creature in yonder. I have striven long to avoid exposure, and I should not like it to come at last. Here, Carter, help him on with his waistcoat. Where did you leave your furred cloak? You can't travel a mile without that, I know, in this damned cold climate. In your room?—Jane, run down to Mr. Mason's room,—the one next mine,—and fetch a cloak you will see there."

Again, I ran, and again returned, bearing an immense mantle lined and edged with fur.

"Now, I've another errand for you," said my untiring master; "you must away to my room again. What a mercy you are shod with velvet, Jane!—a clod-hopping messenger would never do at this juncture. You must open the middle drawer of my toilet-table and take out a little phial and a little glass you will find there,—quick!"

I flew thither and back, bringing the desired vessels.

"That's well! Now, doctor, I shall take the liberty of administering a dose myself; on my own responsibility. I got this cordial at Rome, of an Italian charlatan—a fellow you would have kicked, Carter. It is not a thing to be used indiscriminately, but it is good upon occasion: as now, for instance. Jane, a little water."

He held out the tiny glass, and I half filled it from the water bottle on the wash-stand.

"That will do: — now wet the lip of the phial."

I did so: he measured twelve drops of a crimson liquid, and presented it to Mason.

"Drink, Richard: it will give you the heart you lack, for an hour or so."

"But will it hurt me? — is it inflammatory?"

"Drink! drink! drink!"

Mr. Mason obeyed, because it was evidently useless to resist. He was dressed now: he still looked pale, but he was no longer gory and sullied. Mr. Rochester let him sit three minutes after he had swallowed the liquid; he then took his arm: —

"Now I am sure you can get on your feet," he said: — "try."

The patient rose.

"Carter, take him under the other shoulder. Be of good cheer, Richard; step out: — that's it!"

"I do feel better," remarked Mr. Mason.

"I am sure you do. Now, Jane, trip on before us away to the backstairs; unbolt the side-passage door, and tell the driver of the post-chaise you will see in the yard — or just outside, for I told him not to drive his rattling wheels over the pavement — to be ready; we are coming: and, Jane, if any one is about, come to the foot of the stairs and hem."

It was by this time half-past five, and the sun was on the point of rising; but I found the kitchen still dark and silent. The side-passage door was fastened; I opened it with as little noise as possible: all the yard was quiet; but the gates stood wide open, and there was a post-chaise, with horses ready harnessed, and driver seated on the box, stationed outside. I approached him, and said the gentlemen were coming; he nodded: and then I looked carefully round and listened. The stillness of early morning slumbered everywhere; the curtains were yet drawn over the servants' chamber windows; little birds were just twittering in the blossom-blanched orchard trees, whose boughs drooped like white garlands over the wall enclosing one side of the yard; the carriage horses stamped from time to time in their closed stables: all else was still.

The gentlemen now appeared. Mason, supported by Mr. Rochester and the surgeon, seemed to walk with tolerable ease: they assisted him into the chaise; Carter followed.

"Take care of him," said Mr. Rochester to the latter, "and keep him at your house till he is quite well: I shall ride over in a day or two to see how he gets on. Richard, how is it with you?"

"The fresh air revives me, Fairfax."

"Leave the window open on his side, Carter; there is no wind—good-bye, Dick."

"Fairfax—"

"Well, what is it?"

"Let her be taken care of, let her be treated as tenderly as may be: let her—" he stopped and burst into tears.

"I do my best, and have done it, and will do it," was the answer; he shut up the chaise door, and the vehicle drove away.

"Yet would to God there was an end of all this" added Mr. Rochester, as he closed and barred the heavy yard-gates. This done, he moved with slow step and abstracted air towards a door in the wall bordering the orchard. I, supposing he had done with me, prepared to return to the house; again, however, I heard him call "Jane!" He had opened the portal and stood at it, waiting for me.

"Come where there is some freshness, for a few moments," he said, "that house is a mere dungeon: don't you feel it so?"

"It seems to me a splendid mansion, sir."

"The glamour of inexperience is over your eyes," he answered; "and you see it through a charmed medium: you cannot discern that the gilding is slime and the silk draperies cobwebs; that the marble is sordid slate, and the polished woods mere refuse chips and scaly bark. Now *here* (he pointed to the leafy enclosure we had entered) all is real, sweet, and pure."

He strayed down a walk edged with box; with apple trees, pear trees, and cherry trees on one side, and a border on the other, full of all sorts of old-fashioned flowers, stocks, sweet-williams, primroses, pansies, mingled with southernwood, sweet-briar, and various fragrant herbs. They were fresh now as a succession of April showers and gleams, followed by a lovely spring morning, could make them: the sun was just entering the dappled east, and his light illumined the wreathed and dewy orchard trees and shone down the quiet walks under them.

"Jane, will you have a flower?"

He gathered a half-blown rose, the first on the bush, and offered it to me.

"Thank you, sir."

"Do you like this sunrise, Jane? That sky with its high and light clouds which are sure to melt away as the day waxes warm—this placid and balmy atmosphere?"

"I do, very much."

"You have passed a strange night, Jane?"

"Yes, sir."

"And it has made you look pale—were you afraid when I left you alone with Mason?"

"I was afraid of some one coming out of the inner room."

"But I had fastened the door—I had the key in my pocket: I should have been a careless shepherd if I had left a lamb—my pet lamb—so near a wolf's den, unguarded: you were safe."

"Will Grace Poole live here still, sir?"

"Oh, yes! don't trouble your head about her—put the thing out of your thoughts."

"Yet it seems to me your life is hardly secure while she stays."

"Never fear—I will take care of myself."

"Is the danger you apprehended last night gone by now, sir?"

"I cannot vouch for that till Mason is out of England: nor even then. To live, for me, Jane, is to stand on a crater-crust which may crack and spue fire any day."

"But Mr. Mason seems a man easily led. Your influence, sir, is evidently potent with him: he will never set you at defiance, or wilfully injure you."

"Oh, no! Mason will not defy me; nor, knowing it, will he

hurt me—but, unintentionally, he might in a moment, by one careless word, deprive me, if not of life, yet for ever of happiness."

"Tell him to be cautious, sir: let him know what you fear, and show him how to avert the danger."

He laughed sardonically, hastily took my hand, and as hastily threw it from him.

"If I could do that, simpleton, where would the danger be? Annihilated in a moment. Ever since I have known Mason, I have only had to say to him, 'Do that,' and the thing has been done. But I cannot give him orders in this case: I cannot say, 'Beware of harming me, Richard;' for it is imperative that I should keep him ignorant that harm to me is possible. Now you look puzzled; and I will puzzle you farther. You are my little friend, are you not?"

"I like to serve you, sir, and to obey you in all that is right."

"Precisely: I see you do. I see genuine contentment in your gait, and mien, your eye and face, when you are helping me and pleasing me—working for me, and with me, in, as you characteristically say, *'all that is right'*: for if I bid you do what you thought wrong, there would be no light-footed running, no neat-handed alacrity, no lively glance and animated complexion. My friend would then turn to me, quiet and pale, and would say, 'No, sir; that is impossible: I cannot do it, because it is wrong;' and would become immutable as a fixed star. Well, you too have power over me, and may injure me: yet I dare not show you where I am vulnerable, lest, faithful and friendly as you are, you should transfix me at once."

"If you have no more to fear from Mr. Mason than you have from me, sir, you are very safe."

"God grant it may be so! Here, Jane, is an arbour; sit down."

The arbour was an arch in the wall, lined with ivy; it contained a rustic seat. Mr. Rochester took it, leaving room, however, for me: but I stood before him.

"Sit," he said; "the bench is long enough for two. You don't hesitate to take a place at my side, do you? Is that wrong, Jane?"

I answered him by assuming it: to refuse would, I felt, have been unwise.

"Now, my little friend, while the sun drinks the dew—

while all the flowers in this old garden awake and expand, and the birds fetch their young ones' breakfast out of the Thornfield, and the early bees do their first spell of work—I'll put a case to you; which you must endeavour to suppose your own: but first, look at me, and tell me you are at ease, and not fearing that I err in detaining you, or that you err in staying."

"No, sir; I am content."

"Well, then, Jane, call to aid your fancy:—suppose you were no longer a girl well reared and disciplined, but a wild boy indulged from childhood upwards; imagine yourself in a remote foreign land; conceive that you there commit a capital error, no matter of what nature or from what motives, but one whose consequences must follow you through life and taint all your existence. Mind, I don't say a *crime;* I am not speaking of shedding of blood or any other guilty act, which might make the perpetrator amenable to the law: my word is *error.* The results of what you have done become in time to you utterly insupportable; you take measures to obtain relief: unusual measures, but neither unlawful nor culpable. Still you are miserable; for hope has quitted you on the very confines of life: your sun at noon darkens in an eclipse, which you feel will not leave it till the time of setting. Bitter and base associations have become the sole food of your memory: you wander here and there, seeking rest in exile: happiness in pleasure—I mean in heartless, sensual pleasure—such as dulls intellect and blights feeling. Heart-weary and soul-withered, you come home after years of voluntary banishment; you make a new acquaintance—how or where no matter: you find in this stranger much of the good and bright qualities which you have sought for twenty years, and never before encountered; and they are all fresh, healthy, without soil and without taint. Such society revives, regenerates: you feel better days come back—higher wishes, purer feelings; you desire to recommence your life, and to spend what remains to you of days in a way more worthy of an immortal being. To attain this end, are you justified in over-leaping an obstacle of custom—a mere conventional impediment, which neither your conscience sanctifies nor your judgment approves?"

He paused for an answer: and what was I to say? Oh, for some good spirit to suggest a judicious and satisfactory response! Vain aspiration! The west wind whispered in the ivy round me; but no gentle Ariel borrowed its breath as a medium of speech: the birds sang in the tree-tops; but their song, however sweet, was inarticulate.

Again Mr. Rochester propounded his query:

"Is the wandering and sinful, but now rest-seeking and repentant, man justified in daring the world's opinion, in order to attach to him for ever this gentle, gracious, genial stranger; thereby securing his own peace of mind and regeneration of life?"

"Sir," I answered, "a wanderer's repose or a sinner's reformation should never depend on a fellow-creature. Men and women die; philosophers falter in wisdom, and Christians in goodness: if any one you know has suffered and erred, let him look higher than his equals for strength to amend, and solace to heal."

"But the instrument—the instrument! God, who does the work, ordains the instrument. I have myself—I tell it you without parable—been a worldly, dissipated, restless man; and I believe I have found the instrument for my cure, in—"

He paused: the birds went on carolling, the leaves lightly rustling. I almost wondered they did not check their songs and whispers to catch the suspended revelation: but they would have had to wait many minutes—so long was the silence protracted. At last I looked up at the tardy speaker: he was looking eagerly at me.

"Little friend," said he, in quite a changed tone—while his face changed too; losing all its softness and gravity, and becoming harsh and sarcastic—"you have noticed my tender penchant for Miss Ingram: don't you think if I married her she would regenerate me with a vengeance?"

He got up instantly, went quite to the other end of the walk, and when he came back he was humming a tune.

"Jane, Jane," said he, stopping before me, "you are quite pale with your vigils: don't you curse me for disturbing your rest?"

"Curse you? No, sir."

"Shake hands in confirmation of the word. What cold fingers! They were warmer last night when I touched them at the door of the mysterious chamber. Jane, when will you watch with me again?"

"Whenever I can be useful, sir."

"For instance, the night before I am married! I am sure I shall not be able to sleep. Will you promise to sit up with me to bear me company? To you I can talk of my lovely one: for now you have seen her and know her."

"Yes, sir."

"She's a rare one, is she not, Jane?"

"Yes, sir."

"A strapper—a real strapper, Jane: big, brown, and buxom; with hair just such as the ladies of Carthage must have had. Bless me! there's Dent and Lynn in the stables! Go in by the shrubbery, through that wicket."

As I went one way, he went another, and I heard him in the yard, saying cheeringly:—

"Mason got the start of you all this morning; he was gone before sunrise: I rose at four to see him off."

Chapter Twenty-One

Presentiments are strange things! and so are sympathies; and so are signs: and the three combined make one mystery to which humanity has not yet found the key. I never laughed at presentiments in my life; because I have had strange ones of my own. Sympathies, I believe, exist: (for instance, between far-distant, long-absent, wholly estranged relatives; asserting, notwithstanding their alienation, the unity of the source to which each traces his origin) whose workings baffle mortal comprehension. And signs, for aught we know, may be but the sympathies of Nature with man.

When I was a little girl, only six years old, I, one night, heard Bessie Leaven say to Martha Abbot[10] that she had been

[10]*Bessie Leaven and Martha Abbot:* servants at the Reed house, where Jane once lived as a child

dreaming about a little child; and that to dream of children was a sure sign of trouble, either to one's self or one's kin. The saying might have worn out of my memory, had not a circumstance immediately followed which served indelibly to fix it there. The next day Bessie was sent for home to the deathbed of her little sister.

Of late I had often recalled this saying and this incident; for during the past week scarcely a night had gone over my couch that had not brought with it a dream of an infant: which I sometimes hushed in my arms, sometimes dandled on my knee, sometimes watched playing with daisies on a lawn; or again, dabbling its hands in running water. It was a wailing child this night, and a laughing one the next: now it nestled close to me, and now it ran from me; but whatever mood the apparition evinced, whatever aspect it wore, it failed not for seven successive nights to meet me the moment I entered the land of slumber.

I did not like this iteration of one idea—this strange recurrence of one image; and I grew nervous as bedtime approached and the hour of the vision drew near. It was from companionship with this baby-phantom I had been roused on that moonlight night when I heard the cry; and it was on the afternoon of the day following I was summoned downstairs by a message that some one wanted me in Mrs. Fairfax's room. On repairing thither, I found a man waiting for me, having the appearance of a gentleman's servant: he was dressed in deep mourning, and the hat he held in his hand was surrounded with a crape band.

"I daresay you hardly remember me, Miss," he said, rising as I entered; "but my name is Leaven; I lived coachman with Mrs. Reed[11] when you were at Gateshead eight or nine years since, and I live there still."

"Oh, Robert! how do you do? I remember you very well: you used to give me a ride sometimes on Miss Georgiana's bay pony. And how is Bessie? You are married to Bessie?"

"Yes, Miss: my wife is very hearty, thank you; she brought me another little one about two months since—we have

[11]*Mrs. Reed:* Jane's aunt by marriage. Her dying husband requested her to care for Jane, which she had done against her will. Her harshness and unfairness to Jane had made Jane's early childhood an unhappy one.

three now—and both mother and child are thriving."

"And are the family well at the house, Robert?"

"I am sorry I can't give you better news of them, Miss: they are very badly at present—in great trouble."

"I hope no one is dead," I said, glancing at his black dress. He too looked down at the crape round his hat and replied,—

"Mr. John died yesterday was a week, at his chambers in London."

"Mr. John?"

"Yes."

"And how does his mother bear it?"

"Why you see, Miss Eyre, it is not a common mishap: his life has been very wild: these last three years he gave himself up to strange ways; and his death was shocking."

"I heard from Bessie he was not doing well."

"Doing well! He could not do worse: he ruined his health and his estate amongst the worst men and the worst women. He got into debt and into jail: his mother helped him out twice, but as soon as he was free he returned to his old companions and habits. His head was not strong: the knaves he lived amongst fooled him beyond anything I ever heard. He came down to Gateshead about three weeks ago and wanted Missis to give up all to him. Missis refused: her means have long been much reduced by his extravagance; so he went back again, and the next news was that he was dead. How he died, God knows!—they say he killed himself."

I was silent: the tidings were frightful. Robert Leaven resumed:—

"Missis has been out of health herself for some time: she had got very stout, but was not strong with it; and the loss of money and fear of poverty were quite breaking her down. The information about Mr. John's death and the manner of it came too suddenly: it brought on a stroke. She was three days without speaking; but last Tuesday she seemed rather better: she appeared as if she wanted to say something, and kept making signs to my wife and mumbling. It was only yesterday morning, however, that Bessie understood she was pronouncing your name; and at last she made out the words, 'Bring Jane—fetch Jane Eyre: I want to speak to her.' Bessie is not sure whether she is in her right mind, or means anything by the words; but she told Miss Reed and Miss Georgiana, and advised them to send for you. The young ladies put it off at first: but their mother grew so restless, and said, 'Jane, Jane,' so many times, that at last they consented. I left Gateshead yesterday; and if you can get ready, Miss, I should like to take you back with me early to-morrow morning."

"Yes, Robert, I shall be ready: it seems to me that I ought to go."

"I think so too, Miss. Bessie said she was sure you would not refuse: but I suppose you will have to ask leave before you can get off?"

"Yes; and I will do it now;" and having directed him to the servants' hall, and recommended him to the care of John's wife, and the attentions of John himself, I went in search of Mr. Rochester.

He was not in any of the lower rooms; he was not in the yard, the stables, or the grounds. I asked Mrs. Fairfax if she had seen him;—yes: she believed he was playing billiards with Miss Ingram. To the billiard-room I hastened: the click of balls and the hum of voices resounded thence; Mr. Rochester, Miss Ingram, the two Misses Eshton, and their admirers, were all busied in the game. It required some courage to disturb so interesting a party; my errand, however, was one I could not defer, so I approached the master where he stood at Miss Ingram's side. She turned as I drew near, and looked at me haughtily: her eyes seemed to demand, "What can the creeping creature want now?" and when I said, in a low voice, "Mr. Rochester," she made a movement as if tempted to order me away. I remember her appearance at the moment,—it was very graceful and very striking: she wore a morning robe of sky-blue crape; a gauzy azure scarf was twisted in her hair. She had been all animation with the game, and irritated pride did not lower the expression of her haughty lineaments.

"Does that person want you?" she inquired of Mr. Rochester; and Mr. Rochester turned to see who the "person" was. He made a curious grimace,—one of his strange and equivocal[12] demonstrations—threw down his cue and followed me from the room.

[12]*equivocal:* unclear

"Well, Jane?" he said, as he rested his back against the school-room door, which he had shut.

"If you please, sir, I want leave of absence for a week or two."

"What to do?—Where to go?"

"To see a sick lady who has sent for me."

"What sick lady?—Where does she live?"

"At Gateshead, in—shire."

"—shire? That is a hundred miles off! Who may she be that sends for people to see her that distance?"

"Her name is Reed, sir,—Mrs. Reed."

"Reed of Gateshead? There was a Reed of Gateshead, a magistrate."

"It is his widow, sir."

"And what have you to do with her? How do you know her?"

"Mr. Reed was my uncle,—my mother's brother."

"The deuce he was! You never told me that before: you always said you had no relations."

"None that would own me, sir. Mr. Reed is dead, and his wife cast me off."

"Why?"

"Because I was poor, and burdensome, and she disliked me."

"But Reed left children?—you must have cousins? Sir George Lynn was talking of a Reed of Gateshead, yesterday—who, he said, was one of the veriest rascals in town; and Ingram was mentioning a Georgiana Reed of the same place, who was much admired for her beauty, a season or two ago, in London."

"John Reed is dead, too, sir: he ruined himself and half-ruined his family, and is supposed to have committed suicide. The news so shocked his mother that it brought on an apoplectic attack."

"And what good can you do her? Nonsense, Jane! I would never think of running a hundred miles to see an old lady who will, perhaps, be dead before you reach her: besides, you say she cast you off."

"Yes, sir, but that is long ago; and when her circumstances

were very different: I could not be easy to neglect her wishes now."

"How long will you stay?"

"As short a time as possible, sir."

"Promise me only to stay a week—"

"I had better not pass my word: I might be obliged to break it."

"At all events you *will* come back: you will not be induced under any pretext to take up a permanent residence with her?"

"Oh no! I shall certainly return if all be well."

"And who goes with you? You don't travel a hundred miles alone."

"No, sir, she has sent her coachman."

"A person to be trusted?"

"Yes, sir, he has lived ten years in the family."

Mr. Rochester meditated. "When do you wish to go?"

"Early to-morrow morning, sir."

"Well, you must have some money; you can't travel without money, and I daresay you have not much: I have given you no salary yet. How much have you in the world, Jane?" he asked, smiling.

I drew out my purse; a meagre thing it was. "Five shillings, sir." He took the purse, poured the hoard into his palm and chuckled over it as if its scantiness pleased him. Soon he produced his pocket-book: "Here," said he, offering me a note: it was fifty pounds, and he owed me but fifteen. I told him I had no change.

"I don't want change: you know that. Take your wages."

I declined accepting more than was my due. He scowled at first; then, as if recollecting something, he said:—

"Right, right! Better not give you all now: you would, perhaps, stay away three months if you had fifty pounds. There are ten: it is not plenty?"

"Yes, sir, but now you owe five."

"Come back for it then: I am your banker for forty pounds."

"Mr. Rochester, I may as well mention another matter of business to you while I have the opportunity."

"Matter of business? I'm curious to hear it."

"You have as good as informed me, sir, that you are going shortly to be married?"

"Yes: what then?"

"In that case, sir, Adèle[13] ought to go to school: I am sure you will perceive the necessity of it."

"To get her out of my bride's way; who might otherwise walk over her rather too emphatically. There's sense in the suggestion; not a doubt of it: Adèle, as you say, must go to school; and you, of course, must march straight to—the devil?"

"I hope not, sir: but I must seek another situation somewhere."

"In course!" he exclaimed, with a twang of voice and a distortion of features equally fantastic and ludicrous. He looked at me some minutes.

"And old Madam Reed, or the Misses, her daughters, will be solicited by you to seek a place, I suppose?"

"No, sir; I am not on such terms with my relatives as would justify me in asking favours of them—but I shall advertise."

"You shall walk up the pyramids of Egypt!" he growled. "At your peril you advertise! I wish I had only offered you a sovereign instead of ten pounds. Give me back nine pounds, Jane; I've a use for it."

"And so have I, sir," I returned, putting my hands and my purse behind me. "I could not spare the money on any account."

"Little niggard!" said he, "refusing me a pecuniary request! Give me five pounds, Jane."

"Not five shillings, sir; nor five pence."

"Just let me look at the cash."

"No, sir; you are not to be trusted."

"Jane!"

"Sir?"

"Promise me one thing."

"I'll promise you anything, sir, that I think I am likely to perform."

"Not to advertise: and to trust this quest of a situation to me. I'll find you one in time."

[13]*Adèle:* Rochester's ward and Jane's charge

"I shall be glad so to do, sir, if you, in your turn, will promise that I and Adèle shall be both safe out of the house before your bride enters it."

"Very well! very well! I'll pledge my word on it. You go tomorrow, then?"

"Yes, sir; early."

"Shall you come down to the drawing-room after dinner?"

"No, sir, I must prepare for the journey."

"Then you and I must bid good-bye for a little while?"

"I suppose so, sir."

"And how do people perform that ceremony of parting, Jane? Teach me; I'm not quite up to it."

"They say, Farewell; or any other form they prefer."

"Then say it."

"Farewell, Mr. Rochester, for the present."

"What must I say?"

"The same, if you like, sir."

"Farewell, Miss Eyre, for the present: is that all?"

"Yes."

"It seems stingy, to my notions, and dry, and unfriendly. I should like something else: a little addition to the rite. If one shook hands, for instance; but no,—that would not content me either. So you'll do no more than say Farewell, Jane?"

"It is enough, sir: as much good-will may be conveyed in one hearty word as in many."

"Very likely; but it is blank and cool—'farewell.'"

"How long is he going to stand with his back against that door?" I asked myself; "I want to commence my packing." The dinner-bell rang, and suddenly away he bolted, without another syllable: I saw him no more during the day, and was off before he had risen in the morning. . . .

FOR DISCUSSION

1. How does the atmosphere of the first section of Chapter Twenty contrast with that of the last section? How is this change brought about? What details help to create these varying moods? What

contributes to the creation and maintenance of suspense in the first half of Chapter Twenty?

2. What is the effect of the cry on the people staying at Thornfield Hall? How does Rochester conduct himself? What is the difference between the responses of Jane Eyre and Miss Ingram?
3. What role is Jane called upon to play? Describe her reactions to Rochester in Chapter Twenty. What does Jane's statement—"I like to serve you, sir, and to obey you in all that is right"—reveal about her? What do you learn about Rochester from his reaction to Jane's comment?
4. What are Rochester's principal characteristics? Use details from the two chapters to form your answer. What makes him so mysterious? What contrasts are present in Rochester's behavior and personality?
5. How do you account for Rochester's response to Jane's announcement that she must leave Thornfield Hall for a time? How does the Jane of this episode differ from the Jane of the previous chapter? Why do you think Rochester makes somewhat of a ceremony of their parting?

FOR COMPOSITION

1. Using the information given in this selection, write a sketch of Miss Ingram. Stress the differences between Miss Ingram and Jane Eyre.
2. Read again Rochester's long explanation to Jane of his past experiences. Then in a brief essay, answer in your own words his question beginning "Is the wandering and sinful . . ." (page 271).

THE SHORT STORY IN ENGLAND

The literary scene in nineteenth-century England had been dominated by the novel, which was a vehicle for entertainment and for social criticism. With the turn of the century, however, the short story increased in importance and in popularity. Its development in England was influenced by the principles set down by Edgar Allan Poe, American short-story writer and critic. He contended that a short story should create a single impression and that every element—plot, characters, setting, and dialogue—should contribute to this impression and to the effect which the author wanted to create. This requirement necessitated strict economy and careful artistry.

It is perfectly natural, however, that writers become more interested in one element of the short story than in another. At least for the purposes of a particular story, one element often seems to be stressed. The short stories which follow illustrate how twentieth-century artists have developed interests in particular aspects of the modern short story.

In "The Three Strangers," THOMAS HARDY emphasizes setting. Hardy's view of setting is rather specialized: these scenes not only furnish the background for the events of his stories, they also underscore his convictions about the place of man in the universe. Hardy saw nature as blind, impervious to fleeting concerns of man, and implacable in the control it exerted on the lives of relatively powerless human beings. While many modern writers use natural scenes to make the human affairs they describe more dramatic, Hardy always contrasts the unchanging natural scene with the more tempestuous affairs of men. He is like his contemporaries, however, in using natural settings as a means to make thematic statement more obvious or convincing.

"The Verger" by W. SOMERSET MAUGHAM is a good example of the "well-made story." In such a story, something definite happens. The plot moves swiftly and clearly from one step to the next, and nothing is allowed to distract the author or reader from this well-planned movement. All the other elements of the story are subordinated to the plot, but this type of story still demands a particular talent for narrative. The story not only must involve clear steps internally, it must lead also to a definite climax which signals an unmistakable end of the action. The neatly phrased twist at the end of Maugham's tale makes as clear a point about today's complex society as many more hard-working stories of other writers have failed to do.

"The Wind Blows" illustrates the interest in character evident in many contemporary short stories. What KATHERINE MANSFIELD does in this story is to explore the mind, emotions, and perceptions of a young girl. The story begins as Matilda awakens; that is, as her conscious thoughts begin. The sentences, rhythms, phrases, and vocabulary reveal the girl's state of mind to the reader. The disjointed opening sentences, for example, reflect the confusions of a sleepy mind not yet fully alert. The extraordinary number of action words in the first paragraph—*shaking, rattling, banging, tremble, flutter, wags, falls, swinging, lollop*—add to a sense of purposeless motion which reflects the girl's chaotic emotional state. Gradually the details which the girl notices lead her to a particular conclusion—"everything is ugly." The generalizations gradually focus on one cause of her state of mind: Mother. Throughout the story, the details which the girl chooses to notice—or is able to notice—tell the reader what is happening to her. Thus when one has finished "The

Wind Blows," one has also explored in depth a particular personality.

VIRGINIA WOOLF believed that the incidents of life could not be shaped and presented neatly; they must flow freely as they actually are experienced in the minds of people. In short, men do not focus upon one idea at a time. Rather, each triggering of the senses, each idea grasped at by the mind starts up a reaction similar to that of a pebble in a pool. There is a sort of chain reaction as man's consciousness is touched.

This idea obsessed Mrs. Woolf. Her desire to penetrate to the consciousness of her characters rather than to portray their surface lives attracted her to the stream-of-consciousness technique. Her novels, notably *Mrs. Dalloway,* and her short stories are examples of this form of narrative. The reader finds neither plot, nor an exposition of the relationships among the characters, nor any description of the setting. He does find, rather, an accurate though complex presentation of interrelated sights, sounds, impressions, and thoughts as they are had by a character over a brief period of time. From this internal picture, he must construct what is happening to the character externally. "The New Dress" is a vivid example of this approach.

In some ways E. M. FORSTER'S "The Celestial Omnibus" seems out of place in the twentieth century because it is an allegory—a delightful form which, sadly enough, has gone out of style. In allegory each character represents an abstraction. The events of the story allow the writer to state something about this abstraction. Thus, the major function of allegory is to illustrate a truth or to state a theme. Because recent writers have rebelled against pious moralizing, they have often tried to avoid such obvious attention to theme as allegory involves. Forster's story, however, proves that truth is not necessarily something the writer must approach in a spirit of straight-laced propriety. Irreverent truths also need expressing. "The Celestial Omnibus" has some very irreverent things to say about the wisdom of educated philosophers and thinkers, the relative merits of different forms of reading, and the best way of encountering a book. It also suggests what happens to those who love books "not wisely but too well."

GRAHAM GREENE'S "The End of the Party" emphasizes still other elements of short-story craft: mood and atmosphere. Mood refers to the state of mind or feeling which a writer attempts to create in the reader. Atmosphere, a vaguer term, suggests the over-all feeling in a story conveyed by the setting and the mood. The mood of Greene's story is tense and the atmosphere ominous. He carefully inserts hints and statements which foreshadow the final event and increase the suspense. Ultimately, however, there is more to the story than its suspenseful outcome because Greene leaves the reader, at the end, with a mystery to ponder which is at least as dense as the mystery of fear the story describes.

A matter of the greatest concern to the craftsman of the present century has been the technique of narration. *How* the story is told and *by whom* it is told have seemed at times more important than *what* is told. No contemporary writer worth his salt fails to give maximum attention to the best possible point of view from which to tell his story. Perhaps this interest stems to a large extent from the interest in human psychology and an awareness that what an individual sees or understands can be shaped largely by what he wants to see. Thus, any individual's reliability when discussing any particular set of facts is open to question. The writer, therefore, must decide what kind of narrator will prove most convincing to his reader.

Sometimes the narrator is an impersonal observer whose account of what happens is accepted without question. Often, however, the narrator is a flesh and blood character, with clearly identifiable peculiarities and limitations. Then the narrator himself, with his individual point of view, becomes a factor in the story. This is true most emphatically of ALAN SILLITOE'S "On Saturday Afternoon." The point of the story lies not merely in the grisly events being narrated but in the very special way these events are perceived and presented by a boy from a working-class family. The reader of this story comes to know more (and in a sense to *care* more) about the small boy-narrator—his background, his values, his family, his slum environment, his frame of mind—than he does about the victim of the tragedy.

Thomas Hardy

The Three Strangers

Among the few features of agricultural England which retain an appearance but little modified by the lapse of centuries may be reckoned the high, grassy and furzy downs, coombs,[1] or ewe-leases, as they are indifferently called, that fill a large area of certain counties in the south and south-west. If any mark of human occupation is met with hereon, it usually takes the form of the solitary cottage of some shepherd.

Fifty years ago such a lonely cottage stood on such a down, and may possibly be standing there now. In spite of its loneliness, however, the spot, by actual measurement, was not more than five miles from a county-town. Yet that affected it little. Five miles of irregular upland, during the long inimical seasons, with their sleets, snows, rains, and mists, afford withdrawing space enough to isolate a Timon[2] or a Nebuchadnezzar;[3] much less, in fair weather, to please that less repellent tribe, the poets, philosophers, artists, and others who "conceive and meditate of pleasant things."

Some old earthen camp or barrow,[4] some clump of trees, at least some starved fragment of ancient hedge is usually taken advantage of in the erection of these forlorn dwellings. But, in the present case, such a kind of shelter has been disregarded. Higher Crowstairs, as the house was called, stood quite detached and undefended. The only reason for its precise situation seemed to be the crossing of two footpaths

[1]*coombs:* hollows in the side of a mountain

[2]*Timon:* the protagonist of Shakespeare's *Timon of Athens*, a fifth-century Greek who fled from human contact and lived alone in a cave

[3]*Nebuchadnezzar:* Babylonian king mentioned in the Bible who lived alone in the fields after becoming insane

[4]*barrow:* a hill or mound, often found to be an ancient Anglo-Saxon or Celtic burial site

at right angles hard by, which may have crossed there and thus for a good five hundred years. Hence the house was exposed to the elements on all sides. But, though the wind up here blew unmistakably when it did blow, and the rain hit hard whenever it fell, the various weathers of the winter season were not quite so formidable on the coomb as they were imagined to be by dwellers on low ground. The raw rimes[5] were not so pernicious as in the hollows, and the frosts were scarcely so severe. When the shepherd and his family who tenanted the house were pitied for their sufferings from the exposure, they said that upon the whole they were less inconvenienced by "wuzzes and flames" (hoarses and phlegms) than when they had lived by the stream of a snug neighboring valley.

The night of March 28, 182–, was precisely one of the nights that were wont to call forth these expressions of commiseration. The level rainstorm smote walls, slopes, and hedges like the clothyard shafts of Senlac[6] and Crecy.[7] Such sheep and outdoor animals as had no shelter stood with their buttocks to the winds; while the tails of little birds trying to roost on some scraggy thorn were blown inside-out like umbrellas. The gable-end of the cottage was stained with wet, and the eavesdroppings flapped against the wall. Yet never was commiseration for the shepherd more misplaced. For that cheerful rustic was entertaining a large party in glorification of the christening of his second girl.

The guests had arrived before the rain began to fall, and they were all now assembled in the chief or living room of the dwelling. A glance into the apartment at eight o'clock on this eventful evening would have resulted in the opinion that it was as cosy and comfortable a nook as could be wished for in boisterous weather. The calling of its inhabitant was proclaimed by a number of highly polished sheep crooks without stems that were hung ornamentally over the fire-

[5]*rimes:* accumulated frost formations

[6]*Senlac:* hill in southeastern England near Hastings, where the Normans defeated the Saxons in 1066

[7]*Crecy:* town in northern France where English archers, using *clothyard shafts* or yard-long arrows, defeated the French in 1346 during the Hundred Years' War

place, the curl of each shining crook varying from the antiquated type engraved in the patriarchal pictures of old family Bibles to the most approved fashion of the last local sheep fair. The room was lighted by half a dozen candles having wicks only a trifle smaller than the grease which enveloped them, in candlesticks that were never used but at high-days, holy-days, and family feasts. The lights were scattered about the room, two of them standing on the chimney piece. This position of candles was in itself significant. Candles on the chimney piece always meant a party.

On the hearth, in front of a back-brand to give substance, blazed a fire of thorns, that crackled "like the laughter of the fool."

Nineteen persons were gathered here. Of these, five women, wearing gowns of various bright hues, sat in chairs along the wall; girls shy and not shy filled the window-bench; four men, including Charley Jake, the hedge-carpenter, Elijah New, the parish-clerk, and John Pitcher, a neighboring dairyman, the shepherd's father-in-law, lolled in the settle; a young man and maid, who were blushing over tentative *pour-parlers*[8] on a life-companionship, sat beneath the corner-cupboard; and an elderly engaged man of fifty or upward moved restlessly about from spots where his betrothed was not to the spot where she was. Enjoyment was pretty general, and so much the more prevailed in being unhampered by conventional restrictions. Absolute confidence in each other's good opinion begat perfect ease, while the finishing stroke of manner, amounting to a truly princely serenity, was lent to the majority by the absence of any expression or trait denoting that they wished to get on in the world, enlarge their minds, or do any eclipsing thing whatever—which nowadays so generally nips the bloom and bonhomie[9] of all except the two extremes of the social scale.

Shepherd Fennel had married well, his wife being a dairyman's daughter from a vale at a distance, who brought fifty guineas in her pocket—and kept them there, till they should

[8]*pour-parlers:* talks together
[9]*bonhomie:* good spirits

be required for ministering to the needs of a coming family. This frugal woman had been somewhat exercised as to the character that should be given to the gathering. A sit-still party had its advantages; but an undisturbed position of ease in chairs and settles was apt to lead on the men to such an unconscious deal of toping that they would sometimes fairly drink the house dry. A dancing-party was the alternative; but this, while avoiding the foregoing objection on the score of good drink, had a counterbalancing disadvantage in the matter of good victuals, the ravenous appetites engendered by the exercise causing immense havoc in the buttery. Shepherdess Fennell fell back upon the intermediate plan of mingling short dances with short periods of talk and singing, so as to hinder any ungovernable rage in either. But this scheme was entirely confined to her own gentle mind: the shepherd himself was in the mood to exhibit the most reckless phases of hospitality.

The fiddler was a boy of those parts, about twelve years of age, who had a wonderful dexterity in jigs and reels, though his fingers were so small and short as to necessitate a constant shifting for the high notes, from which he scrambled back to the first position with sounds not of unmixed purity of tone. At seven the shrill tweedle-dee of this youngster had begun, accompanied by a booming ground-bass from Elijah New, the parish-clerk, who had thoughtfully brought with him his favorite musical instrument, the serpent.[10] Dancing was instantaneous, Mrs. Fennel privately enjoining the players on no account to let the dance exceed the length of a quarter of an hour.

But Elijah and the boy, in the excitement of their position, quite forgot the injunction. Moreover, Oliver Giles, a man of seventeen, one of the dancers, who was enamored of his partner, a fair girl of thirty-three rolling years, had recklessly handed a new crown-piece to the musicians, as a bribe to keep going as long as they had muscle and wind. Mrs. Fennel, seeing the steam begin to generate on the countenances of her guests, crossed over and touched the fiddler's elbow and

[10]*serpent:* an archaic bass wind instrument, similar to the trumpet

put her hand on the serpent's mouth. But they took no notice, and fearing she might lose her character of genial hostess if she were to interfere too markedly, she retired and sat down helpless. And so the dance whizzed on with cumulative fury, the performers moving in their planet-like courses, direct and retrograde, from apogee to perigee,[11] till the hand of the well-kicked clock at the bottom of the room had traveled over the circumference of an hour.

While these cheerful events were in course of enactment within Fennel's pastoral dwelling, an incident having considerable bearing on the party had occurred in the gloomy night without. Mrs. Fennel's concern about the growing fierceness of the dance corresponded in point of time with the ascent of a human figure to the solitary hill of Higher Crowstairs from the direction of the distant town. This personage strode on through the rain without a pause, following the little-worn path which, further on in its course, skirted the shepherd's cottage.

It was nearly the time of full moon, and on this account, though the sky was lined with a uniform sheet of dripping cloud, ordinary objects out of doors were readily visible. The sad, wan light revealed the lonely pedestrian to be a man of supple frame; his gait suggested that he had somewhat passed the period of perfect and instinctive agility, though not so far as to be otherwise than rapid of motion when occasion required. At a rough guess, he might have been about forty years of age. He appeared tall, but a recruiting sergeant, or other person accustomed to the judging of men's heights by the eye, would have discerned that this was chiefly owing to his gauntness, and that he was not more than five-feet-eight or nine.

Notwithstanding the regularity of his tread, there was caution in it, as in that of one who mentally feels his way; and despite the fact that it was not a black coat nor a dark garment of any sort that he wore, there was something about him which suggested that he naturally belonged to the black-coated

[11]*apogee and perigee:* the points at which the rotating moon is farthest and nearest to the earth

tribes[12] of men. His clothes were of fustian,[13] and his boots hobnailed, yet in his progress he showed not the mud-accustomed bearing of hobnailed and fustianed peasantry.

By the time that he had arrived abreast of the shepherd's premises the rain came down, or rather came along, with yet more determined violence. The outskirts of the little settlement partially broke the force of wind and rain, and this induced him to stand still. The most salient of the shepherd's domestic erections was an empty sty at the forward corner of his hedgeless garden, for in these latitudes the principle of masking the homelier features of your establishment by a conventional frontage was unknown. The traveler's eye was attracted to this small building by the pallid shine of the wet slates that covered it. He turned aside, and, finding it empty, stood under the pent-roof for shelter.

While he stood, the boom of the serpent within the adjacent house, and the lesser strains of the fiddler, reached the spot as an accompaniment to the surging hiss of the flying rain on the sod, its louder beating on the cabbage leaves of the garden, on the eight or ten beehives just discernible by the path, and its dripping from the eaves into a row of buckets and pans that had been placed under the walls of the cottage. For at Higher Crowstairs, as at all such elevated domiciles, the grand difficulty of housekeeping was an insufficiency of water; and a casual rainfall was utilized by turning out, as catchers, every utensil that the house contained. Some queer stories might be told of the contrivances for economy in suds and dishwaters that are absolutely necessitated in upland habitations during the droughts of summer. But at this season there were no such exigencies; a mere acceptance of what the skies bestowed was sufficient for an abundant store.

At last the notes of the serpent ceased and the house was silent. This cessation of activity aroused the solitary pedestrian from the reverie into which he had elapsed, and, emerging from the shed, with an apparently new intention, he

[12]*black-coated tribes:* artisans or office workers
[13]*fustian:* coarse cotton

walked up the path to the house door. Arrived here, his first act was to kneel down on a large stone beside the row of vessels, and to drink a copious draught from one of them. Having quenched his thirst, he rose and lifted his hand to knock, but paused with his eye upon the panel. Since the dark surface of the wood revealed absolutely nothing, it was evident that he must be mentally looking through the door, as if he wished to measure thereby all the possibilities that a house of this sort might include, and how they might bear upon the question of his entry.

In his indecision he turned and surveyed the scene around. Not a soul was anywhere visible. The garden path stretched downward from his feet, gleaming like the track of a snail; the roof of the little well (mostly dry), the well-cover, the top rail of the garden gate, were varnished with the same dull liquid glaze; while, far away in the vale, a faint whiteness of more than usual extent showed that the rivers were high in the meads. Beyond all this winked a few bleared lamplights through the beating drops—lights that denoted the siutation of the county-town from which he had appeared to come. The absence of all notes of life in that direction seemed to clinch his intentions, and he knocked at the door.

Within, a desultory chat had taken the place of movement and musical sound. The hedge-carpenter was suggesting a song to the company, which nobody just then was inclined to undertake, so that the knock afforded a not unwelcome diversion.

"Walk in!" said the shepherd, promptly.

The latch clicked upward, and out of the night our pedestrian appeared upon the door mat. The shepherd arose, snuffed two of the nearest candles, and turned to look at him.

Their light disclosed that the stranger was dark in complexion and not unprepossessing as to feature. His hat, which for a moment he did not remove, hung low over his eyes, without concealing that they were large, open, and determined, moving with a flash rather than a glance round the room. He seemed pleased with his survey, and, baring his shaggy head, said, in a rich, deep voice: "The rain is so heavy, friends, that I ask leave to come in and rest awhile."

"To be sure, Stranger," said the shepherd. "And faith, you've been lucky in choosing your time, for we are having a bit of a fling for a glad cause—though, to be sure, a man could hardly wish that glad cause to happen more than once a year."

"Nor less," spoke up a woman. "For 'tis best to get your family over and done with, as soon as you can, so as to be all the earlier out of the fag o't."

"And what may be this glad cause?" asked the stranger.

"A birth and christening," said the shepherd.

The stranger hoped his host might not be made unhappy either by too many or too few of such episodes and, being invited by a gesture to a pull at the mug, he readily acquiesced. His manner, which, before entering, had been so dubious, was now altogether that of a careless and candid man.

"Late to be traipsing athwart this coomb—hey?" said the engaged man of fifty.

"Late it is, Master, as you say.—I'll take a seat in the chimney corner, if you have nothing to urge against it, Ma'am; for I am a little moist on the side that was next the rain."

Mrs. Shepherd Fennel assented, and made room for the self-invited comer, who, having got completely inside the chimney corner, stretched out his legs and arms with the expansiveness of a person quite at home.

"Yes, I am rather cracked in the vamp,"[14] he said freely, seeing that the eyes of the shepherd's wife fell upon his boots, "and I am not well fitted either. I have had some rough times lately, and have been forced to pick up what I can get in the way of wearing, but I must find a suit better fit for working-days when I reach home."

"One of hereabouts?" she inquired.

"Not quite that—further up the country."

"I thought so. And so be I; and by your tongue you come from my neighborhood."

"But you would hardly have heard of me," he said quickly. "My time would be long before yours, Ma'am, you see."

This testimony to the youthfulness of his hostess had the effect of stopping her cross-examination.

[14]*vamp:* the part of a shoe above the sole and in front of the ankle seam

"There is only one thing more wanted to make me happy," continued the newcomer, "and that is a little baccy, which I am sorry to say I am out of."

"I'll fill your pipe," said the shepherd.

"I must ask you to lend me a pipe likewise."

"A smoker, and no pipe about 'ee?"

"I have dropped it somewhere on the road."

The shepherd filled and handed him a new clay pipe, saying, as he did so, "Hand me your baccy-box—I'll fill that too, now I am about it."

The man went through the movement of searching his pockets.

"Lost that too?" said his entertainer, with some surprise.

"I am afraid so," said the man with some confusion. "Give it to me in a screw of paper." Lighting his pipe at the candle with a suction that drew the whole flame into the bowl, he resettled himself in the corner and bent his looks upon the faint steam from his damp legs, as if he wished to say no more.

Meanwhile the general body of guests had been taking little notice of this visitor by reason of an absorbing discussion in which they were engaged with the band about a tune for the next dance. The matter being settled, they were about to stand up when an interruption came in the shape of another knock at the door.

At sound of the same the man in the chimney corner took up the poker and began stirring the brands as if doing it thoroughly were the one aim of his existence; and a second time the shepherd said, "Walk in!" In a moment another man stood upon the straw-woven doormat. He too was a stranger.

This individual was one of a type radically different from the first. There was more of the commonplace in his manner, and a certain jovial cosmopolitanism sat upon his features. He was several years older than the first arrival, his hair being slightly frosted, his eyebrows bristly, and his whiskers cut back from his cheeks. His face was rather full and flabby, and yet it was not altogether a face without power. A few grog-blossoms marked the neighborhood of his nose. He flung back his long drab greatcoat, revealing that beneath it he wore a suit of cinder-gray shade throughout, large heavy seals, of some metal or other that would take a polish, dangling from his fob as his only personal ornament. Shaking the water drops from his low-crowned glazed hat, he said, "I must ask for a few minutes' shelter, comrades, or I shall be wetted to my skin before I get to Casterbridge."

"Make yourself at home, Master," said the shepherd, perhaps a trifle less heartily than on the first occasion. Not that Fennel had the least tinge of niggardliness in his composition; but the room was far from large, spare chairs were not numerous, and damp companions were not altogether desirable at close quarters for the women and girls in their bright-colored gowns.

However, the second comer, after taking off his greatcoat, and hanging his hat on a nail in one of the ceiling-beams as if he had been specially invited to put it there, advanced and sat down at the table. This had been pushed so closely into the chimney corner, to give all available room to the dancers, that its inner edge grazed the elbow of the man who had ensconced himself by the fire; and thus the two strangers were brought into close companionship. They nodded to each other by way of breaking the ice of unacquaintance, and the first stranger handed his neighbor the family mug—a huge vessel of brown ware, having its upper edge worn away like a threshold by the rub of whole generations of thirsty lips that had gone the way of all flesh, and bearing the following inscription burnt upon its rotund side in yellow letters:

THERE IS NO FUN
UNTIL I CUM.

The other man, nothing loath,[15] raised the mug to his lips, and drank on, and on, and on—till a curious blueness overspread the countenance of the shepherd's wife, who had regarded with no little surprise the first stranger's free offer to the second of what did not belong to him to dispense.

"I knew it!" said the toper to the shepherd with much satisfaction. "When I walked up your garden before coming

[15]*nothing loath:* not hesitant

in, and saw the hives all of a row, I said to myself, 'Where there's bees there's honey, and where there's honey there's mead.' But mead of such a truly comfortable sort as this I really didn't expect to meet in my older days." He took yet another pull at the mug, till it assumed an ominous elevation.

"Glad you enjoy it!" said the shepherd warmly.

"It is goodish mead," assented Mrs. Fennel, with an absence of enthusiasm which seemed to say that it was possible to buy praise for one's cellar at too heavy a price. "It is trouble enough to make—and really I hardly think we shall make any more. For honey sells well, and we ourselves can make shift with a drop o' small mead and metheglin[16] for common use from the comb-washings."

"Oh, but you'll never have the heart!" reproachfully cried the stranger in cinder-gray, after taking up the mug a third time and setting it down empty. "I love mead, when 'tis old like this, as I love to go to church o' Sundays, or to relieve the needy any day of the week."

"Ha, ha, ha!" said the man in the chimney corner, who, in spite of the taciturnity induced by the pipe of tobacco, could not or would not refrain from this slight testimony to his comrade's humor.

Now the old mead of those days, brewed of the purest first-year or maiden honey, four pounds to the gallon—with its due complement of white of eggs, cinnamon, ginger, cloves, mace, rosemary, yeast, and processes of working, bottling, and cellaring—tasted remarkably strong; but it did not taste so strong as it actually was. Hence presently, the stranger in cinder-gray at the table, moved by its creeping influence, unbuttoned his waistcoat, threw himself back in his chair, spread his legs, and made his presence felt in various ways.

"Well, well, as I say," he resumed, "I am going to Casterbridge, and to Casterbridge I must go. I should have been almost there by this time; but the rain drove me into your dwelling, and I'm not sorry for it."

[16]*small mead and metheglin:* a type of alcoholic beverage weaker than mead, but also made from fermented honey and water

"You don't live in Casterbridge?" said the shepherd.

"Not as yet; though I shortly mean to move there."

"Going to set up in trade, perhaps?"

"No, no," said the shepherd's wife. "It is easy to see that the gentleman is rich, and don't want to work at anything."

The cinder-gray stranger paused, as if to consider whether he would accept that definition of himself. He presently rejected it by answering. "Rich is not quite the word for me, Dame. I do work, and I must work. And even if I only get to Casterbridge by midnight I must begin work there at eight tomorrow morning, Yes, het or wet, blow or snow, famine or sword, my day's work tomorrow must be done."

"Poor man! Then, in spite o' seeming, you be worse off than we," replied the shepherd's wife.

"'Tis the nature of my trade, men and maidens. 'Tis the nature of my trade more than my poverty. . . . But really and truly I must up and off, or I shan't get a lodging in the town." However, the speaker did not move, and directly added, "There's time for one more draught of friendship before I go; and I'd perform it at once if the mug were not dry."

"Here's a mug o' small," said Mrs. Fennel. "Small, we call it, though to be sure 'tis only the first wash o' the combs."

"No," said the stranger, disdainfully. "I won't spoil your first kindness by partaking o' your second."

"Certainly not," broke in Fennel. "We don't increase and multiply every day, and I'll fill the mug again." He went away to the dark place under the stairs where the barrel stood. The shepherdess followed him.

"Why should you do this?" she said, reproachfully, as soon as they were alone. "He's emptied it once, though it held enough for ten people; and now he's not contented wi' the small, but must needs call for more o' the strong! And a stranger unbeknown to any of us. For my part, I don't like the look o' the man at all."

"But he's in the house, my honey; and 'tis a wet night, and a christening. Daze it, what's a cup of mead more or less? There'll be plenty more next bee-burning."

"Very well—this time, then," she answered, looking wistfully at the barrel. "But what is the man's calling, and where is he one of, that he should come in and join us like this?"

"I don't know. I'll ask him again."

The catastrophe of having the mug drained dry at one pull by the stranger in cinder-gray was effectually guarded against this time by Mrs. Fennel. She poured out his allowance in a small cup, keeping the large one at a discreet distance from him. When he had tossed off his portion the shepherd renewed his inquiry about the stranger's occupation.

The latter did not immediately reply, and the man in the chimney corner, with sudden demonstrativeness, said, "Anybody may know my trade—I'm a wheelwright."

"A very good trade for these parts," said the shepherd.

"And anybody may know mine—if they've the sense to find it out," said the stranger in cinder-gray.

"You may generally tell what a man is by his claws," observed the hedge-carpenter, looking at his own hands. "My fingers be as full of thorns as an old pincushion is of pins."

The hands of the man in the chimney corner instinctively sought the shade, and he gazed into the fire as he resumed his pipe. The man at the table took up the hedge-carpenter's remark, and added smartly, "True; but the oddity of my trade is that, instead of setting a mark upon me, it sets a mark upon my customers."

No observation being offered by anybody in elucidation of this enigma, the shepherd's wife once more called for a song. The same obstacles presented themselves as at the former time—one had no voice, another had forgotten the first verse. The stranger at the table, whose soul had now risen to a good working temperature, relieved the difficulty by exclaiming that, to start the company, he would sing himself. Thrusting one thumb into the armhole of his waistcoat, he waved the other hand in the air, and, with an extemporizing gaze at the shining sheep-crooks above the mantelpiece, began:

O my trade it is the rarest one,
Simple shepherds all—
My trade is a sight to see;
For my customers I tie, and take
them up on high,
And waft 'em to a far countree!

The room was silent when he had finished the verse—with one exception, that of the man in the chimney corner, who at the singer's word, "Chorus!" joined him in a deep bass voice of musical relish:

And waft 'em to a far countree!

Oliver Giles, John Pitcher the dairyman, the parish-clerk, the engaged man of fifty, the row of young women against the wall, seemed lost in thought not of the gayest kind. The shepherd looked meditatively on the ground, the shepherdess gazed keenly at the singer, and with some suspicion; she was doubting whether this stranger were merely singing an old song from recollection, or was composing one there and then for the occasion. All were as perplexed at the obscure revelation as the guests at Belshazzar's Feast,[17] except the man in the chimney corner, who quietly said, "Second verse, stranger," and smoked on.

The singer thoroughly moistened himself from his lips inward, and went on with the next stanza as requested:

My tools are but common ones,
Simple shepherds all—
My tools are no sight to see:
A little hempen string, and a post
whereon to swing,
Are implements enough for me!

Shepherd Fennel glanced round. There was no longer any doubt that the stranger was answering his question rhythmically. The guests one and all started back with suppressed exclamations. The young woman engaged to the man of fifty fainted halfway, and would have proceeded, but finding him wanting in alacrity for catching her she sat down trembling.

[17]*Belshazzar's Feast:* The Old Testament account describes writing which appeared on the wall during this feast and prophesied the destruction of Babylon.

"Oh, he's the—!" whispered the people in the background, mentioning the name of an ominous public officer. "He's come to do it! 'Tis to be at Casterbridge jail tomorrow—the man for sheep-stealing—the poor clockmaker we heard of, who used to live away at Shottsford and had no work to do—Timothy Summers, whose family were astarving, and so he went out of Shottsford by the highroad, and took a sheep in open daylight, defying the farmer and the farmer's wife and the farmer's lad, and every man jack among 'em. He" (and they nodded toward the stranger of the deadly trade) "is come from up the country to do it because there's not enough to do in his own county-town, and he's got the place here now our own county-man's dead; he's going to live in the same cottage under the prison wall."

The stranger in cinder-gray took no notice of this whispered string of observations, but again wetted his lips. Seeing that his friend in the chimney corner was the only one who reciprocated his joviality in any way, he held out his cup toward that appreciative comrade, who also held out his own. They clinked together, the eyes of the rest of the room hanging upon the singer's actions. He parted his lips for the third verse; but at that moment another knock was audible upon the door. This time the knock was faint and hesitating.

The company seemed scared; the shepherd looked with consternation toward the entrance, and it was with some effort that he resisted his alarmed wife's deprecatory glance, and uttered for the third time the welcoming words, "Walk in!"

The door was gently opened, and another man stood upon the mat. He, like those who had preceded him, was a stranger. This time it was a short, small personage, of fair complexion, and dressed in a decent suit of dark clothes.

"Can you tell me the way to—?" he began: when, gazing round the room to observe the nature of the company among whom he had fallen, his eyes lighted on the stranger in cinder-gray. It was just at the instant when the latter, who had thrown his mind into his song with such a will that he scarcely heeded the interruption, silenced all whispers and inquiries by bursting into his third verse:

Tomorrow is my working day,
Simple shepherds all—
Tomorrow is a working day for me:
For the farmer's sheep is slain, and
lad who did it ta'en,
And on his soul may God ha' merc-y!

The stranger in the chimney corner, waving cups with the singer so heartily that his mead splashed over the hearth, repeated in his bass voice as before:

And on his soul may God ha'
merc-y!

All this time the third stranger had been standing in the doorway. Finding now that he did not come forward or go on speaking, the guests particularly regarded him. They noticed to their surprise that he stood before them the picture of abject terror—his knees trembling, his hand shaking so violently that the door-latch by which he supported himself rattled audibly: his white lips were parted, and his eyes fixed on the merry officer of justice in the middle of the room. A moment more and he had turned, closed the door, and fled.

"What a man can it be?" said the shepherd.

The rest, between the awfulness of their late discovery and the odd conduct of this third visitor, looked as if they knew not what to think, and said nothing. Instinctively they withdrew further and further from the grim gentleman in their midst, whom some of them seemed to take for the Prince of Darkness himself, till they formed a remote circle, an empty space of floor being left between them and him— . . . *circulus, cujus centrum diabolus.*[18] The room was so silent—though there were more than twenty people in it—that nothing could be heard but the patter of the rain against the window-shutters, accompanied by the occasional hiss of a stray drop that fell down the chimney into the fire, and the steady puffing

[18]*circulus . . . diabolus:* a circle enclosing the devil at its center

of the man in the corner, who had now resumed his pipe of long clay.

The stillness was unexpectedly broken. The distant sound of a gun reverberated through the air—apparently from the direction of the county-town.

"Be jiggered!" cried the stranger who had sung the song, jumping up.

"What does that mean?" asked several.

"A prisoner escaped from the jail—that's what it means."

All listened. The sound was repeated, and none of them spoke but the man in the chimney corner, who said quietly, "I've often been told that in this county they fire a gun at such times; but I never heard it till now."

"I wonder if it is *my* man?" murmured the personage in cinder-gray.

"Surely it is!" said the shepherd involuntarily. "And surely we've zeed him! That little man who looked in at the door by now, and quivered like a leaf when he zeed ye and heard your song!"

"His teeth chattered, and the breath went out of his body," said the dairyman.

"And his heart seemed to sink within him like a stone," said Oliver Giles.

"And he bolted as if he'd been shot at," said the hedge-carpenter.

"True—his teeth chattered, and his heart seemed to sink; and he bolted as if he'd been shot at," slowly summed up the man in the chimney corner.

"I didn't notice it," remarked the hangman.

"We were all awondering what made him run off in such a fright," faltered one of the women against the wall, "and now 'tis explained!"

The firing of the alarm-gun went on at intervals, low and sullenly, and their suspicions became a certainty. The sinister gentleman in cinder-gray roused himself. "Is there a constable here?" he asked, in thick tones. "If so, let him step forward."

The engaged man of fifty stepped quavering out from the wall, his betrothed beginning to sob on the back of the chair.

"You are a sworn constable?"

"I be, Sir."

"Then pursue the criminal at once, with assistance, and bring him back here. He can't have gone far."

"I will, Sir, I will—when I've got my staff. I'll go home and get it, and come sharp here, and start in a body."

"Staff!—never mind your staff; the man'll be gone!"

"But I can't do nothing without my staff—can I, William, and John, and Charles Jake? No; for there's the king's royal crown apainted on en in yaller and gold, and the lion and the unicorn, so as when I raise en up and hit my prisoner, 'tis made a lawful blow thereby. I wouldn't 'tempt to take up a man without my staff—no, not I. If I hadn't the law to gie me courage, why, instead o' my taking up him he might take up me!"

"Now, I'm a king's man myself, and can give you authority enough for this," said the formidable officer in gray. "Now then, all of ye, be ready. Have ye any lanterns?"

"Yes—have ye any lanterns?—I demand it!" said the constable.

"And the rest of you able-bodied—"

"Able-bodied men—yes—the rest of ye!" said the constable.

"Have you some good stout staves and pitchforks—"

"Staves and pitchforks—in the name o' the law! And take 'em in yer hands and go in quest, and do as we in authority tell ye!"

Thus aroused, the men prepared to give chase. The evidence was, indeed, though circumstantial, so convincing, that but little argument was needed to show the shepherd's guests that after what they had seen it would look very much like connivance if they did not instantly pursue the unhappy third stranger, who could not as yet have gone more than a few hundred yards over such uneven country.

A shepherd is always well provided with lanterns; and, lighting these hastily, and with hurdle-staves in their hands, they poured out of the door, taking a direction along the crest of the hill, away from the town, the rain having fortunately a little abated.

Disturbed by the noise, or possibly by unpleasant dreams

of her baptism, the child who had been christened began to cry heartbrokenly in the room overhead. These notes of grief came down through the chinks of the floor to the ears of the women below, who jumped up one by one, and seemed glad of the excuse to ascend and comfort the baby, for the incidents of the last half-hour greatly oppressed them. Thus in the space of two or three minutes the room on the ground-floor was deserted quite.

But it was not for long. Hardly had the sound of footsteps died away when a man returned round the corner of the house from the direction the pursuers had taken. Peeping in at the door, and seeing nobody there, he entered leisurely. It was the stranger of the chimney corner, who had gone out with the rest. The motive of his return was shown by his helping himself to a cut piece of skimmer-cake that lay on a ledge beside where he had sat, and which he had apparently forgotten to take with him. He also poured out half a cup more mead from the quantity that remained, ravenously eating and drinking these as he stood. He had not finished when another figure came in just as quietly—his friend in cinder-gray.

"Oh—you here?" said the latter, smiling. "I thought you had gone to help in the capture." And this speaker also revealed the object of his return by looking solicitously round for the fascinating mug of old mead.

"And I thought you had gone," said the other, continuing his skimmer-cake with some effort.

"Well, on second thoughts, I felt there were enough without me," said the first confidentially, "and such a night as it is, too. Besides, 'tis the business o' the Government to take care of its criminals—not mine."

"True; so it is. And I felt as you did, that there were enough without me."

"I don't want to break my limbs running over the humps and hollows of this wild country."

"Nor I neither, between you and me."

"These shepherd-people are used to it—simple-minded souls, you know, stirred up to anything in a moment. They'll have him ready for me before the morning, and no trouble to me at all."

"They'll have him, and we shall have saved ourselves all labor in the matter."

"True, true. Well, my way is to Casterbridge; and 'tis as much as my legs will do to take me that far. Going the same way?"

"No, I am sorry to say! I have to get home over there" (he nodded indefinitely to the right), "and I feel as you do, that it is quite enough for my legs to do before bedtime."

The other had by this time finished the mead in the mug, after which, shaking hands heartily at the door, and wishing each other well, they went their several ways.

In the meantime the company of pursuers had reached the end of the hog's-back elevation which dominated this part of the down. They had decided on no particular plan of action; and, finding that the man of the baleful trade was no longer in their company, they seemed quite unable to form any such plan now. They descended in all directions down the hill, and straightway several of the party fell into the snare set by Nature for all misguided midnight ramblers over this part of the cretaceous[19] formation. The "lanchets," or flint slopes, which belted the escarpment at intervals of a dozen yards, took the less cautious ones unawares, and losing their footing on the rubbly steep they slid sharply downward, the lanterns rolling from their hands to the bottom, and there lying on their sides till the horn[20] was scorched through.

When they had again gathered themselves together, the shepherd, as the man who knew the country best, took the lead, and guided them round these treacherous inclines. The lanterns, which seemed rather to dazzle their eyes and warn the fugitive than to assist them in the exploration, were extinguished, due silence was observed; and in this more rational order they plunged into the vale. It was a grassy, briery, moist defile, affording some shelter to any person who had sought it; but the party perambulated it in vain, and ascended on the other side. Here they wandered apart, and after an interval closed together again to report progress. At the

[19]*cretaceous:* chalky
[20]*horn:* scraped horn used for lantern holders instead of glass

second time of closing in they found themselves near a lonely ash, the single tree on this part of the coomb, probably sown there by a passing bird some fifty years before. And here, standing a little to one side of the trunk, as motionless as the trunk itself appeared the man they were in quest of, his outline being well defined against the sky beyond. The band noiselessly drew up and faced him.

"Your money or your life!" said the constable sternly to the still figure.

"No, no," whispered John Pitcher. "'Tisn't our side ought to say that. That's the doctrine of vagabonds like him, and we be on the side of the law."

"Well, well," replied the constable, impatiently; "I must say something, mustn't I? and if you had all the weight o' this undertaking upon your mind, perhaps you'd say the wrong thing, too!—Prisoner at the bar, surrender in the name of the Father—the Crown, I mane!"

The man under the tree seemed now to notice them for the first time, and, giving them no opportunity whatever for exhibiting their courage, he strolled slowly toward them. He was, indeed, the little man, the third stranger; but his trepidation had in a great measure gone.

"Well, travelers," he said, "did I hear you speak to me?"

"You did; you've got to come and be our prisoner at once!" said the constable. "We arrest 'ee on the charge of not biding in Casterbridge jail in a decent proper manner to be hung tomorrow morning. Neighbors, do your duty, and seize the culpet!"

On hearing the charge, the man seemed enlightened, and, saying not another word, resigned himself with preternatural civility to the search-party, who, with their staves in their hands, surrounded him on all sides, and marched him back toward the shepherd's cottage.

It was eleven o'clock by the time they arrived. The light shining from the open door, a sound of men's voices within, proclaimed to them as they approached the house that some new events had arisen in their absence. On entering they discovered the shepherd's living-room to be invaded by two officers from Casterbridge jail, and a well-known magistrate who lived at the nearest country-seat, intelligence of the escape having become generally circulated.

"Gentlemen," said the constable, "I have brought back your man—not without risk and danger; but every one must do his duty! He is inside this circle of able-bodied persons, who have lent me useful aid, considering their ignorance of Crown work.—Men, bring forward your prisoner!" And the third stranger was led to the light.

"Who is this?" said one of the officials.

"The man," said the constable.

"Certainly not," said the turnkey; and the first corroborated his statement.

"But how can it be otherwise?" asked the constable. "Or why was he so terrified at sight o' the singing instrument of the law who sat there?" Here he related the strange behavior of the third stranger on entering the house during the hangman's song.

"Can't understand it," said the officer coolly. "All I know is that it is not the condemned man. He's quite a different character from this one; a gauntish fellow, with dark hair and eyes, rather good-looking, and with a musical bass voice that if you heard it once you'd never mistake as long as you lived."

"Why, souls—'twas the man in the chimney corner!"

"Hey—what?" said the magistrate, coming forward after inquiring particulars from the shepherd in the background. "Haven't you got the man after all?"

"Well, Sir," said the constable, "he's the man we were in search of, that's true; and yet he's not the man we were in search of. For the man we were in search of was not the man we wanted, Sir, if you understand my everyday way; for 'twas the man in the chimney corner!"

"A pretty kettle of fish altogether!" said the magistrate. "You had better start for the other man at once."

The prisoner now spoke for the first time. The mention of the man in the chimney corner seemed to have moved him as nothing else could do. "Sir," he said, stepping forward to the magistrate, "take no more trouble about me. The time is come when I may as well speak. I have done nothing; my crime is that the condemned man is my brother. Early this afternoon I left home at Shottsford to tramp it all the way to Casterbridge jail to bid him farewell. I was benighted, and called here to rest and ask the way. When I opened the door I saw before me the very man, my brother, that I thought to see in the condemned cell at Casterbridge. He was in this chimney corner; and jammed close to him, so that he could not have got out if he had tried, was the executioner who'd come to take his life, singing a song about it and not knowing that it was his victim who was close by, joining in to save appearances. My brother looked a glance of agony at me, and I know he meant, 'Don't reveal what you see; my life depends on it.' I was so terror-struck that I could hardly stand, and, not knowing what I did, I turned and hurried away."

The narrator's manner and tone had the stamp of truth, and his story made a great impression on all around. "And do you know where your brother is at the present time?" asked the magistrate.

"I do not. I have never seen him since I closed this door."

"I can testify to that, for we've been between ye ever since," said the constable.

"Where does he think to fly to?—what is his occupation?"

"He's a watch-and-clock-maker, Sir."

"'A said 'a was a wheelwright—a wicked rogue," said the constable.

"The wheels of clocks and watches he meant, no doubt," said Shepherd Fennel. "I thought his hands were palish for's trade."

"Well, it appears to me that nothing can be gained by retaining this poor man in custody," said the magistrate; "your business lies with the other, unquestionably."

And so the little man was released offhand; but he looked nothing the less sad on that account, it being beyond the power of magistrate or constable to raze out the written troubles in his brain, for they concerned another whom he regarded with more solicitude than himself. When this was done, and the man had gone his way, the night was found to be so far advanced that it was deemed useless to renew the search before the next morning.

Next day, accordingly, the quest for the clever sheep-stealer became general and keen, to all appearance at least.

But the intended punishment was cruelly disproportioned to the transgression, and the sympathy of a great many countryfolk in that district was strongly on the side of the fugitive. Moreover, his marvelous coolness and daring in hob-and-nobbing with the hangman, under the unprecedented circumstances of the shepherd's party, won their admiration. So that it may be questioned if all those who ostensibly made themselves so busy in exploring woods and fields and lanes were quite so thorough when it came to the private examination of their own lofts and out-houses.

Stories were afloat of a mysterious figure being occasionally seen in some old overgrown trackway or other, remote from turnpike roads, but when a search was instituted in any of these suspected quarters nobody was found. Thus the days and weeks passed without tidings.

In brief, the bass-voiced man of the chimney corner was never recaptured. Some said that he went across the sea, others that he did not, but buried himself in the depths of a populous city. At any rate, the gentleman in cinder-gray never did his morning's work at Casterbridge, nor met anywhere at all, for business purposes, the genial comrade with whom he had passed an hour of relaxation in the lonely house on the coomb.

The grass has long been green on the graves of Shepherd Fennel and his frugal wife; the guests who made up the christening party have mainly followed their entertainers to the tomb; the baby in whose honor they all had met is a matron in the sere and yellow leaf. But the arrival of the three strangers at the shepherd's that night, and the details connected therewith, is a story as well-known as ever in the country about Higher Crowstairs.

FOR DISCUSSION

1. What effect does Hardy's careful and detailed description of the natural setting have on the story? What difference would it make if all such description were omitted? What relationship

between man and nature does such a setting suggest? How is the suggestion relevant to the whole story?

2. How would you describe Hardy's prose style? Are his sentences crisp and concise or long and rambling? Are his vocabulary and syntax those of everyday speech or are they more formal? How else can you describe the prose? How does such prose affect the story?
3. Do you think Hardy had symbolic overtones in mind when he said the house was undefended from the elements and was near a crossroads? Why or why not?
4. How do the rain and cold help create the right mood for the incident in the story? To what extent does the setting reflect, and to what extent does it contrast with, events of the tale?
5. What view of the lower classes does this story present? What attitude does Hardy seem to take toward such people?
6. What clues throughout the story foreshadow the surprise twist at the end? Do any statements mislead you?
7. Though touches of humor are not usually associated with Hardy's work, several mildly amusing incidents appear here. What is the basis of such humor?
8. What elements in this story might explain the fact that the tale outlived those who attended the christening?

FOR COMPOSITION

1. Write an essay on the social implications of such a story as "The Three Strangers." For example, what does the story imply about the law and about disproportionately severe punishment for crimes? What other implications about society and cultural mores do you find here?
2. Write an essay describing Hardy's method of characterization. For example, what devices does he use to portray the three strangers? How does he clearly differentiate them?

W. Somerset Maugham

The Verger

There had been a christening that afternoon at St. Peter's, Neville Square, and Albert Edward Foreman still wore his verger's[1] gown. He kept his new one, its folds as full and stiff as though it were made not of alpaca but of perennial bronze, for funerals and weddings (St. Peter's, Neville Square, was a church much favored by the fashionable for these ceremonies), and now he wore only his second best. He wore it with complacence;[2] for it was the dignified symbol of his office, and without it (when he took it off to go home) he had the disconcerting sensation of being somewhat insufficiently clad. He took pains with it; he pressed it and ironed it himself. During the sixteen years he had been verger of this church he had had a succession of such gowns; but he had never been able to throw them away when they were worn out, and the complete series, neatly wrapped up in brown paper, lay in the bottom drawer of the wardrobe in his bedroom.

The verger busied himself quietly, replacing the painted wooden cover on the marble font, taking away a chair that had been brought for an infirm old lady, and waited for the vicar[3] to have finished in the vestry so that he could tidy up in there and go home. Presently he saw him walk across the chancel, genuflect in front of the high altar, and come down the aisle; but he still wore his cassock.

"What's he 'anging about for?" the verger said to himself. "Don't 'e know I want my tea?"

The vicar had been but recently appointed, a red-faced, energetic man in his early forties, and Albert Edward still

[1]*verger:* attendant to a clergyman
[2]*complacence:* contentment
[3]*vicar:* minister in charge of a church

regretted his predecessor, a clergyman of the old school who preached leisurely sermons in a silvery voice and dined out a great deal with his more aristocratic parishioners. He liked things in church to be just so, but he never fussed; he was not like this new man who wanted to have his finger in every pie. But Edward was tolerant. St. Peter's was in a very good neighborhood and the parishioners were a very nice class of people. The new vicar had come from the East End, and he couldn't be expected to fall in all at once with the discreet ways of his fashionable congregation.

"All this 'ustle," said Albert Edward. "But give 'im time; he'll learn."

When the vicar had walked down the aisle so far that he could address the verger without raising his voice more than was becoming in a place of worship, he stopped.

"Foreman, will you come into the vestry for a minute?" I have something to say to you."

"Very good, sir."

The vicar waited for him to come up and they walked up the church together.

"A very nice christening, I thought, sir. Funny 'ow the baby stopped cryin' the moment you took him."

"I've noticed they very often do," said the vicar, with a little smile. "After all, I've had a good deal of practice with them."

It was a source of subdued pride to him that he could nearly always quiet a whimpering infant by the manner in which he held it, and he was not unconscious of the amused admiration with which mothers and nurses watched him settle the baby in the crook of his surpliced arm. The verger knew that it pleased him to be complimented on his talent.

The vicar preceded Albert Edward into the vestry. Albert Edward was a trifle surprised to find the two churchwardens there. He had not seen them come in. They gave him pleasant nods.

"Good afternoon, my lord. Good afternoon, sir," he said to one after the other.

They were elderly men, both of them, and they had been

churchwardens almost as long as Albert Edward had been verger. They were sitting now at a handsome refectory table[4] that the old vicar had brought many years before from Italy, and the vicar sat down in the vacant chair between them. Albert Edward faced them, the table between him and them, and wondered with slight uneasiness what was the matter. He remembered still the occasion on which the organist had got into trouble and the bother they had had to hush things up. In a church like St. Peter's, Neville Square, they couldn't afford a scandal. On the vicar's red face was a look of resolute benignity, but the others bore an expression that was slightly troubled.

"He's been naggin' them, he' as," said the verger to himself. "He's jockeyed them into doin' something, but they don't 'alf like it. That's what it is; you mark my words."

But his thoughts did not appear on Albert Edward's clean-cut and distinguished features. He stood in a respectful but not obsequious[5] attitude. He had been in service[6] before he was appointed to his ecclesiastical office, but only in very good houses, and his deportment was irreproachable. Starting as a pageboy in the household of a merchant prince, he had risen by due degrees from the position of fourth to first footman; for a year he had been singlehanded butler to a widowed peeress and, till the vacancy occurred at St. Peter's, butler with two men under him in the house of a retired ambassador. He was tall, spare, grave, and dignified. He looked, if not like a duke, at least like an actor of the old school who specialized in dukes' parts. He had tact, firmness, and self-assurance. His character was unimpeachable.[7]

The vicar began briskly.

"Foreman, we've got something rather unpleasant to say to you. You've been here a great many years, and I think his lordship and the general agree with me that you've fulfilled the duties of your office to the satisfaction of everybody concerned."

The two churchwardens nodded.

[4]*refectory table:* long, narrow table with heavy legs
[5]*obsequious:* overly submissive
[6]*service:* employed as a household servant
[7]*unimpeachable:* above criticism

"But a most extraordinary circumstance came to my knowledge the other day and I felt it my duty to impart it to the churchwardens. I discovered to my astonishment that you could neither read nor write."

The verger's face betrayed no sign of embarrassment.

"The last vicar knew that, sir," he replied. "He said it didn't make no difference. He always said there was a great deal too much education in the world for 'is taste."

"It's the most amazing thing I ever heard," cried the general. "Do you mean to say that you've been verger of this church for sixteen years and never learned to read or write?"

"I went into service when I was twelve, sir. The cook in the first place tried to teach me once, but I didn't seem to 'ave the knack for it, and then what with one thing and another I never seemed to 'ave the time. I've never really found the want of it. I think a lot of these young fellows waste a lot of time readin' when they might be doin' something useful."

"But don't you want to know the news?" said the other churchwarden. "Don't you ever want to write a letter?"

"No, me lord. I seem to manage very well without. And of late years, now they've all these pictures in the papers, I get to know what's goin' on pretty well. Me wife's quite a scholar, and if I want to write a letter she writes it for me. It's not as if I was a bettin' man."

The two churchwardens gave the vicar a troubled glance and then looked down at the table.

"Well, Foreman, I've talked the matter over with these gentlemen and they quite agree with me that the situation is impossible. At a church like St. Peter's, Neville Square, we cannot have a verger who can neither read nor write."

Albert Edward's thin, sallow face reddened and he moved uneasily on his feet, but he made no reply.

"Understand me, Foreman, I have no complaint to make against you. You do your work quite satisfactorily. I have the highest opinion both of your character and of your capacity, but we haven't the right to take the risk of some accident that might happen owing to your lamentable ignorance. It's a matter of prudence as well as of principle."

"But couldn't you learn, Foreman?" asked the general.

"No, sir, I'm afraid I couldn't—not now. You see, I'm not as young as I was, and, if I couldn't seem able to get the letters in me 'ead when I was a nipper, I don't think there's much chance of it now."

"We don't want to be harsh with you, Foreman," said the vicar. "But the churchwardens and I have quite made up our minds. We'll give you three months, and if at the end of that time you cannot read and write I'm afraid you'll have to go."

Albert Edward had never liked the new vicar. He'd said from the beginning that they'd made a mistake when they gave him St. Peter's. He wasn't the type of man they wanted with a classy congregation like that. And now he straightened himself a little. He knew his value and he wasn't going to allow himself to be put upon.

"I'm very sorry, sir; I'm afraid it's no good. I'm too old a dog to learn new tricks. I've lived a good many years without knowin' 'ow to read and write, and without wishin' to praise myself—self-praise is no recommendation—I don't mind sayin' I've done my duty in that state of life in which it 'as pleased a merciful providence to place me, and if I *could* learn now I don't know as I'd want to."

"In that case, Foreman, I'm afraid you must go."

"Yes, sir, I quite understand. I shall be 'appy to 'and in my resignation as soon as you've found somebody to take my place."

But when Albert Edward, with his usual politeness, had closed the church door behind the vicar and the two churchwardens, he could not sustain the air of unruffled dignity with which he had borne the blow inflicted upon him, and his lips quivered. He walked slowly back to the vestry and hung up on its proper peg his verger's gown. He sighed as he thought of all the grand funerals and smart weddings it had seen. He tidied everything up, put on his coat, and hat in hand walked down the aisle. He locked the church door behind him. He strolled across the square; but, deep in sad thoughts, he did not take the street that led him home, where a nice strong cup of tea awaited him—he took the wrong turning.

He walked slowly along. His heart was heavy. He did not know what he should do with himself. He did not fancy the notion of going back to domestic service; after being his own master for so many years—for the vicar and churchwardens could say what they liked; it was he that had run St. Peter's, Neville Square—he could scarcely demean himself by accepting a situation.[8] He had saved a tidy sum, but not enough to live on without doing something; and life seemed to cost more every year. He had never thought to be troubled with such questions. The vergers of St. Peter's, like the popes of Rome, were there for life. He had often thought of the pleasant reference the vicar would make, in his sermon at evensong the first Sunday after his death, to the long and faithful service and the exemplary character of their late verger, Albert Edward Foreman.

He sighed deeply. Albert Edward was a nonsmoker and a total abstainer, but with a certain latitude; that is to say, he liked a glass of beer with his dinner and when he was tired he enjoyed a cigarette. It occurred to him now that one would comfort him and, since he did not carry them, he looked about him for a shop where he could buy a packet of Gold Flakes. He did not at once see one and walked on a little. It was a long street, with all sorts of shops in it; but there was not a single one where you could buy cigarettes.

"That's strange," said Albert Edward.

To make sure, he walked right up the street again. No, there was no doubt about it. He stopped and looked reflectively up and down.

"I can't be the only man as walks along this street and wants a fag," he said. "I shouldn't wonder but what a fellow might do very well with a little shop here. Tobacco and sweets, you know."

He gave a sudden start.

"That's an idea," he said. "Strange 'ow things come to you when you least expect it."

He turned, walked home, and had his tea.

"You're very silent this afternoon, Albert," his wife remarked.

"I'm thinkin'," he said.

He considered the matter from every point of view, and next

[8]*situation:* position as a household servant

day he went along the street and by good luck found a little shop to let that looked as though it would exactly suit him. Twenty-four hours later he had taken it and, when a month after that he left St. Peter's, Neville Square, forever, Albert Edward Foreman set up in business as a tobacconist and newsagent. His wife said it was a dreadful comedown after being verger of St. Peter's; but he answered that you had to move with the times, the church wasn't what it was, and 'enceforward he was going to render unto Caesar what was Caesar's. Albert Edward did very well. He did so well that in a year or so it struck him that he might take a second shop and put a manager in. He looked for another long street that hadn't got a tobacconist in it and when he found it, and a shop to let, took it and stocked it. This was a success too. Then it occurred to him that if he could run two he could run half a dozen; so he began walking about London, and whenever he found a long street that had no tobacconist, and a shop to let, he took it. In the course of ten years he had acquired no less than ten shops and he was making money hand over fist. He went round to all of them himself every Monday, collected the week's takings and took them to the bank.

One morning when he was there, paying in a bundle of notes and a heavy bag of silver, the cashier told him that the manager would like to see him. He was shown into an office and the manager shook hands with him.

"Mr. Foreman, I wanted to have a talk to you about the money you've got on deposit with us. D'you know exactly how much it is?"

"Not within a pound or two, sir; but I've got a pretty rough idea."

"Apart from what you paid in this morning, it's a little over thirty thousand pounds. That's a very large sum to have on deposit and I should have thought you'd do better to invest it."

"I wouldn't want to take no risk, sir. I know it's safe in the bank."

"You needn't have the least anxiety. We'll make you out a list of absolutely gilt-edged securities. They'll bring you in a better rate of interest than we can possibly afford to give you."

A troubled look settled on Mr. Foreman's distinguished face.

"I've never 'ad anything to do with stocks and shares and I'd 'ave to leave it all in your 'ands," he said.

The manager smiled.

"We'll do everything. All you'll have to do next time you come in is just to sign the transfers."

"I could do that all right," said Albert uncertainly. "But 'ow should I know what I was signin'?"

"I suppose you can read," said the manager a trifle sharply.

Mr. Foreman gave him a disarming smile.

"Well, sir, that's just it. I can't. I know it sounds funny like, but there it is! I can't read or write—only me name, an' I only learned to do that when I went into business."

The manager was so surprised that he jumped up from his chair.

"That's the most extraordinary thing I ever heard."

"You see, it's like this, sir—I never 'ad the opportunity until it was too late, and then some'ow I wouldn't. I got obstinate like."

The manager stared at him as though he were a prehistoric monster.

"And do you mean to say that you've built up this important business and amassed a fortune of thirty thousand pounds without being able to read or write? Good God, man, what would you be now if you had been able to?"

"I can tell you that, sir," said Mr. Foreman, a little smile on his still aristocratic features. "I'd be verger of St. Peter's, Neville Square."

FOR DISCUSSION

1. What do you consider the real cause of the conflict between the vicar and the verger? Find evidence in the story that there is a conflict and that the verger's illiteracy is perhaps not the only reason for his dismissal.
2. Prior to the meeting with the churchwardens, the verger re-

marks, "He's been naggin' them, he 'as. He's jockeyed them into doin' something, but they don't 'alf like it." How well has the verger sized up the situation?
3. What difference does the verger see between the old vicar and the new one? What view of education did the last vicar hold? Why did he hold this view? What arguments can you give for or against it?
4. In your opinion, was Foreman's success in his new business the result of character, of luck, or of something else? Explain.
5. In his critical writings Maugham emphasized that the main aim of a writer is to entertain: "he seeks to prove nothing. He paints a picture and sets it before you." Of course, Maugham continued, this picture must be convincing. The writer hopes to make you believe in the world he has created, to make you accept "his view of the universe." What "view of the universe" does Maugham present in this story? Judging by the ending would you say it is or is not, ironical? Cite evidence from the story to support your answer.

FOR COMPOSITION

1. Imagine that you are the vicar. Write an official version of the replacement of the verger, in which you include your own version of his conduct in his office during your ministry. Or recount the event as it would be related by one of the churchwardens to his wife.
2. Often what seems to be misfortune turns out, in the long run, to be good fortune. Write an account based on your own experience or observation which illustrates the truth of this idea.
3. Discuss the justice of the verger's dismissal. Consider his qualifications as opposed to his illiteracy and his attitude toward it. Explain why you do, or do not, think the churchwardens and the vicar were justified in their action.

Katherine Mansfield

The Wind Blows

Suddenly—dreadfully—she wakes up. What has happened? Something dreadful has happened. No—nothing has happened. It is only the wind shaking the house, rattling the windows, banging a piece of iron on the roof and making her bed tremble. Leaves flutter past the window, up and away; down in the avenue a whole newspaper wags in the air like a lost kite and falls, spiked on a pine tree. It is cold. Summer is over—it is autumn— everything is ugly. The carts rattle by, swinging from side to side; two Chinamen lollop along under their wooden yokes with the straining vegetable baskets—their pigtails and blue blouses fly out in the wind. A white dog on three legs yelps past the gate. It is all over! What is? Oh, everything! And she begins to plait her hair with shaking fingers, not daring to look in the glass. Mother is talking to grandmother in the hall.

"A perfect idiot! Imagine leaving anything out on the line in weather like this. . . . Now my best little Teneriffe-work teacloth is simply in ribbons. *What* is that extraordinary smell? It's the porridge burning. Oh, heavens—this wind!"

She has a music lesson at ten o'clock. At the thought the minor movement of the Beethoven begins to play in her head, the trills long and terrible like little rolling drums. . . . Marie Swainson runs into the garden next door to pick the "chrysanths" before they are ruined. Her skirt flies up above her waist; she tries to beat it down, to tuck it between her legs while she stoops, but it is no use—up it flies. All the trees and bushes beat about her. She picks as quickly as she can, but she is quite distracted. She doesn't mind what she does—she pulls the plants up by the roots and bends and twists them, stamping her foot and swearing.

"For heaven's sake keep the front door shut! Go round to the back," shouts someone. And then she hears Bogey:

"Mother, you're wanted on the telephone. Telephone, Mother. It's the butcher."

How hideous life is—revolting, simply revolting. . . . And now her hat-elastic's snapped. Of course it would. She'll wear her old tam and slip out the back way. But Mother has seen.

"Matilda. Matilda. Come back im-me-diately! What on earth have you got on your head? It looks like a tea cosy. And why have you got that mane of hair on your forehead."

"I can't come back, Mother. I'll be late for my lesson."

"Come back immediately!"

She won't. She won't. She hates Mother. "Go to hell," she shouts, running down the road.

In waves, in clouds, in big round whirls the dust comes stinging, and with it little bits of straw and chaff and manure. There is a loud roaring sound from the trees in the gardens, and standing at the bottom of the road outside Mr. Bullen's gate she can hear the sea sob: "Ah! . . . Ah! . . . Ah-h!" But Mr. Bullen's drawing-room is as quiet as a cave. The windows are closed, the blinds half pulled, and she is not late. The-girl-before-her has just started playing MacDowell's "To an Iceberg." Mr. Bullen looks over at her and half smiles.

"Sit down," he says. "Sit over there in the sofa corner, little lady."

How funny he is. He doesn't exactly laugh at you . . . but there is just something. . . . Oh, how peaceful it is here. She likes this room. It smells of art serge[1] and stale smoke and chrysanthemums . . . there is a big vase of them on the mantelpiece behind the pale photograph of Rubinstein[2] . . . *à mon ami*[3] *Robert Bullen*. . . . Over the black glittering piano hangs "Solitude"—a dark tragic woman draped in white, sitting on a rock, her knees crossed, her chin on her hands.

"No, no!" says Mr. Bullen, and he leans over the other girl, puts his arms over her shoulders and plays the passage for her. The stupid—she's blushing! How ridiculous.

Now the-girl-before-her has gone; the front door slams.

[1]*serge:* suit fabric
[2]*Rubinstein:* a famous pianist
[3]*à mon ami:* to my friend (French)

Mr. Bullen comes back and walks up and down, very softly, waiting for her. What an extraordinary thing. Her fingers tremble so that she can't undo the knot in the music satchel. It's the wind. . . . And her heart beats so hard she feels it must lift her blouse up and down. Mr. Bullen does not say a word. The shabby red piano seat is long enough for two people to sit side by side. Mr. Bullen sits down by her.

"Shall I begin with scales," she asks, squeezing her hands together. "I had some arpeggios, too."

But he does not answer. She doesn't believe he even hears . . . and then suddenly his fresh hand with the ring on it reaches over and opens Beethoven.

"Let's have a little of the old master," he says.

But why does he speak so kindly—so awfully kindly—and as though they had known each other for years and years and knew everything about each other.

He turns the page slowly. She watches his hand—it is a very nice hand and always looks as though it had just been washed.

"Here we are," says Mr. Bullen.

Oh, that kind voice—Oh, that minor movement. Here come the little drums. . . .

"Shall I take the repeat?"

"Yes, dear child."

His voice is far, far too kind. The crotchets and quavers[4] are dancing up and down the stave like little black boys on a fence. Why is he so . . . She will not cry—she has nothing to cry about. . . .

"What is it, dear child?"

Mr. Bullen takes her hands. His shoulder is there—just by her head. She leans on it ever so little, her cheek against the springy tweed.

"Life is so dreadful," she murmurs, but she does not feel it's dreadful at all. He says something about "waiting" and "marking time" and "that rare thing, a woman," but she does not hear. It is so comfortable . . . for ever . . .

Suddenly the door opens and in pops Marie Swainson, hours before her time.

[4]*crotchets and quavers:* quarter notes and eighth notes

"Take the allegretto a little faster," says Mr. Bullen, and gets up and begins to walk up and down again.

"Sit in the sofa corner, little lady," he says to Marie.

The wind, the wind. It's frightening to be here in her room by herself. The bed, the mirror, the white jug and basin gleam like the sky outside. It's the bed that is frightening. There it lies, sound asleep. . . . Does Mother imagine for one moment that she is going to darn all those stockings knotted up on the quilt like a coil of snakes? She's not. No, Mother. I do not see why I should. . . . The wind—the wind! There's a funny smell of soot blowing down the chimney. Hasn't anyone written poems to the wind? . . . "I bring fresh flowers to the leaves and showers." . . . What nonsense.

"Is that you, Bogey?"

"Come for a walk round the esplanade, Matilda. I can't stand this any longer."

"Right-o. I'll put on my ulster.[5] Isn't it an awful day!" Bogey's ulster is just like hers. Hooking the collar she looks at herself in the glass. Her face is white, they have the same excited eyes and hot lips. Ah, they know those two in the glass. Good-bye, dears; we shall be back soon.

"This is better, isn't it?"

"Hook on," says Bogey.

They cannot walk fast enough. Their heads bent, their legs just touching, they stride like one eager person through the town, down the asphalt zigzag where the fennel grows wild and on to the esplanade. It is dusky—just getting dusky. The wind is so strong that they have to fight their way through it, rocking like two old drunkards. All the poor little pahutukawas on the esplanade are bent to the ground.

"Come on! Come on! Let's get near."

Over by the breakwater the sea is very high. They pull off their hats and her hair blows across her mouth, tasting of salt. The sea is so high that the waves do not break at all; they thump against the rough stone wall and suck up the weedy, dripping steps. A fine spray skims from the water

[5]*ulster:* long, loose overcoat.

right across the esplanade. They are covered with drops. The inside of her mouth tastes wet and cold.

Bogey's voice is breaking. When he speaks he rushes up and down the scale. It's funny—it makes you laugh—and yet it just suits the day. The wind carries their voices—away fly the sentences like little narrow ribbons.

"Quicker! Quicker!"

It is getting very dark. In the harbour the coal hulks show two lights—one high on a mast, and one from the stern.

"Look, Bogey. Look over there."

A big black steamer with a long loop of smoke streaming, with the portholes lighted, with lights everywhere, is putting out to sea. The wind does not stop her; she cuts through the waves, making for the open gate between the pointed rocks that leads to . . . It's the light that makes her look so awfully beautiful and mysterious. . . . *They* are on board leaning over the rail arm in arm.

" . . . Who are they?"

" . . . Brother and sister."

"Look, Bogey, there's the town. Doesn't it look small? There's the post office clock chiming for the last time. There's the esplanade where we walked that windy day. Do you remember? I cried at my music lesson that day—how many years ago! Good-bye, little island, good-bye. . . ."

Now the dark stretches a wing over the tumbling water. They can't see those two any more. Good-bye, good-bye. Don't forget. . . . But the smoke is gone, now.

The wind—the wind.

FOR DISCUSSION

1. Describe Matilda's mood in the first part of the story? To what does she attribute it? What occasions her resentful thoughts about her mother? Are they justified? Explain.
2. The effect of the wind is emphasized during Matilda's walk to her music lesson. What is that effect? Why does Matilda's mood suddenly change when she arrives at the music lesson?

3. What purpose is served by the music lesson episode? Why does Matilda cry during the lesson? What hints do the music teacher's comments give you of the real cause of Matilda's feelings?
4. As Matilda thinks about the wind, she recalls a line of poetry from Shelley's "The Cloud." Why does she say, "What nonsense"? Note that the wind can be interpreted both literally and symbolically. What is it a symbol of? Why is it an appropriate symbol?
5. Discuss the use of the mirror in the story. Where and why is it mentioned? What parallel is suggested between the scene in which Matilda and Bogey look into the mirror before their walk and the one in which they watch the ship? The ship is a real object seen by Matilda and Bogey. It is also a symbol of what Matilda wishes. What is this wish?
6. What truth about life does Matilda discover at the end of the story? What causes the change in her outlook? Tell why you think the change is permanent or temporary.
7. This story seems to fall into more than one part. What is the function of each part? What details in the sentences signal the changes?

FOR COMPOSITION

1. Discuss in an essay the way in which Miss Mansfield's sentences reflect (or help create) the mood and events of the story. You may wish to concentrate on sentence lengths and ryhthms, verb tenses, or punctuation patterns.
2. Matilda responded differently to her mother and to her music teacher. In a short composition point out the ways in which her responses were different and why.

Virginia Woolf

The New Dress

Mable had her first suspicion that something was wrong as she took her cloak off and Mrs. Barnet, while handing her the mirror and touching the brushes and thus drawing her attention, perhaps rather markedly, to all the appliances for tidying and improving hair, complexion, clothes, which existed on the dressing table, confirmed the suspicion—that it was not right, not quite right, which growing stronger as she went upstairs and springing at her, with conviction as she greeted Clarissa Dalloway, she went straight to the far end of the room, to a shaded corner where a looking-glass hung and looked. No! It was not *right.* And at once the misery which she always tried to hide, the profound dissatisfaction—the sense she had had, ever since she was a child, of being inferior to other people—set upon her, relentlessly, remorselessly, with an intensity which she could not beat off, as she would when she woke at night at home, by reading Borrow or Scott; for oh these men, oh these women, all were thinking—"What's Mabel wearing? What a fright she looks! What a hideous new dress!"—their eyelids flickering as they came up and then their lids shutting rather tight. It was her own appalling inadequacy; her cowardice; her mean, water-sprinkled blood that depressed her. And at once the whole of the room where, for ever so many hours, she had planned with the little dressmaker how it was to go, seemed sordid, repulsive; and her own drawing-room so shabby, and herself, going out, puffed up with vanity as she touched the letters on the hall table and said: "How dull!" to show off—all this now seemed unutterably silly, paltry, and provincial. All this had been absolutely destroyed, shown up, exploded, the moment she came into Mrs. Dalloway's drawing-room.

What she had thought that evening when, sitting over the teacups, Mrs. Dalloway's invitation came, was that, of course, she could not be fashionable. It was absurd to pretend it even—fashion meant cut, meant style, meant thirty guineas at least—but why not be original? Why not be herself, anyhow? And, getting up, she had taken that old fashion book of her mother's, a Paris fashion book of the time of the Empire, and had thought how much prettier, more dignified, and more womanly they were then, and so set herself—oh, it was foolish—trying to be like them, pluming herself in fact, upon being modest and old-fashioned and very charming, giving herself up, no doubt about it, to an orgy of self-love, which deserved to be chastised, and so rigged herself out like this.

But she dared not look in the glass. She could not face the whole horror—the pale yellow, idiotically old-fashioned silk dress with its long skirt and its high sleeves and its waist and all the things that looked so charming in the fashion book, but not on her, not among all these ordinary people. She felt like a dressmaker's dummy standing there, for young people to stick pins into.

"But, my dear, it's perfectly charming!" Rose Shaw said, looking her up and down with that little satirical pucker of the lips which she expected—Rose herself being dressed in the height of the fashion, precisely like everybody else, always.

We are all like flies trying to crawl over the edge of the saucer, Mable thought, and repeated the phrase as if she were crossing herself, as if she were trying to find some spell to annul this pain, to make this agony endurable. Tags of Shakespeare, lines from books she had read ages ago, suddenly came to her when she was in agony, and she repeated them over and over again. "Flies trying to crawl," she repeated. If she could say that over often enough and make herself see the flies, she would become numb, chill, frozen, dumb. Now she could see flies crawling slowly out of a saucer of milk with their wings stuck together; and she strained and strained (standing in front of the looking-glass, listening to Rose Shaw) to make herself see Rose Shaw and all the other people there as flies, trying to hoist themselves out of something, or into something, meagre, insignificant, toiling flies. But she could not see them like that, not other people. She saw herself like that—she was a fly, but the others were dragonflies, butterflies, beautiful insects, dancing, fluttering, skimming, while she alone dragged herself up out of the saucer. (Envy and spite, the most detestable of the vices, were her chief faults.)

"I feel like some dowdy, decrepit, horribly dingy old fly," she said, making Robert Haydon stop just to hear her say that, just to reassure herself by furbishing up a poor weak-kneed phrase and so showing how detached she was, how witty, that she did not feel in the least out of anything. And, of course, Robert Haydon answered something quite polite, quite insincere, which she saw through instantly, and said to herself, directly he went (again from some book), "Lies, lies, lies!" For a party makes things either much more real, or much less real, she thought; she saw in a flash to the bottom of Robert Haydon's heart; she saw through everything. She saw the truth. *This* was true, this drawing-room, this self, and the other false. Miss Milan's little work-room was really terribly hot, stuffy, sordid. It smelt of clothes and cabbage cooking; and yet, when Miss Milan put the glass in her hand, and she looked at herself with the dress on, finished, an extraordinary bliss shot through her heart. Suffused with light, she sprang into existence. Rid of cares and wrinkles, what she had dreamed of herself was there—a beautiful woman. Just for a second (she had not dared look longer, Miss Milan wanted to know about the length of the skirt), there looked at her, framed in the scrolloping mahogany, a grey-white, mysteriously smiling, charming girl, the core of herself, the soul of herself; and it was not vanity only, not only self-love that made her think it good, tender, and true. Miss Milan said that the skirt could not well be longer; if anything the skirt, said Miss Milan, puckering her forehead, considering with all her wits about her, must be shorter; and she felt, suddenly, honestly, full of love for Miss Milan, much, much fonder of Miss Milan than of any one in the whole world, and could have cried for pity that she should be crawling on the floor with her mouth full of pins, and her face red and her eyes bulging—that one human being should be doing this for another, and she saw them all as human beings merely, and herself going off to her party, and Miss Milan pulling the cover over the canary's cage, or letting him pick a hemp-seed from between her lips, and the thought of it, of this side of human nature and its patience and its endurance and its being content with such miserable, scanty, sordid, little pleasures filled her eyes with tears.

And now the whole thing had vanished. The dress, the room, the love, the pity, the scrolloping looking-glass, and the canary's cage—all had vanished, and here she was in a corner of Mrs. Dalloway's drawing-room, suffering tortures, woken wide awake to reality.

But it was all so paltry, weak-blooded, and petty-minded to care so much at her age with two children, to be still so utterly dependent on people's opinions and not have principles or convictions, not to be able to say as other people did, "There's Shakespeare! There's death! We're all weevils in a captain's biscuit"—or whatever it was that people did say.

She faced herself straight in the glass; she pecked at her left shoulder; she issued out into the room, as if spears were thrown at her yellow dress from all sides. But instead of looking fierce or tragic, as Rose Shaw would have done—Rose would have looked like Boadicea—she looked foolish and self-conscious, and simpered like a schoolgirl and slouched across the room positively slinking, as if she were a beaten mongrel, and looked at a picture, an engraving. As if one went to a party to look at a picture! Everybody knew why she did it—it was from shame, from humiliation.

"Now the fly's in the saucer," she said to herself, "right in the middle, and can't get out, and the milk," she thought, rigidly staring at the picture, "is sticking its wings together."

"It's so old-fashioned," she said to Charles Burt, making him stop (which by itself he hated) on his way to talk to some one else.

She meant, or she tried to make herself think that she meant, that it was the picture and not her dress, that was old-fashioned. And one word of praise, one word of affection from Charles would have made all the difference to her at the moment. If he had only said, "Mabel, you're looking charming to-night!" it would have changed her life. But then she ought to have been truthful and direct. Charles said nothing of the kind, of course. He was malice itself. He always saw through one, especially if one were feeling particularly mean, paltry, or feeble-minded.

"Mabel's got a new dress!" he said, and the poor fly was absolutely shoved into the middle of the saucer. Really, he would like her to drown, she believed. He had no heart, no fundamental kindness, only a veneer of friendliness. Miss Milan was much more real, much kinder. If only one could feel that and stick to it, always. "Why," she asked herself—replying to Charles much too pertly, letting him see that she was out of temper, or "ruffled" as he called it ("Rather ruffled?" he said and went on to laugh at her with some woman over there)—"Why," she asked herself, "can't I feel one thing always, feel quite sure that Miss Milan is right, and Charles wrong and stick to it, feel sure about the canary and pity and love and not be whipped all round in a second by coming into a room full of people?" It was her odious, weak, vacillating character again, always giving at the critical moment and not being seriously interested in conchology, etymology, botany, archeology, cutting up potatoes and watching them fructify like Mary Dennis, like Violet Searle.

Then Mrs. Holman, seeing her standing there, bore down upon her. Of course a thing like a dress was beneath Mrs. Holman's notice, with her family always tumbling downstairs or having the scarlet fever. Could Mabel tell her if Elmthorpe was ever let for August and September? Oh, it was a conversation that bored her unutterably!—it made her furious to be treated like a house agent or a messenger boy, to be made use of. Not to have value, that was it, she thought, trying to grasp something hard, something real, while she tried to answer sensibly about the bathroom and the south aspect and the hot water to the top of the house; and all the time she could see little bits of her yellow dress in the round looking-glass which made them all the size of boot-buttons or tadpoles; and it was amazing to think how much humiliation and agony and self-loathing and effort and passionate ups and downs of feeling were contained in a thing the size of a three-penny bit. And what was still odder, this thing, this Mabel Waring, was separate, quite disconnected; and though Mrs. Holman (the black button) was leaning forward and telling her how her eldest boy had strained his heart running, she could see her, too, quite detached in the looking-glass, and it was impossible that the black dot, leaning forward, gesticulating, should make the yellow dot, sitting solitary, self-centred, feel what the black dot was feeling, yet they pretended.

"So impossible to keep boys quiet"—that was the kind of thing one said.

And Mrs. Holman, who could never get enough sympathy and snatched what little there was greedily, as if it were her right (but she deserved much more for there was her little girl who had come down this morning with a swollen knee-joint), took this miserable offering and looked at it suspiciously, grudgingly, as if it were a halfpenny when it ought to have been a pound and put it away in her purse, must put up with it, mean and miserly though it was, times being hard, so very hard; and on she went, creaking, injured Mrs. Holman, about the girl with the swollen joints. Ah, it was tragic, this greed, this clamour of human beings, like a row of cormorants, barking and flapping their wings for sympathy—it was tragic, could one have felt it and not merely pretended to feel it!

But in her yellow dress to-night she could not wring out one drop more; she wanted it all, all for herself. She knew (she kept on looking into the glass, dipping into that dreadfully showing-up blue pool) that she was condemned, despised, left like this in a backwater, because of her being like this a feeble, vacillating creature; and it seemed to her that the yellow dress was a penance which she had deserved, and if she had been dressed like Rose Shaw, in lovely, clinging green with a ruffle of swansdown, she would have deserved that; and she thought that there was no escape for her—none whatever. But it was not her fault altogether, after all. It was being one of a family of ten; never having money enough, always skimping and paring; and her mother carrying great cans, and the linoleum worn on the stair edges, and one sordid little domestic tragedy after another—nothing catastrophic, the sheep farm failing, but not utterly; her eldest brother marrying beneath him but not very much—there was no romance, nothing extreme about them all. They petered out respectably in seaside resorts; every watering-place had one of her aunts even now asleep in some lodging with the front windows not quite facing the sea. That was so like them—they had to squint at things always. And she had done the same—she was just like her aunts. For all her dreams of living in India, married to some hero like Sir Henry Lawrence, some empire builder (still the sight of a native in a turban filled her with romance), she had failed utterly. She had married Hubert, with his safe, permanent underling's job in the Law Courts, and they managed tolerably in a smallish house, without proper maids, and hash when she was alone or just bread and butter, but now and then—Mrs Holman was off, thinking her the most dried-up, unsympathetic twig she had ever met, absurdly dressed, too, and would tell every one about Mabel's fantastic appearance—now and then, thought Mabel Waring, left alone on the blue sofa, punching the cushion in order to look occupied, for she would not join Charles Burt and Rose Shaw, chattering like magpies and perhaps laughing at her by the fireplace—now and then, there did come to her delicious moments, reading the other night in bed, for instance, or down by the sea on the sand in the sun, at Easter—let her recall it—a great tuft of pale sand-grass standing all twisted like a shock of spears against the sky, which was blue like a smooth china egg, so firm, so hard, and then the melody of the waves—"Hush, hush," they said, and the children's shouts paddling—yes, it was a divine moment, and there she lay, she felt, in the hand of the Goddess who was the world; rather a hard-hearted, but very beautiful Goddess, a little lamb laid on the altar (one did think these silly things, and it didn't matter so long as one never said them). And also with Hubert sometimes she had quite unexpectedly—carving the mutton for Sunday lunch, for no reason, opening a letter, coming into a room—divine moments, when she said to herself (for she would never say this to anybody else), "This is it. This has happened. This is it!" And the other way about it was equally surprising—that is, when everything was arranged—music, weather, holidays, every reason for happiness was there—then nothing happened at all. One wasn't happy. It was flat, just flat, that was all.

Her wretched self again, no doubt! She had always been a fretful, weak, unsatisfactory mother, a wobbly wife, lolling about in a kind of twilight existence with nothing very clear or very bold, or more one thing than another, like all her brothers and sisters, except perhaps Herbert—they were all the same poor water-veined creatures who did nothing. Then in the midst of this creeping, crawling life, suddenly she was on the crest of a wave. That wretched fly—where had she read the story that kept coming into her mind about the fly and the saucer?—struggled out. Yes, she had those moments. But now that she was forty, they might come more and more seldom. By degrees she would cease to struggle any more. But that was deplorable! That was not to be endured! That made her feel ashamed of herself!

She would go to the London Library to-morrow. She would find some wonderful, helpful, astonishing book, quite by chance, a book by a clergyman, by an American no one had ever heard of; or she would walk down the Strand and drop, accidentally, into a hall where a miner was telling about the life in the pit, and suddenly she would become a new person. She would be absolutely transformed. She would wear a uniform; she would be called Sister Somebody; she would never give a thought to clothes again. And for ever after she would be perfectly clear about Charles Burt and Miss Milan and this room and that room; and it would be always, day after day, as if she were lying in the sun or carving the mutton. It would be it!

So she got up from the blue sofa, and the yellow button in the looking-glass got up too, and she waved her hand to Charles and Rose to show them she did not depend on them one scrap, and the yellow button moved out of the looking-glass, and all the spears were gathered into her breast as she walked towards Mrs. Dalloway and said, "Good night."

"But it's too early to go," said Mrs. Dalloway, who was always so charming.

"I'm afraid I must," said Mabel Waring. "But," she added

in her weak, wobbly voice which only sounded ridiculous when she tried to strengthen it, "I have enjoyed myself enormously."

"I have enjoyed myself," she said to Mr. Dalloway, whom she met on the stairs.

"Lies, lies, lies!" she said to herself, going downstairs, and "Right in the saucer!" she said to herself as she thanked Mrs. Barnet for helping her and wrapped herself, round and round and round, in the Chinese cloak she had worn these twenty years.

FOR DISCUSSION

1. How does the author help you to learn about Mabel's past? What hints are given about her family? How has her present situation been influenced by the events in her past?
2. What was Mabel's reason for choosing this particular style of dress? Is it, as she claims, "idiotically old-fashioned"? If not, why do those who meet her act as if it were? Or do they? Explain.
3. Mabel is characterized chiefly by her thoughts and actions. What exactly are her character traits? What forces motivate her actions?
4. From whose point of view is the story told? Does this perspective provide you with a true picture of life as represented in Mrs. Dalloway's drawing room? Do all the incidents related by Mabel really occur? If not, which episodes are real? which are not?
5. Is Mabel snubbed by her acquaintances, or is she accepted by the group in which she moves? Are the guests aware of Mabel's feelings or are they unfeeling people? Discuss fully.
6. While reading the story you have probably felt as ill at ease and embarrassed as Mabel; it is with relief you accompany her to the cloakroom. How do you account for her change of feeling as she prepares to go home? Is there any significance in the fact that on leaving she wraps herself "round and round and round, in the Chinese cloak she had worn these twenty years"?
7. State the theme of this story in your own words and cite sentences or passages which help to express this idea.

FOR COMPOSITION

1. Doubtless you have had occasion to feel inadequate to a situation in which you found yourself. In a short narrative, describe such a situation and your feelings at that time.
2. Imagine you are one of the men or women who attended Mrs. Dalloway's party. Write an entry in your diary after returning home, describing your reaction to Mabel.

E. M. Foster

The Celestial Omnibus

I

The boy who resided at Agathox Lodge, 28, Buckingham Park Road, Surbiton,[1] had often been puzzled by the old signpost that stood almost opposite. He asked his mother about it, and she replied that it was a joke, and not a very nice one, which had been made many years back by some naughty young men, and that the police ought to remove it. For there were two strange things about this sign-post: firstly, it pointed up a blank alley, and, secondly, it had painted on it, in faded characters, the words, "To Heaven."

"What kind of young men were they?" he asked.

"I think your father told me that one of them wrote verses, and was expelled from the University and came to grief in other ways. Still, it was a long time ago. You must ask your father about it. He will say the same as I do, that it was put up as a joke."

"So it doesn't mean anything at all?"

She sent him up-stairs to put on his best things, for the Bonses were coming to tea, and he was to hand the cake-stand.

It struck him, as he wrenched on his tightening trousers, that he might do worse than ask Mr. Bons about the sign-post. His father, though very kind, always laughed at him—shrieked with laughter whenever he or any other child asked a question or spoke. But Mr. Bons was serious as well as kind. He had a beautiful house and lent one books, he was a church-warden, and a candidate for the County Council; he had donated to the Free Library enormously, he presided over the Literary Society, and had Members of Parliament to stop

[1]*Surbiton:* suburban town southwest of London

with him—in short, he was probably the wisest person alive.

Yet even Mr. Bons could only say that the sign-post was a joke—the joke of a person named Shelley.

"Of course!" cried the mother; "I told you so, dear. That was the name."

"Had you never heard of Shelley?" asked Mr. Bons.

"No," said the boy, and hung his head.

"But is there no Shelley in the house?"

"Why, yes!" exclaimed the lady, in much agitation. "Dear Mr. Bons, we aren't such Philistines[2] as that. Two at the least. One a wedding present, and the other, smaller print, in one of the spare rooms."

"I believe we have seven Shelleys," said Mr. Bons, with a slow smile. Then he brushed the cake crumbs off his stomach, and, together with his daughter, rose to go.

The boy, obeying a wink from his mother, saw them all the way to the garden gate, and when they had gone he did not at once return to the house, but gazed for a little up and down Buckingham Park Road.

His parents lived at the right end of it. After No. 39 the quality of the houses dropped very suddenly, and 64 had not even a separate servants' entrance. But at the present moment the whole road looked rather pretty, for the sun had just set in splendour, and the inequalities of rent were drowned in a saffron afterglow. Small birds twittered, and the bread-winners' train shrieked musically down through the cutting—that wonderful cutting which has drawn to itself the whole beauty out of Surbiton, and clad itself, like any Alpine valley, with the glory of the fir and the silver birch and the primrose. It was this cutting that had first stirred desires within the boy—desires for something just a little different, he knew not what, desires that would return whenever things were sunlit, as they were this evening, running up and down, till he would feel quite unusual all over, and as likely as not would want to cry. This evening he was even sillier, for he slipped across the road toward the signpost and began to run up the blank alley.

[2]*Philistines:* uncultured persons

The alley runs between high walls—the walls of the gardens of "Ivanhoe" and "Belle Vista" respectively. It smells a little all the way, and is scarcely twenty yards long, including the turn at the end. So not unnaturally the boy soon came to a standstill. "I'd like to kick that Shelley," he exclaimed, and glanced idly at a piece of paper which was pasted on the wall. Rather an odd piece of paper, and he read it carefully before he turned back. This is what he read:

S. AND C. R. C. C.

Alteration in Service.

Owing to lack of patronage the Company are regretfully compelled to suspend the hourly service, and to retain only the

Sunrise and Sunset Omnibuses,

which will run as usual. It is to be hoped that the public will patronize an arrangement which is intended for their convenience. As an extra inducement, the Company will, for the first time, now issue

Return Tickets!

(available one day only), which may be obtained of the driver. Passengers are again reminded that *no tickets are issued at the other end,* and that no complaints in this connection will receive consideration from the Company. Nor will the Company be responsible for any negligence or stupidity on the part of Passengers, nor for Hailstorms, Lightning, Loss of Tickets, nor for any Act of God.

For the Direction.

Now he had never seen this notice before, nor could he imagine where the omnibus went to. S. of course was for Surbiton, and R.C.C. meant Road Car Company. But what was the meaning of the other C.? Coombe and Malden, perhaps, or possibly "City." Yet it could not hope to compete with the South-Western. The whole thing, the boy reflected, was run on hopelessly unbusiness-like lines. Why no tickets from the other end? And what an hour to start! Then he realized that unless the notice was a hoax, an omnibus[3] must have been starting just as he was wishing the Bonses good-bye. He peered at the ground through the gathering dusk, and there he saw what might or might not be the marks of wheels. Yet nothing had come out of the alley. And he had never seen an omnibus at any time in the Buckingham Park Road. No: it must be a hoax, like the signposts, like the fairy tales, like the dreams upon which he would wake suddenly in the night. And with a sigh he stepped from the alley—right into the arms of his father.

Oh, how his father laughed! "Poor, poor Popsey!" he cried. "Diddums! Diddums! Diddums think he'd walky-palky up to Evvink!" And his mother, also convulsed with laughter, appeared on the steps of Agathox Lodge. "Don't, Bob!" she gasped. "Don't be so naughty! Oh, you'll kill me! Oh, leave the boy alone!"

But all that evening the joke was kept up. The father implored to be taken too. Was it a very tiring walk? Need one wipe one's shoes on the door-mat? And the boy went to bed feeling faint and sore, and thankful for only one thing—that he had not said a word about the omnibus. It was a hoax, yet through his dreams it grew more and more real, and the streets of Surbiton, through which he saw it driving, seemed instead to become hoaxes and shadows. And very early in the morning he woke with a cry, for he had had a glimpse of its destination.

He struck a match, and its light fell not only on his watch but also on his calendar, so that he knew it to be half-an-hour to sunrise. It was pitch dark, for the fog had come down from London in the night, and all Surbiton was wrapped in its embraces. Yet he sprang out and dressed himself, for he was determined to settle once for all which was real: the omnibus or the streets. "I shall be a fool one way or the other," he thought, "until I know." Soon he was shivering in the road under the gas lamp that guarded the entrance to the alley.

To enter the alley itself required some courage. Not only was it horribly dark, but he now realized that it was an im-

[3]*omnibus:* a large coach

possible terminus for an omnibus. If it had not been for a policeman, whom he heard approaching through the fog, he would never have made the attempt. The next moment he had made the attempt and failed. Nothing. Nothing but a blank alley and a very silly boy gaping at its dirty floor. It *was* a hoax. "I'll tell papa and mamma," he decided. "I deserve it. I deserve that they should know. I am too silly to be alive." And he went back to the gate of Agathox Lodge.

There he remembered that his watch was fast. The sun was not risen; it would not rise for two minutes. "Give the bus every chance," he thought cynically, and returned into the alley.

But the omnibus was there.

II

It had two horses, whose sides were still smoking from their journey, and its two great lamps shone through the fog against the alley's walls, changing their cobwebs and moss into tissues of fairyland. The driver was huddled up in a cape. He faced the blank wall, and how he had managed to drive in so neatly and so silently was one of the many things that the boy never discovered. Nor could he imagine how ever he would drive out.

"Please," his voice quavered through the foul brown air, "Please, is that an omnibus?"

"Omnibus west," said the driver, without turning round. There was a moment's silence. The policeman passed, coughing, by the entrance of the alley. The boy crouched in the shadow, for he did not want to be found out. He was pretty sure, too, that it was a Pirate; nothing else, he reasoned, would go from such odd places and at such odd hours.

"About when do you start?" He tried to sound nonchalant.

"At sunrise."

"How far do you go?"

"The whole way."

"And I can have a return ticket which will bring me all the way back?"

"You can."

"Do you know, I half think I'll come." The driver made no answer. The sun must have risen, for he unhitched the brake. And scarcely had the boy jumped in before the omnibus was off.

How? Did it turn? There was no room. Did it go forward? There was a blank wall. Yet it was moving—moving at a stately pace through the fog, which had turned from brown to yellow. The thought of warm bed and warmer breakfast made the boy feel faint. He wished he had not come. His parents would not have approved. He would have gone back to them if the weather had not made it impossible. The solitude was terrible; he was the only passenger. And the omnibus, though well-built, was cold and somewhat musty. He drew his coat round him, and in so doing chanced to feel his pocket. It was empty. He had forgotten his purse.

"Stop!" he shouted. "Stop!" And then, being of a polite disposition, he glanced up at the painted notice-board so that he might call the driver by name. "Mr. Browne! stop; O, do please stop!"

Mr. Browne did not stop, but he opened a little window and looked in at the boy. His face was a surprise, so kind it was and modest.

"Mr. Browne, I've left my purse behind. I've not got a penny. I can't pay for the ticket. Will you take my watch, please? I am in the most awful hole."

"Tickets on this line," said the driver, "whether single or return, can be purchased by coinage from no terrene mint. And a chronometer,[4] though it had solaced the vigils of Charlemagne, or measured the slumbers of Laura, can acquire by no mutation[5] the doublecake that charms the fangless Cerberus[6] of Heaven!" So saying, he handed in the necessary ticket, and, while the boy said "Thank you," continued:

[4]*chronometer:* timepiece
[5]*mutation:* change
[6]*Cerberus:* in classical mythology, the three-headed dog who guarded the entrance to Hades

"Titular pretensions, I know it well, are vanity. Yet they merit no censure when uttered on a laughing lip, and in an homonymous[7] world are in some sort useful, since they do serve to distinguish one Jack from his fellow. Remember me, therefore, as Sir Thomas Browne."

"Are you a Sir? Oh, sorry!" He had heard of these gentlemen drivers. "It *is* good of you about the ticket. But if you go on at this rate, however does your bus pay?"

"It does not pay. It was not intended to pay. Many are the faults of my equipage; it is compounded too curiously of foreign woods; its cushions tickle erudition[8] rather than promote repose; and my horses are nourished not on the evergreen pastures of the moment, but on the dried bents and clovers of Latinity. But that it pays!—that error at all events was never intended and never attained."

"Sorry again," said the boy rather hopelessly. Sir Thomas looked sad, fearing that, even for a moment, he had been the cause of sadness. He invited the boy to come up and sit beside him on the box, and together they journeyed on through the fog, which was now changing from yellow to white. There were no houses by the road; so it must be either Putney Heath or Wimbledon Common.

"Have you been a driver always?"

"I was a physician once."

"But why did you stop? Weren't you good?"

"As a healer of bodies I had scant success, and several score of my patients preceded me. But as a healer of the spirit I have succeeded beyond my hopes and my deserts. For though my draughts were not better nor subtler than those of other men, yet, by reason of the cunning goblets wherein I offered them, the queasy soul was ofttimes tempted to sip and be refreshed."

"The queasy soul," he murmured; "if the sun sets with trees in front of it, and you suddenly come strange all over, is that a queasy soul?"

[7]*homonymous:* having the same name
[8]*erudition:* learning

"Have you felt that?"

"Why yes."

After a pause he told the boy a little, a very little, about the journey's end. But they did not chatter much, for the boy, when he liked a person, would as soon sit silent in his company as speak, and this, he discovered, was also the mind of Sir Thomas Browne and of many others with whom he was to be acquainted. He heard, however, about the young man Shelley, who was now quite a famous person, with a carriage of his own, and about some of the other drivers who are in the service of the Company. Meanwhile the light grew stronger, though the fog did not disperse. It was now more like mist than fog, and at times would travel quickly across them, as if it was part of a cloud. They had been ascending, too, in a most puzzling way; for over two hours the horses had been pulling against the collar, and even if it were Richmond Hill they ought to have been at the top long ago. Perhaps it was Epsom, or even the North Downs; yet the air seemed keener than that which blows on either. And as to the name of their destination, Sir Thomas Browne was silent.

Crash!

"Thunder, by Jove!" said the boy, "and not so far off either. Listen to the echoes! It's more like mountains."

He thought, not very vividly, of his father and mother. He saw them sitting down to sausages and listening to the storm. He saw his own empty place. Then there would be questions, alarms, theories, jokes, consolations. They would expect him back at lunch. To lunch he would not come, nor to tea, but he would be in for dinner, and so his day's truancy would be over. If he had had his purse he would have bought them presents—not that he should have known what to get them.

Crash!

The peal and the lightning came together. The cloud quivered as if it were alive, and torn streamers of mist rushed past. "Are you afraid?" asked Sir Thomas Browne.

"What is there to be afraid of? Is it much farther?"

The horses of the omnibus stopped just as a ball of fire burst up and exploded with a ringing noise that was deafening but clear, like the noise of a blacksmith's forge. All the cloud was shattered.

"Oh, listen, Sir Thomas Browne! No, I mean look; we shall get a view at last. No, I mean listen; that sounds like a rainbow!"

The noise had died into the faintest murmur, beneath which another murmur grew, spreading stealthily, steadily, in a curve that widened but did not vary. And in widening curves a rainbow was spreading from the horses' feet into the dissolving mists.

"But how beautiful! What colours! Where will it stop? It is more like the rainbows you can tread on. More like dreams."

The colour and the sound grew together. The rainbow spanned an enormous gulf. Clouds rushed under it and were pierced by it, and still it grew, reaching forward, conquering the darkness, until it touched something that seemed more solid than a cloud.

The boy stood up. "What is that out there?" he called. "What does it rest on, out at that other end?"

In the morning sunshine a precipice shone forth beyond the gulf. A precipice—or was it a castle? The horses moved. They set their feet upon the rainbow.

"Oh, look!" the boy shouted. "Oh, listen! Those caves—or are they gateways? Oh, look between those cliffs at those ledges. I see people! I see trees!"

"Look also below," whispered Sir Thomas. "Neglect not the diviner Acheron."

The boy looked below, past the flames of the rainbow that licked against their wheels. The gulf also had cleared, and in its depths there flowed an everlasting river. One sunbeam entered and struck a green pool, and as they passed over he saw three maidens rise to the surface of the pool, singing, and playing with something that glistened like a ring.

"You down in the water—" he called.

They answered, "You up on the bridge—" There was a burst of music. "You up on the bridge, good luck to you. Truth in the depth, truth on the height."

"You down in the water, what are you doing?"

Sir Thomas Browne replied: "They sport in the mancipiary possession of their gold"; and the omnibus arrived.

III

The boy was in disgrace. He sat locked up in the nursery of Agathox Lodge, learning poetry for a punishment. His father had said, "My boy! I can pardon anything but untruthfulness," and had caned him, saying at each stroke, "There is *no* omnibus, *no* driver, *no* bridge, *no* mountain; you are a *truant*, a *guttersnipe*, a *liar*." His father could be very stern at times. His mother had begged him to say he was sorry. But he could not say that. It was the greatest day of his life, in spite of the caning and the poetry at the end of it.

He had returned punctually at sunset—driven not by Sir Thomas Browne, but by a maiden lady who was full of quiet fun. They had talked of omnibuses and also of barouche[9] landaus. How far away her gentle voice seemed now! Yet it was scarcely three hours since he had left her up the alley.

His mother called through the door. "Dear, you are to come down and to bring your poetry with you."

He came down, and found that Mr. Bons was in the smoking-room with his father. It had been a dinner party.

"Here is the great traveller!" said his father grimly. "Here is the young gentleman who drives in an omnibus over rainbows, while young ladies sing to him." Pleased with his wit, he laughed.

"After all," said Mr. Bons, smiling, "there is something a little like it in Wagner. It is odd how, in quite illiterate minds, you will find glimmers of Artistic Truth. The case interests me. Let me plead for the culprit. We have all romanced in our time, haven't we?"

"Hear how kind Mr. Bons is," said his mother, while his father said, "Very well. Let him say his Poem, and that will do. He is going away to my sister on Tuesday, and *she* will cure him of this alley-slopering." (Laughter.) "Say your Poem."

The boy began, "'Standing aloof in giant ignorance.'"

His father laughed again—roared. "One for you, my son!

[9]*barouche:* a four-wheeled carriage

'Standing aloof in giant ignorance!' I never knew these poets talked sense. Just describes you. Here, Bons, you go in for poetry. Put him through it, will you, while I fetch up the whisky?"

"Yes, give me the Keats," said Mr. Bons. "Let him say his Keats to me."

So for a few moments the wise man and the ignorant boy were left alone in the smoking-room.

"'Standing aloof in giant ignorance, of thee I dream and of the Cyclades, as one who sits ashore and longs perchance to visit—'"

"Quite right. To visit what?"

"'To visit dolphin coral in deep seas,'" said the boy, and burst into tears.

"Come, come! why do you cry?"

"Because—because all these words that only rhymed before, now that I've come back they're me."

Mr. Bons laid the Keats down. The case was more interesting than he had expected. "*You?*" he exclaimed. "This sonnet, *you?*"

"Yes—and look further on: 'Aye, on the shores of darkness there is light, and precipices show untrodden green.' It *is* so, sir. All these things are true."

"I never doubted it," said Mr. Bons, with closed eyes.

"You—then you believe me? You believe in the omnibus and the driver and the storm and that return ticket I got for nothing and—"

"Tut, tut! No more of your yarns, my boy, I meant that I never doubted the essential truth of Poetry. Some day, when you have read more, you will understand what I mean."

"But Mr. Bons, it *is* so. There *is* light upon the shores of darkness. I have seen it coming. Light and a wind."

"Nonsense," said Mr. Bons.

"If I had stopped! They tempted me. They told me to give up my ticket—for you cannot come back if you lose your ticket. They called from the river for it, and indeed I was tempted, for I have never been so happy as among those precipices. But I thought of my mother and father, and that I must fetch them. Yet they will not come, though the road starts opposite our house. It has all happened as the people up there warned me, and Mr. Bons has disbelieved me like every one else. I have been caned. I shall never see that mountain again."

"What's that about me?" said Mr. Bons, sitting up in his chair very suddenly.

"I told them about you, and how clever you were, and how many books you had, and they said, 'Mr. Bons will certainly disbelieve you.'"

"Stuff and nonsense, my young friend. You grow impertinent. I—well—I will settle the matter. Not a word to your father. I will cure you. To-morrow evening I will myself call here to take you for a walk, and at sunset we will go up this alley opposite and hunt for your omnibus, you silly little boy."

His face grew serious, for the boy was not disconcerted, but leapt about the room singing, "Joy joy! I told them you would believe me. We will drive together over the rainbow. I told them that you would come." After all, could there by anything in the story? Wagner? Keats? Shelley? Sir Thomas Browne? Certainly the case was interesting.

And on the morrow evening, though it was pouring with rain, Mr. Bons did not omit to call at Agathox Lodge.

The boy was ready, bubbling with excitement, and skipping about in a way that rather vexed the President of the Literary Society. They took a turn down Buckingham Park Road, and then—having seen that no one was watching them—slipped up the alley. Naturally enough (for the sun was setting) they ran straight against the omnibus.

"Good heavens!" exclaimed Mr. Bons. "Good gracious heavens!"

It was not the omnibus in which the boy had driven first, nor yet that in which he had returned. There were three horses—black, gray, and white, the gray being the finest. The driver, who turned round at the mention of goodness and of heaven, was a sallow man with terrifying jaws and sunken eyes. Mr. Bons, on seeing him, gave a cry as if of recognition, and began to tremble violently.

The boy jumped in.

"Is it possible?" cried Mr. Bons. "Is the impossible possible?"

"Sir; come in, sir. It is such a fine omnibus. Oh, here is his name—Dan some one."[10]

Mr. Bons sprang in too. A blast of wind immediately slammed the omnibus door, and the shock jerked down all the omnibus blinds, which were very weak on their springs.

"Dan . . . Show me. Good gracious heavens! we're moving."

"Hooray!" said the boy.

Mr. Bons became flustered. He had not intended to be kidnapped. He could not find the door-handle, nor push up the blinds. The omnibus was quite dark, and by the time he had struck a match, night had come on outside also. They were moving rapidly.

"A strange, a memorable adventure," he said, surveying the interior of the omnibus, which was large, roomy, and constructed with extreme regularity, every part exactly answering to every other part. Over the door (the handle of which was outside) was written, "Lasciate ogni baldanza voi che entrate"[11]—at least, that was what was written, but Mr. Bons said that it was Lashy arty something, and that baldanza[12] was a mistake for speranza.[13] His voice sounded as if he was in church. Meanwhile, the boy called to the cadaverous[14] driver for two return tickets. They were handed in without a word. Mr. Bons covered his face with his hand and again trembled. "Do you know who that is!" he whispered, when the little window had shut upon them. "It is the impossible."

"Well, I don't like him as much as Sir Thomas Browne, though I shouldn't be surprised if he had even more in him."

"More in him?" He stamped irritably. "By accident you have made the greatest discovery of the century, and all you can say is that there is more in this man. Do you remember those vellum[15] books in my library, stamped with red

[10]*Dan some one:* Dante
[11]*Lasciate . . . entrate:* Abandon all courage, ye who enter here
[12]*baldanza:* courage
[13]*speranza:* hope
[14]*cadaverous:* pale, death-like
[15]*vellum:* rich calfskin binding

lilies? This—sit still, I bring you stupendous news!—*this is the man who wrote them.*"

The boy sat quite still. "I wonder if we shall see Mrs. Gamp?" he asked, after a civil pause.

"Mrs. —?"

"Mrs. Gamp and Mrs. Harris. I like Mrs. Harris. I came upon them quite suddenly. Mrs. Gamp's bandboxes have moved over the rainbow so badly. All the bottoms have fallen out, and two of the pippins off her bedstead tumbled into the stream."

"Out there sits the man who wrote my vellum books!" thundered Mr. Bons, "and you talk to me of Dickens and of Mrs. Gamp?"

"I know Mrs. Gamp so well," he apologized. "I could not help being glad to see her. I recognized her voice. She was telling Mrs. Harris about Mrs. Prig."

"Did you spend the whole day in her elevating company?"

"Oh, no. I raced. I met a man who took me out beyond to a race-course. You run, and there are dolphins out at sea."

"Indeed. Do you remember the man's name?"

"Achilles. No; he was later. Tom Jones."

Mr. Bons sighed heavily. "Well, my lad, you have made a miserable mess of it. Think of a cultured person with your opportunities! A cultured person would have known all these characters and known what to have said to each. He would not have wasted his time with a Mrs. Gamp or a Tom Jones. The creations of Homer, of Shakespeare, and of Him who drives us now, would alone have contented him. He would not have raced. He would have asked intelligent questions."

"But, Mr. Bons," said the boy humbly, "you will be a cultured person. I told them so."

"True, true, and I beg you not to disgrace me when we arrive. No gossiping. No running. Keep close to my side, and never speak to these Immortals unless they speak to you. Yes, and give me the return tickets. You will be losing them."

The boy surrendered the tickets, but felt a little sore. After all, he had found the way to this place. It was hard first to be disbelieved and then to be lectured. Meanwhile, the rain had stopped, and moonlight crept into the omnibus through the cracks in the blinds.

"But how is there to be a rainbow?" cried the boy.

"You distract me," snapped Mr. Bons. "I wish to meditate on beauty. I wish to goodness I was with a reverent and sympathetic person."

The lad bit his lip. He made a hundred good resolutions. He would imitate Mr. Bons all the visit. He would not laugh, or run, or sing, or do any of the vulgar things that must have disgusted his new friends last time. He would be very careful to pronounce their names properly, and to remember who knew whom. Achilles did not know Tom Jones—at least, so Mr. Bons said. The Duchess of Malfi was older than Mrs. Gamp—at least, so Mr. Bons said. He would be self-conscious, reticent, and prim. He would never say he liked any one. Yet, when the blind flew up at a chance touch of his head, all these good resolutions went to the winds, for the omnibus had reached the summit of a moonlit hill, and there was the chasm, and there, across it, stood the old precipices, dreaming, with their feet in the everlasting river. He exclaimed, "The mountain! Listen to the new tune in the water! Look at the camp fires in the ravines," and Mr. Bons, after a hasty glance, retorted, "Water? Camp fires? Ridiculous rubbish. Hold your tongue. There is nothing at all."

Yet, under his eyes, a rainbow formed, compounded not of sunlight and storm, but of moonlight and the spray of the river. The three horses put their feet upon it. He thought it the finest rainbow he had seen, but did not dare to say so, since Mr. Bons said that nothing was there. He leant out—the window had opened—and sang the tune that rose from the sleeping waters.

"The prelude to Rhinegold?" said Mr. Bons suddenly. "Who taught you these *leitmotifs?*"[16] He, too, looked out of the window. Then he behaved very oddly. He gave a choking cry, and fell back on to the omnibus floor. He writhed and kicked. His face was green.

[16]*leitmotifs:* musical passages associated with certain characters in Wagner's operas. In *The Rhinegold* a rainbow bridge is built across the Rhine to Valhalla, the castle of the gods.

"Does the bridge make you dizzy?" the boy asked.

"Dizzy!" gasped Mr. Bons. "I want to go back. Tell the driver."

But the driver shook his head.

"We are nearly there," said the boy. "They are asleep. Shall I call? They will be so pleased to see you, for I have prepared them."

Mr. Bons moved. They moved over the lunar rainbow, which ever and ever broke away behind their wheels. How still the night was! Who would be sentry at the Gate?

"I am coming," he shouted, again forgetting the hundred resolutions. "I am returning—I, the boy."

"The boy is returning," cried a voice to other voices, who repeated, "The boy is returning."

"I am bringing Mr. Bons with me."

Silence.

"I should have said Mr. Bons is bringing me with him."

Profound silence.

"Who stands sentry?"

"Achilles."

And on the rocky causeway, close to the springing of the rainbow bridge, he saw a young man who carried a wonderful shield.

"Mr. Bons, it is Achilles, armed."

"I want to go back," said Mr. Bons.

The last fragment of the rainbow melted, the wheels sang upon the living rock, the door of the omnibus burst open. Out leapt the boy—he could not resist—and sprang to meet the warrior, who, stooping suddenly, caught him on his shield.

"Achilles!" he cried, "let me get down, for I am ignorant and vulgar, and I must wait for that Mr. Bons of whom I told you yesterday."

But Achilles raised him aloft. He crouched on the wonderful shield, on heroes and burning cities, on vineyards graven in gold, on every dear passion, every joy, on the entire image of the Mountain that he had discovered, encircled, like it, with an everlasting stream. "No, no," he protested, "I am not worthy. It is Mr. Bons who must be up here."

But Mr. Bons was whimpering, and Achilles trumpeted and cried, "Stand upright upon my shield!"

"Sir, I did not mean to stand! something made me stand. Sir, why do you delay? Here is only the great Achilles, whom you knew."

Mr. Bons screamed, "I see no one. I see nothing. I want to go back." Then he cried to the driver, "Save me! Let me stop in your chariot. I have honoured you. I have quoted you. I have bound you in vellum. Take me back to my world."

The driver replied, "I am the means and not the end. I am the food and not the life. Stand by yourself, as that boy has stood. I cannot save you. For poetry is a spirit; and they that would worship it must worship in spirit and in truth."

Mr. Bons—he could not resist—crawled out of the beautiful omnibus. His face appeared, gaping horribly. His hands followed, one gripping the step, the other beating the air. Now his shoulders emerged, his chest, his stomach. With a shriek of "I see London," he fell—fell against the hard, moonlit rock, fell into it as if it were water, fell through it, vanished, and was seen by the boy no more.

"Where have you fallen to, Mr. Bons? Here is a procession arriving to honour you with music and torches. Here come the men and women whose names you know. The mountain is awake, the river is awake, over the racecourse the sea is awaking those dolphins, and it is all for you. They want you—"

There was the touch of fresh leaves on his forehead. Some one had crowned him.

ΤΕΛΟΣ[17]

From the *Kingston Gazette*, *Surbiton Times*,
and *Raynes Park Observer*

> The body of Mr. Septimus Bons has been found in a shockingly mutilated condition in the vicinity of the Bermondsey gasworks.

[17]ΤΕΛΟΣ: the end, consummation (Greek)

> The deceased's pockets contained a sovereign-purse, a silver cigar-case, a bijou[18] pronouncing dictionary, and a couple of omnibus tickets. The unfortunate gentleman had apparently been hurled from a considerable height. Foul play is suspected, and a thorough investigation is pending by the authorities.

[18]*bijou:* small

FOR DISCUSSION

1. At what point in the story do the real and unreal become one for the boy? What object of the real world is the means of the boy's entry into the unreal world? Where does this object come from? What is the reaction of the adults to it?
2. What aspects of the boy's real life make him susceptible to the kind of experience he has? What is it that "first stirred desires within the boy"?
3. What qualities of personality does Sir Thomas Browne reveal in his trip with the boy? What does his language show about him? What do you think accounts for the congeniality between the boy and Sir Thomas Browne?
4. What does the celestial region look like? Who are the inhabitants of this region? How do you account for the boy's lack of fear or hesitation in this strange environment?
5. Compare the reactions of the three adults to the boy's account of his trip. How is he punished? In what way does the punishment backfire? What characteristics of the father are revealed by his treatment of the boy after his return?
6. Why does Mr. Bons consent to go with the boy on the second day? What does his warning to the boy not to tell his father reveal about Bons? What is Bons's reaction to the boy's account of his acquaintances of the previous day? What warning does Bons give to the boy before their arrival? Why is the boy unable to follow it?
7. What difference is there in the boy's and Mr. Bons's reaction to the celestial regions? Find details earlier in the story which prepare you for Bons's reaction. In the light of his interest in literature and his considerable knowledge, why do you think he

was so fearful? Explain the meaning of the driver's answer to Bons when he demanded to be taken back to his world. How does Bons's fear lead to his death?

8. Since this is an allegory (see page 383), the various parts of the story have more than a literal meaning. Suggest possible allegorical interpretations of the description of the celestial regions; the free ticket and the lack of ticket sale at the other end; Bons's concern with the status of the people to whom the boy spoke; Bons's death.

FOR COMPOSITION

1. Rewrite Sir Thomas Browne's speeches to the boy in ordinary conversational English.
2. Write a character sketch of Sir Thomas Browne. Do not overlook the humor in the caricature-like presentation of Browne and the remarkable relationship he is able to achieve with the eager, naive boy.

Graham Greene

The End of the Party

Peter Morton woke with a start to face the first light. Through the window he could see a bare bough dropping across a frame of silver. Rain tapped against the glass. It was January the fifth.

He looked across a table, on which a night-light had guttered into a pool of water, at the other bed. Francis Morton was still asleep, and Peter lay down again with his eyes on his brother. It amused him to imagine that it was himself whom he watched, the same hair, the same eyes, the same lips and line of cheek. But the thought soon palled, and the mind went back to the fact which lent the day importance. It was the fifth of January. He could hardly believe that a year had passed since Mrs. Henne-Falcon had given her last children's party.

Francis turned suddenly upon his back and threw an arm across his face, blocking his mouth. Peter's heart began to beat fast, not with pleasure now but with uneasiness. He sat up and called across the table, "Wake up." Francis's shoulders shook and he waved a clenched fist in the air, but his eyes remained closed. To Peter Morton the whole room seemed suddenly to darken, and he had the impression of a great bird swooping. He cried again, "Wake up," and once more there was silver light and the touch of rain on the windows. Francis rubbed his eyes. "Did you call out?" he asked.

"You are having a bad dream," Peter said with confidence. Already experience had taught him how far their minds reflected each other. But he was the elder, by a matter of minutes, and that brief extra interval of light, while his brother still struggled in pain and darkness, had given him self-reliance and an instinct of protection towards the other who was afraid of so many things.

"I dreamed that I was dead," Francis said.

"What was it like?" Peter asked with curiosity.

"I can't remember," Francis said, and his eyes turned with relief to the silver of day, as he allowed the fragmentary memories to fade.

"You dreamed of a big bird."

"Did I?" Francis accepted his brother's knowledge without question, and for a little the two lay silent in bed facing each other, the same green eyes, the same nose tilting at the tip, the same firm lips parted, and the same premature modelling of the chin. The fifth of January, Peter thought again, his mind drifting idly from the image of cakes to the prizes which might be won. Egg-and-spoon races, spearing apples in basins of water, blind-man's buff.

"I don't want to go," Francis said suddenly. "I suppose Joyce will be there . . . Mabel Warren." Hateful to him, the thought of a party shared with those two. They were older than he. Joyce was eleven and Mabel Warren thirteen. Their long pigtails swung superciliously to a masculine stride. Their sex humiliated him, as they watched him fumble with his egg, from under lowered scornful lids. And last year . . . he turned his face away from Peter, his cheeks scarlet.

"What's the matter?" Peter asked.

"Oh, nothing. I don't think I'm well, I've got a cold. I oughtn't to go to the party."

Peter was puzzled. "But, Francis, is it a bad cold?"

"It will be a bad cold if I go to the party. Perhaps I shall die."

"Then you mustn't go," Peter said with decision, prepared to solve all difficulties with one plain sentence, and Francis let his nerves relax in a delicious relief, ready to leave everything to Peter. But though he was grateful he did not turn his face towards his brother. His cheeks still bore the badge of a shameful memory, of the game of hide-and-seek last year in the darkened house, and of how he had screamed when Mabel Warren put her hand suddenly upon his arm. He had not heard her coming. Girls were like that. Their shoes never squeaked. No boards whined under their tread. They slunk like cats on padded claws. When the nurse came in with hot water Francis lay tranquil, leaving everything to Peter. Peter said, "Nurse, Francis has got a cold."

The tall starched woman laid the towels across the cans and said, without turning, "The washing won't be back till tomorrow. You must lend him some of your handkerchiefs."

"But, Nurse," Peter asked, "hadn't he better stay in bed?"

"We'll take him for a good walk this morning," the nurse said. "Wind'll blow away the germs. Get up now, both of you," and she closed the door behind her.

"I'm sorry," Peter said, and then, worried at the sight of a face creased again by misery and foreboding, "Why don't you just stay in bed? I'll tell mother you felt too ill to get up." But such a rebellion against destiny was not in Francis's power. Besides, if he stayed in bed they would come up and tap his chest and put a thermometer in his mouth and look at his tongue, and they would discover that he was malingering.[1] It was true that he felt ill, a sick empty sensation in his stomach and a rapidly beating heart, but he knew that the cause was only fear, fear of the party, fear of being made to hide by himself in the dark, uncompanioned by Peter and with no night-light to make a blessed breach.

"No, I'll get up," he said, and then with sudden desperation, "But I won't go to Mrs. Henne-Falcon's party. I swear on the Bible I won't." Now surely all would be well, he thought. God would not allow him to break so solemn an oath. He would show him a way. There was all the morning before him and all the afternoon until four o'clock. No need to worry now when the grass was still crisp with the early frost. Anything might happen. He might cut himself or break his leg or really catch a bad cold. God would manage somehow.

He had such confidence in God that when at breakfast his mother said, "I hear you have a cold, Francis," he made light of it. "We should have heard more about it," his mother said with irony, "if there was not a party this evening," and Francis smiled uneasily, amazed and daunted by her ignorance of him. His happiness would have lasted longer if, out for a walk that morning, he had not met Joyce. He was alone

[1]*malingering:* pretending illness

with his nurse, for Peter had leave to finish a rabbit-hutch in the woodshed. If Peter had been there he would have cared less; the nurse was Peter's nurse also, but now it was as though she were employed only for his sake, because he could not be trusted to go for a walk alone. Joyce was only two years older and she was by herself.

She came striding towards them, pigtails flapping. She glanced scornfully at Francis and spoke with ostentation to the nurse. "Hello, Nurse. Are you bringing Francis to the party this evening? Mabel and I are coming." And she was off again down the street in the direction of Mabel Warren's home, consciously alone and self-sufficient in the long empty road. "Such a nice girl," the nurse said. But Francis was silent, feeling again the jump-jump of his heart, realizing how soon the hour of the party would arrive. God had done nothing for him, and the minutes flew.

They flew too quickly to plan any evasion, or even to prepare his heart for the coming ordeal. Panic nearly overcame him when, all unready, he found himself standing on the door-step, with coat-collar turned up against a cold wind, and the nurse's electric torch making a short luminous trail through the darkness. Behind him were the lights of the hall and the sound of a servant laying the table for dinner, which his mother and father would eat alone. He was nearly overcome by a desire to run back into the house and call out to his mother than he would not go to the party, that he dared not go. They could not make him go. He could almost hear himself saying those final words, breaking down for ever, as he knew instinctively, the barrier of ignorance that saved his mind from his parents' knowledge. "I'm afraid of going. I won't go. I daren't go. They'll make me hide in the dark, and I'm afraid of the dark. I'll scream and scream and scream." He could see the expression of amazement on his mother's face, and then the cold confidence of a grown-up's retort. "Don't be silly. You must go. We've accepted Mrs. Henne-Falcon's invitation."

But they couldn't make him go; hesitating on the door-step while the nurse's feet crunched across the frost-covered grass to the gate, he knew that. He would answer, "You can say I'm ill. I won't go. I'm afraid of the dark." And his mother, "Don't be silly. You know there's nothing to be afraid of in the dark." But he knew the falsity of that reasoning; he knew how they taught also that there was nothing to fear in death, and how fearfully they avoided the idea of it. But they couldn't make him go to the party. "I'll scream. I'll scream."

"Francis, come along." He heard the nurse's voice across the dimly phosphorescent[2] lawn and saw the small yellow circle of her torch wheel from tree to shrub and back to tree again. "I'm coming," he called with despair, leaving the lighted doorway of the house; he couldn't bring himself to lay bare his last secrets and end reserve between his mother and himself, for there was still in the last resort a further appeal possible to Mrs. Henne-Falcon. He comforted himself with that, as he advanced steadily across the hall, very small, towards her enormous bulk. His heart beat unevenly, but he had control now over his voice, as he said with meticulous accent, "Good evening, Mrs. Henne-Falcon. It was very good of you to ask me to your party." With his strained face lifted towards the curve of her breasts, and his polite set speech, he was like an old withered man. For Francis mixed very little with other children. As a twin he was in many ways an only child. To address Peter was to speak to his own image in a mirror, an image a little altered by a flaw in the glass, so as to throw back less a likeness of what he was than of what he wished to be, what he would be without his unreasoning fear of darkness, footsteps of strangers, the flight of bats in dusk-filled gardens.

"Sweet child," said Mrs. Henne-Falcon absent-mindedly, before, with a wave of her arms, as though the children were a flock of chickens, she whirled them into her set programme of entertainments: egg-and-spoon races, three-legged races, the spearing of apples, games which held for Francis nothing worse than humiliation. And in the frequent intervals when nothing was required of him and he could stand alone in corners as far removed as possible from Mabel Warren's scornful gaze, he was able to plan how he might avoid the approaching terror of the dark. He knew there was nothing

[2]*phosphorescent:* glowing with light

to fear until after tea, and not until he was sitting down in a pool of yellow radiance cast by the ten candles on Colin Henne-Falcon's birthday cake did he become fully conscious of the imminence of what he feared. Through the confusion of his brain, now assailed suddenly by a dozen contradictory plans, he heard Joyce's high voice down the table. "After tea we are going to play hide-and-seek in the dark."

"Oh, no," Peter said, watching Francis's troubled face with pity and an imperfect understanding, "don't let's. We play that every year."

"But it's in the programme," cried Mabel Warren. "I saw it myself. I looked over Mrs. Henne-Falcon's shoulder. Five o'clock, tea. A quarter to six to half-past, hide-and-seek in the dark. It's all written down in the programme."

Peter did not argue, for if hide-and-seek had been inserted in Mrs. Henne-Falcon's programme, nothing which he could say could avert it. He asked for another piece of birthday cake and sipped his tea slowly. Perhaps it might be possible to delay the game for a quarter of an hour, allow Francis at least a few extra minutes to form a plan, but even in that Peter failed, for children were already leaving the table in twos and threes. It was his third failure, and again, the reflection of an image in another's mind, he saw a great bird darken his brother's face with its wings. But he upbraided himself silently for his folly, and finished his cake encouraged by the memory of that adult refrain, "There's nothing to fear in the dark." The last to leave the table, the brothers came together to the hall to meet the mustering and impatient eyes of Mrs. Henne-Falcon.

"And now," she said, "we will play hide-and-seek in the dark."

Peter watched his brother and saw, as he had expected, the lip tighten. Francis, he knew, had feared this moment from the beginning of the party, had tried to meet it with courage and had abandoned the attempt. He must have prayed desperately for cunning to evade the game, which was now welcomed with cries of excitement by all the other children. "Oh, do let's." "We must pick sides." "Is any of the house out of bounds?" "Where shall home be?"

"I think," said Francis Morton, approaching Mrs. Henne-Falcon, his eyes focused unwaveringly on her exuberant breasts, "it will be no use my playing. My nurse will be calling for me very soon."

"Oh, but your nurse can wait, Francis," said Mrs. Henne-Falcon absent-mindedly, while she clapped her hands together to summon to her side a few children who were already straying up the wide staircase to upper floors. "Your mother will never mind."

That had been the limit of Francis's cunning. He had refused to believe that so well prepared an excuse could fail. All that he could say now, still in the precise tone which other children hated, thinking it a symbol of conceit, was, "I think I had better not play." He stood motionless, retaining, though afraid, unmoved features. But the knowledge of his terror, or the reflection of the terror itself, reached his brother's brain. For the moment, Peter Morton could have cried aloud with the fear of bright lights going out, leaving him alone in an island of dark surrounded by the gentle lapping of strange footsteps. Then he remembered that the fear was not his own, but his brother's. He said impulsively to Mrs. Henne-Falcon, "Please. I don't think Francis should play. The dark makes him jump so." They were the wrong words. Six children began to sing, "Cowardy, cowardy custard," turning torturing faces with the vacancy of wide sunflowers toward Francis Morton.

Without looking at his brother, Francis said, "Of course I will play. I am not afraid. I only thought . . ." But he was already forgotten by his human tormentors and was able in loneliness to contemplate the approach of the spiritual, the more unbounded, torture. The children scrambled round Mrs. Henne-Falcon, their shrill voices pecking at her with questions and suggestions. "Yes, anywhere in the house. We will turn out all the lights. Yes, you can hide in the cupboards. You must stay hidden as long as you can. There will be no home."

Peter, too, stood apart, ashamed of the clumsy manner in which he had tried to help his brother. Now he could feel, creeping in at the corners of his brain, all Francis's resentment of his championing. Several children ran upstairs, and the lights on the top floor went out. Then darkness came down like the wings of a bat and settled on the landing. Others began to put out the lights at the edge of the hall, till the children were all gathered in the central radiance of the chandelier, while the bats squatted round on hooded wings and waited for that, too, to be extinguished.

"You and Francis are on the hiding side," a tall girl said, and then the light was gone, and the carpet wavered under his feet with the sibilance[3] of footfalls, like small cold draughts, creeping away into corners.

"Where's Francis?" he wondered. "If I join him he'll be less frightened of all these sounds." "These sounds" were the casing of silence. The squeak of a loose board, the cautious closing of a cupboard door, the whine of a finger drawn along polished wood.

Peter stood in the centre of the dark deserted floor, not listening but waiting for the idea of his brother's whereabouts to enter his brain. But Francis crouched with fingers on his ears, eyes uselessly closed, mind numbed against impressions, and only a sense of strain could cross the gap of dark. Then a voice called "Coming," and as though his brother's self-possession had been shattered by the sudden cry, Peter Morton jumped with his fear. But it was not his own fear. What in his brother was a burning panic, admitting no ideas except those which added to the flame, was in him an altruistic[4] emotion that left the reason unimpaired. "Where, if I were Francis, should I hide?" Such, roughly, was his thought. And because he was, if not Francis himself, at least a mirror to him, the answer was immediate. "Between the oak bookcase on the left of the study door and the leather settee." Peter Morton was unsurprised by the swiftness of the response. Between the twins there could be no jargon of telepathy.[5] They had been together in the womb, and they could not be parted.

Peter Morton tiptoed towards Francis's hiding place. Oc-

[3]*sibilance:* whispering sound
[4]*altruistic:* unselfish concern for others
[5]*telepathy:* unspoken understanding

casionally a board rattled, and because he feared to be caught by one of the soft questers through the dark, he bent and untied his laces. A tag struck the floor and the metallic sound set a host of cautious feet moving in his direction. But by that time he was in his stockings and would have laughed inwardly at the pursuit had not the noise of someone stumbling on his abandoned shoes made his heart trip in the reflection of another's surprise. No more boards revealed Peter Morton's progress. On stockinged feet he moved silently and unerringly towards his object. Instinct told him that he was near the wall, and, extending a hand, he laid the fingers across his brother's face.

Francis did not cry out, but the leap of his own heart revealed to Peter a proportion of Francis's terror. "It's all right," he whispered, feeling down the squatting figure until he captured a clenched hand. "It's only me. I'll stay with you." And grasping the other tightly, he listened to the cascade of whispers his utterance had caused to fall. A hand touched the bookcase close to Peter's head and he was aware of how Francis's fear continued in spite of his presence. It was less intense, more bearable, he hoped, but it remained. He knew that it was his brother's fear and not his own that he experienced. The dark to him was only an absence of light; the groping hand that of a familiar child. Patiently he waited to be found.

He did not speak again, for between Francis and himself touch was the most intimate communion. By way of joined hands thought could flow more swiftly than lips could shape themselves round words. He could experience the whole progress of his brother's emotion, from the leap of panic at the unexpected contact to the steady pulse of fear, which now went on and on with the regularity of a heart-beat. Peter Morton thought with intensity, "I am here. You needn't be afraid. The lights will go on again soon. That rustle, that movement is nothing to fear. Only Joyce, only Mabel Warren." He bombarded the drooping form with thoughts of safety, but he was conscious that the fear continued. "They are beginning to whisper together. They are tired of looking for us. The lights will go on soon. We shall have won. Don't be afraid. That was only someone on the stairs. I believe it's Mrs. Henne-Falcon. Listen. They are feeling for the lights." Feet moving on a carpet, hands brushing a wall, a curtain pulled apart, a clicking handle, the opening of a cupboard door. In the case above their heads a loose book shifted under a touch. "Only Joyce, only Mabel Warren, only Mrs. Henne-Falcon," a crescendo of reassuring thought before the chandelier burst, like a fruit tree, into bloom.

The voices of the children rose shrilly into the radiance. "Where's Peter?" "Have you looked upstairs?" "Where's Francis?" but they were silenced again by Mrs. Henne-Falcon's scream. But she was not the first to notice Francis Morton's stillness, where he had collapsed against the wall at the touch of his brother's hand. Peter continued to hold the clenched fingers in an arid and puzzled grief. It was not merely that his brother was dead. His brain, too young to realize the full paradox, yet wondered with an obscure self-pity why it was that the pulse of his brother's fear went on and on, when Francis was now where he had been always told there was no more terror and no more darkness.

FOR DISCUSSION

1. How is the significance of the day quickly established? What details build up the atmosphere of the entire day? What is the effect of this atmosphere on the story?
2. Why is Peter happy when he awakens? What turns his happiness to anxiety? What is the relationship between the twins? Use details from the story to point out the extent of this relationship. Describe Francis and Peter from the information Greene gives about them.
3. Read again the last paragraph of the story. Why had Peter's earlier attempts to protect Francis failed? Why does this ultimate attempt fail? Why is Peter's grief a "puzzled" one? How do you account for Peter's continuing to feel Francis' fear at the end of the story?
4. How does Greene build up and maintain suspense? How does the tone of the story contribute to its effect?

Alan Sillitoe

On Saturday Afternoon

I once saw a bloke try to kill himself. I'll never forget the day because I was sitting in the house one Saturday afternoon, feeling black and fed-up because everybody in the family had gone to the pictures, except me who'd for some reason been left out of it. 'Course, I didn't know then that I would soon see something you can never see in the same way on the pictures, a real bloke stringing himself up. I was only a kid at the time, so you can imagine how much I enjoyed it.

I've never known a family to look as black as our family when they're fed-up. I've seen the old man with his face so dark and full of murder because he ain't got no fags[1] or was having to use saccharine to sweeten his tea, or even for nothing at all, that I've backed out of the house in case he got up from his fireside chair and came for me. He just sits, almost on top of the fire, his oil-stained Sunday-joint maulers[2] opened out in front of him and facing inwards to each other, his thick shoulders scrunched forward, and his dark brown eyes staring into the fire. Now and again he'd say a dirty word, for no reason at all, the worst word you can think of, and when he starts saying this you know it's time to clear out. If mam's in it gets worse than ever, because she says sharp to him: "What are yo' looking so bleddy black for?" as if it might be because of something she's done, and before you know what's happening he's tipped up a tableful of pots and mam's gone out of the house crying. Dad hunches back over the fire and goes on swearing. All because of a packet of fags.

I once saw him broodier than I'd ever seen him, so that I thought he'd gone crackers[3] in a quiet sort of way—until a

[1]*fags:* cigarettes
[2]*maulers:* hands
[3]*gone crackers:* gone crazy

fly flew to within a yard of him. Then his hand shot out, got it, and slung it crippled into the roaring fire. After that he cheered up a bit and mashed some tea.

Well, that's where the rest of us get our black looks from. It stands to reason we'd have them with a dad who carries on like that, don't it? Black looks run in the family. Some families have them and some don't. Our family has them right enough, and that's certain, so when we're fed-up we're really fed-up. Nobody knows why we get as fed-up as we do or why it gives us these black looks when we are. Some people get fed-up and don't look bad at all: they seem happy in a funny sort of way, as if they've just been set free from clink[4] after being in there for something they didn't do, or come out of the pictures after sitting plugged for eight hours at a bad film, or just missed a bus they ran half a mile for and seen it was the wrong one just after they'd stopped running—but in our family it's murder for the others if one of us is fed-up. I've asked myself lots of times what it is, but I can never get any sort of answer even if I sit and think for hours, which I must admit I don't do, though it looks good when I say I do. But I sit and think for long enough, until mam says to me, at seeing me scrunched up over the fire like dad: "What are yo' looking so black for?" So I've just got to stop thinking about it in case I get really black and fed-up and go the same way as dad, tipping up a tableful of pots and all.

Mostly I suppose there's nothing to look so black for: though it's nobody's fault and you can't blame anyone for looking black because I'm sure it's summat in the blood. But on this Saturday afternoon I was looking so black that when dad came in from the bookie's he said to me: "What's up wi' yo'?"

"I feel badly," I fibbed. He'd have had a fit if I'd said I was only black because I hadn't gone to the pictures.

"Well have a wash," he told me.

"I don't want a wash," I said, and that was a fact.

"Well, get outside and get some fresh air then," he shouted.

[4]*clink:* prison

I did as I was told, double-quick, because if ever dad goes as far as to tell me to get some fresh air I know it's time to get away from him. But outside the air wasn't so fresh, what with that bloody great bike factory bashing away at the yard-end. I didn't know where to go, so I walked up the yard a bit and sat down near somebody's back gate.

Then I saw this bloke who hadn't lived long in our yard. He was tall and thin and had a face like a parson except that he wore a flat cap and had a moustache that drooped, and looked as though he hadn't had a square meal for a year. I didn't think much o' this at the time: but I remember that as he turned in by the yard-end one of the nosy gossiping women who stood there every minute of the day except when she trudged to the pawnshop with her husband's bike or best suit, shouted to him: "What's that rope for, mate?"

He called back: "It's to 'ang messen wi', missis," and she cackled at his bloody good joke so loud and long you'd think she never heard such a good 'un, though the next day she cackled on the other side of her fat face.

He walked by me puffing a fag and carrying his coil of brand-new rope, and he had to step over me to get past. His boot nearly took my shoulder off, and when I told him to watch where he was going I don't think he heard me because he didn't even look round. Hardly anybody was about. All the kids were still at the pictures, and most of their mams and dads were downtown doing the shopping.

The bloke walked down the yard to his back door, and having nothing better to do because I hadn't gone to the pictures I followed him. You see, he left his back door open a bit so I gave it a push and went in. I stood there, just watching him, sucking my thumb, the other hand in my pocket. I suppose he knew I was there, because his eyes were moving more natural now, but he didn't seem to mind. "What are yer going to do wi' that rope, mate?" I asked him.

"I'm going ter 'ang messen, lad," he told me, as though he'd done it a time or two already, and people had usually asked him questions like this beforehand.

"What for mate?" He must have thought I was a nosy young bogger.[5]

[5]*bogger:* rascal, scamp

"'Cause I want to, that's what for," he said, clearing all the pots off the table and pulling it to the middle of the room. Then he stood on it to fasten the rope to the light-fitting. The table creaked and didn't look very safe, but it did him for what he wanted.

"It wain't hold up, mate," I said to him, thinking how much better it was being here than sitting in the pictures and seeing the Jungle Jim serial.

But he got nettled now and turned on me. "Mind yer own business."

I thought he was going to tell me to scram, but he didn't. He made ever such a fancy knot with that rope, as though he'd been a sailor or summat, and as he tied it he was whistling a fancy tune to himself. Then he got down from the table and pushed it back to the wall, and put a chair in its place. He wasn't looking black at all, nowhere near as black as anybody in our family when they're feeling fed-up. If ever he'd looked only half as black as our dad looked twice a week he'd have hanged himself years ago, I couldn't help thinking. But he was making a good job of that rope all right, as though he'd thought about it a lot anyway, and as though it was going to be the last thing he'd ever do. But I knew something he didn't know, because he wasn't standing where I was. I knew the rope wouldn't hold up, and I told him so, again.

"Shut yer gob[6]," he said, but quiet like, "or I'll kick yer out."

I didn't want to miss it, so I said nothing. He took his cap off and put it on the dresser, then he took his coat off, and his scarf, and spread them out on the sofa. I wasn't a bit frightened, like I might be now at sixteen, because it was interesting. And being only ten I'd never had a chance to see a bloke hang himself before. We got pally, the two of us, before he slipped the rope around his neck.

"Shut the door," he asked me, and I did as I was told. "Ye're a good lad for your age," he said to me while I sucked my thumb, and he felt in his pockets and pulled out all that was inside, throwing the handful of bits and bobs on the table; fag-packet and peppermints, a pawn-ticket, an old

[6]*gob:* mouth

comb, and a few coppers. He picked out a penny and gave it to me, saying: "Now listen ter me, young 'un. I'm going to 'ang messen, and when I'm swinging I want you to gi' this chair a bloody good kick and push it away. All right?"

I nodded.

He put the rope around his neck, and then took it off like it was a tie that didn't fit. "What are yer going to do it for, mate?" I asked again.

"Because I'm fed-up," he said, looking very unhappy. "And because I want to. My missus left me, and I'm out o' work."

I didn't want to argue, because the way he said it, I knew he couldn't do anything else except hang himself. Also there was a funny look in his face: even when he talked to me I swear he couldn't see me. It was different to the black looks my old man puts on, and I suppose that's why my old man would never hang himself, worse luck, because he never gets a look into his clock like this bloke had. My old man's look stares at you, so that you have to back down and fly out of the house: this bloke's look looked *through* you, so that you could face it and know it wouldn't do you any harm. So I saw now that dad would never hang himself because he could never get the right sort of look into his face, in spite of the fact that he'd been out of work often enough. Maybe mam would have to leave him first, and then he might do it; but no—I shook my head—there wasn't much chance of that even though he did lead her a dog's life.

"Yer wain't forget to kick that chair away?" he reminded me, and I swung my head to say I wouldn't. So my eyes were popping and I watched every move he made. He stood on the chair and put the rope around his neck so that it fitted this time still whistling his fancy tune. I wanted to get a better goz[7] at the knot, because my pal was in the scouts, and would ask to know how it was done, and if I told him later he'd let me know what happened at the pictures in the Jungle Jim serial, so's I could have my cake and eat it as well, as mam says, tit for tat. But I thought I'd better not ask the bloke to tell me, and I stayed back in my corner. The last thing he did was take the wet dirty butt-end from his lips and sling it into

[7]*goz:* look

the empty firegrate, following it with his eyes to the black fireback where it landed—as if he was then going to mend a fault in the lighting like any electrician.

Suddenly his long legs wriggled and his feet tried to kick the chair, so I helped him as I'd promised I would and took a runner at it as if I was playing centre-forward for Notts Forest,[8] and the chair went scooting back against the sofa, dragging his muffler to the floor as it tipped over. He swung for a bit, his arms chafing like he was a scarecrow flapping birds away, and he made a noise in his throat as if he'd just took a dose of salts and was trying to make them stay down.

Then there was another sound, and I looked up and saw a big crack come in the ceiling, like you see on the pictures when an earthquake's happening, and the bulb began circling round and round as though it was a space ship. I was just beginning to get dizzy when, thank Christ, he fell down with such a horrible thump on the floor that I thought he'd broke every bone he'd got. He kicked around for a bit, like a dog that's got colic bad. Then he lay still.

I didn't stay to look at him. "I told him that rope wouldn't hold up," I kept saying to myself as I went out of the house, tut-tutting because he hadn't done the job right, hands stuffed deep into my pockets and nearly crying at the balls-up he'd made of everything. I slammed his gate so hard with disappointment that it nearly dropped off its hinges.

Just as I was going back up the yard to get my tea at home, hoping the others had come back from the pictures so's I wouldn't have anything to keep on being black about, a copper passed me and headed for the bloke's door. He was striding quickly with his head bent forward, and I knew that somebody had narked.[9] They must have seen him buy the rope and then tipped-off the cop. Or happen the old hen at the yard-end had finally caught on. Or perhaps he'd even told somebody himself, because I supposed that the bloke who'd strung himself up hadn't much known what he was doing, especially with the look I'd seen in his eyes. But that's

[8] *Notts Forest:* a well-known football (soccer) team
[9] *narked:* informed (as to the police)

how it is, I said to myself, as I followed the copper back to the bloke's house, a poor bloke can't even hang himself these days.

When I got back the copper was slitting the rope from his neck with a pen-knife, then he gave him a drink of water, and the bloke opened his peepers. I didn't like the copper, because he'd got a couple of my mates sent to approved school[10] for pinching lead piping from lavatories.

"What did you want to hang yourself for?" he asked the bloke, trying to make him sit up. He could hardly talk, and one of his hands was bleeding from where the light-bulb had smashed. I knew that rope wouldn't hold up, but he hadn't listened to me. I'll never hang myself anyway, but if I want to I'll make sure I do it from a tree or something like that, not a light fitting. "Well, what did you do it for?"

"Because I wanted to," the bloke croaked.

"You'll get five years for this," the copper told him. I'd crept back into the house and was sucking my thumb in the same corner.

"That's what yo' think," the bloke said, a normal frightened look in his eyes now. "I only wanted to hang myself."

"Well," the copper said, taking out his book, "it's against the law, you know."

"Nay," the bloke said, "it can't be. It's my life, ain't it?"

"You might think so," the copper said, "but it ain't."

He began to suck the blood from his hand. It was such a little scratch though that you couldn't see it. "That's the first thing I knew," he said.

"Well I'm telling you," the copper told him.

'Course, I didn't let on to the copper that I'd helped the bloke to hang himself. I wasn't born yesterday, nor the day before yesterday either.

"It's a fine thing if a bloke can't tek his own life," the bloke said, seeing he was in for it.

"Well he can't," the copper said, as if reading out of his book and enjoying it. "It ain't your life. And it's a crime to take your own life. It's killing yourself. It's suicide."

[10] *approved school:* a kind of reform school

The bloke looked hard, as if every one of the copper's words meant six-months cold.[11] I felt sorry for him, and that's a fact, but if only he'd listened to what I'd said and not depended on that light-fitting. He should have done it from a tree, or something like that.

He went up the yard with the copper like a peaceful lamb, and we all thought that that was the end of that.

But a couple of days later the news was flashed through to us—even before it got to the *Post* because a woman in our yard worked at the hospital of an evening dishing grub out and tidying up. I heard her spilling it to somebody at the yard-end. "I'd never 'ave thought it. I thought he'd got that daft idea out of his head when they took him away. But no. Wonders'll never cease. Chucked 'issen from the hospital window when the copper who sat near his bed went off for a pee. Would you believe it? Dead? Not much 'e ain't."

He'd heaved himself at the glass, and fallen like a stone on to the road. In one way I was sorry he'd done it, but in another I was glad; because he'd proved to the coppers and everybody whether it was his life or not all right. It was marvellous though, the way the brainless bastards had put him in a ward six floors up, which finished him off, proper, even better than a tree.

All of which will make me think twice about how black I sometimes feel. The black coal-bag locked inside you, and the black look it puts on your face, doesn't mean you're going to string yourself up or sling yourself under a double-decker or chuck yourself out of a window or cut your throat with a sardine-tin or put your head in the gas-oven or drop your rotten sack-bag of a body on to a railway line, because when you're feeling that black you can't even move from your chair. Anyhow, I know I'll never get so black as to hang myself, because hanging don't look very nice to me, and never will, the more I remember old what's-his-name swinging from the light-fitting.

More than anything else, I'm glad now I didn't go to the pictures that Saturday afternoon when I was feeling black and ready to do myself in. Because you know, I shan't ever

[11]*six-months cold:* six months of imprisonment

kill myself. Trust me. I'll stay alive half-barmy till I'm a hundred and five, and then go out screaming blue murder because I want to stay where I am.

FOR DISCUSSION

1. The very first paragraph—indeed, the first sentence—of "On Saturday Afternoon" tells you that this story differs in significant respects from the other short stories in this section. How would you characterize these differences?
2. The boy telling the story does and says some things that are quite "babyish," and other things that are almost shockingly mature. Give some examples of both. How old do you think the boy is? On what do you base this estimate?
3. The author establishes that the boy telling the story has certain personal qualities: shrewdness, keen powers of observation, curiosity, realism, and a sharp sense of self-interest. Identify the parts of the story that convey each of these qualities to the reader. Are there any other qualities which you feel are conveyed?
4. Does the boy have any awareness that a terrible human tragedy is being unfolded before him? What effect is gained by the repeated references to the "Jungle Jim serial"?
5. Although the boy expresses himself in what might be considered "nonstandard" English, he uses many vivid and striking phrases, such as "the black coal-bag locked inside you." Find some other examples of this. Do you think that a boy with the background indicated would actually be capable of such language?
6. One critic has said of this story that it is "chillingly grim but also strangely exhilarating." The grimness is obvious, but where is the "exhilaration"? (Take a look at the last paragraph.)

FOR COMPOSITION

1. Imagine that this story is being told by an American boy of a background similar to that of the narrator. What changes would there be in the language, the references, the point of view? Select any part of the story that you like particularly, and "Americanize" it.
2. The boy in this story feels that he has learned something very valuable from the events he observed. What is that "something"? Develop this in a short composition.

About the Authors

Jane Austen (1775-1817) was born in Hampshire, England, in the country parish where her father was curate. She spent most of her life in the kind of rural area that was to form the setting of her novels, among the kind of people who inhabited her novels. Miss Austen was the seventh of eight children, and she delighted in the company of her family. She did not separate herself from her surroundings to write; instead she wrote all of her books in the family room of her house in the midst of family activities, ready always to stop writing to visit with friends or to play with her large brood of nieces and nephews. She never married, but she was far from being a typical spinster. She possessed many of the qualities that her heroines showed—wit, a critical sense, a vivid imagination, and an excellent sense of humor.

In 1811 *Sense and Sensibility* was published and in 1813, *Pride and Prejudice.* These were followed by *Mansfield Park* (1814), *Emma* (1816), and *Persuasion* and *Northanger Abbey* in 1818, the year after her death. All of her novels were published anonymously.

Charlotte Brontë (1816-1855) was born in Yorkshire into the unusual family of an unusual father. Patrick Brontë was a proud, moody Irishman. The early death of his wife left him with six children, whose care he put into the hands of a sister-in-law completely unequipped to deal with these precocious children. The two eldest girls died in childhood leaving Charlotte, Bramwell, Emily, and Anne. They attended schools infrequently, preferring instead the secluded life of the Yorkshire moors and their own companionship to formal classrooms. Their very extensive reading, their father's fantastic stories that he occasionally found time to tell them, their familiarity with the wildness and bleakness of the Yorkshire countryside, and their own original and active imaginations led the children to create fantasy worlds of great romance, adventure, and intrigue. The children wrote stories about these places, and later, Charlotte and Emily were to bring elements of these wonder-worlds into their novels.

Charlotte was the strongest of all the children and therefore the one most able to attend and do well at school. She even arranged a stay at a Belgian school for herself and Emily to better prepare themselves to be teachers in a school of their own. Gradually, Charlotte, Emily, and Anne began to write for publication using the names Currer, Ellis, and Acton Bell. In 1847, Charlotte's *Jane Eyre* was published, and shortly thereafter, Emily's *Wuthering Heights.* The following year, however, was probably the most painful of Charlotte's life, for Bramwell, Emily, and Anne died. In the following four years, Charlotte completed her second and third novels, *Shirley* and *Villette.* In 1854 she accepted the proposal of Arthur Bell Nichols, her father's curate, but nine months later, weakened by a very difficult pregnancy, she died.

John Bunyan (1628-1688), the son of a Bedfordshire family that had come down in the world, was a tinker by trade, like his father. An imaginative and sensitive youth, he had strong feelings of guilt for his sins, which were a love of sports (especially tip-cat, a forerunner of cricket), bell-ringing, and bad language. When he married, at the age of twenty, his wife brought him as a dowry two books: *The Plain Man's Path-way to Heaven* and *The Practice of Piety.* They had an important influence on his tortured religious development which, eventually, led him into active preaching in a Baptist congregation at Bedford.

Hardly more than a boy when he served in the Parliamentary Army, Bunyan was never a leader of national prominence in the Puritan movement. Despite his wife's courageous appeal, he was passed over in the general pardon granted those awaiting trial at the coronation of Charles II in 1661. During his twelve years in prison he wrote and supported his wife and four children by making laces. After his release, he was licensed and served as pastor for a wide area until 1675 when he was jailed again for a few months. It was then that he began Part I of *The Pilgrim's Progress* (1678); the second part appeared in 1684. He also wrote his remarkable spiritual autobiography, *Grace Abounding to the Chief of Sinners* (1666), and two other allegories, *The Life and Death of Mr. Badman* (1680) and *The Holy War* (1682).

Joseph Conrad (1857-1924) was born Jozef Teodor Konrad Nalecz Korzeniowski in the Ukraine region of Poland. He belonged to a family dedicated to the liberation of their country from a succession of occupying powers. When Conrad was six, he was taken into exile by his parents, who died soon after, leaving him in the care of an uncle. At the age of seventeen Conrad went to southern France and joined the French marine service. A few years later he joined the English service, in which he served for sixteen years, advancing through the ranks to become captain of a ship. In 1894 in London, he went back to the writing he had started at sea, and published his first book, *Almayer's Folly.* This and other works brought him recognition as a writer, but he did not achieve popular success or financial security for a number of years. Some of his best-known works are *Lord Jim, Heart of Darkness, The Nigger of the Narcissus,* and *Victory.* He is unusual for achieving fame as a master of style in a language he learned as an adult.

Charles Dickens (1812-1870), born in Portsea, England, was the second of the eight children of John and Elizabeth Dickens. His father, a talented but very impractical man, burdened by the expenses of a large family, was continually poor. Dickens received little formal education but compensated for this lack by voracious reading and by developing the habit of observing acutely the world he lived in. When Dickens was twelve, his father was imprisoned for debt, and according to the custom of the times, his family went to live with him in prison. Dickens, however, considered old enough at twelve to be on his own, got work in a shoe factory and lived alone in truly pitiful surroundings. Although this employment lasted only a few months, it was to have a permanent effect on Dickens. Through this crushing experience, he learned at first hand of the degradation of the poor; of the cruelty and injustice of society's institutions and many of its laws; of the helplessness and unhappiness of so many children, and of the cruelty of a law keeping a bankrupt man in prison until he could pay his debts. All of this he later put into his novels.

Dickens worked as an office boy for a law firm, studied stenography, and at seventeen was a shorthand reporter in court. He became a newspaper reporter and published a number of sketches of London life. Just after his twenty-fourth birthday, the first installments of *Pickwick Papers* were published and he married Catherine Hogarth. The *Pickwick Papers* was enormously successful and Dickens' career was firmly launched. He was to go on to write some twenty novels, to own and edit a magazine, to raise a family of ten children, to become wealthy, and to be constantly driven by his own restlessness and ambition to maintain an awesome schedule of work. His deep awareness of the evils of society made this theme a fundamental part of his writing and involved him in many charitable causes. His continuing need "for means of blowing my superfluous steam off" and his love of the dramatic led him to act in amateur theatricals, and, more importantly, to give readings of his own works. He had an enormous success touring England and America with these readings.

He was professionally successful, but his personal life was unhappy, and after twenty-three years of marriage, he and his wife separated. He became even more involved in his work, although his health was noticeably deteriorating. He went again to America to give readings and achieved a tremendous financial success. His health, however, was fatally weakened, and after one more year of strenuous activity, he died. At his death, he was undoubtedly one of England's most popular and widely-read novelists.

Henry Fielding (1707-1754), was born a gentleman; his father was a well-born but financially poor army officer and his mother was the daughter of a famous jurist. Fielding was well-educated, attending Eton, where he discovered his deep love of literature, and the University of Lieden, which he left, however, without taking a degree. He settled in London and wrote for the stage, producing some popular pieces and, more importantly, some strongly satiric pieces. He aimed his satire at the prime minister, Sir Robert Walpole. The thrusts by Fielding and other dramatists caused Walpole to issue a Licensing Act (1737) designed to keep from the stage any unpopular work. Fielding was in effect put out of a job. Because he was married and with family responsibilities and because he seemed to have a capacity for meeting the peculiar challenges of his life, he resumed his study of law that he had begun in Lieden. Three years later he was admitted to the bar, and after that combined his career as a writer with that of a lawyer.

Fielding's wife and a daughter died in 1742 and their deaths affected him deeply. In the same year, his first novel, *Joseph Andrews,* was published. His own health declined and his extravagant habits caused him always to be in economic straits, thus adding to his difficulties. But the urbane, witty, and highly intelligent Fielding continued writing and working, now as a magistrate, even helping to stop a serious crime wave. In 1747, he married his wife's former maid and with her had two sons and a daughter. In 1749, he published *Tom Jones.* His health worsened, so in 1754, in an attempt to find a better climate, he took his family to Lisbon, Portugal, where he died.

E. M. Forster (1879–1970) is eminent as a novelist, a short story writer, and a critic. In his fiction, he has made important use of contrasts: between different temperaments and ways of life, between different cultures, and between illusion and reality. *A Passage to India,* probably his best-known novel, contrasts the English and Indian cultures and temperaments to show how misunderstandings and prejudices prevent the development of rewarding human relationships. Other works include *Aspects of the Novel,* Forster's most important work of criticism, and his collections of essays entitled *Abinger Harvest* and *Two Cheers for Democracy.*

The first of Forster's short stories appeared early in this century but were not published in book form until 1911, after the publication of his first four novels. Many of these stories have a vein of fantasy and mythology, and deal, in one way or another, with the theme which has preoccupied him in all of his work; namely, the endless conflict between the world of the spirit and the everyday world of compromise and conventions.

Graham Greene (1904-   ), the son of a Hertfordshire schoolmaster, comes from a well-educated family and is distantly related to Robert Louis Stevenson. He attended Oxford University and, after graduating, became a sub-editor of the London *Times,* and later the Literary Editor of *The Spectator.* He has travelled widely in the Americas, and lived for a time in Mexico, a country which furnished settings for several of his works. Converted to Roman Catholicism as an adult, his religion is reflected in his later work. Along with his preoccupation with abnormal psychology, he is particularly interested in the varied nature of religious emotion. While Greene uncovers his characters' weaknesses relentlessly, he never loses his compassion for them. Instead, he insists on the need for pity and mercy in one's judgment of others.

A prolific writer, Greene has written a group of thrillers, which he calls "entertainments." These include *The Ministry of Fear, The Third Man,* and *Our Man in Havana.* His reputation rests, however, on his more serious novels. The best-known include *The Power and the Glory, The Heart of the Matter, A Burnt-Out Case,* and most recently, *The Comedians.* In 1962 he was awarded an honorary Doctor of Literature degree by Cambridge University.

Thomas Hardy (1840-1928) was born in a small hamlet in Dorset, a rural section of southern England which became the famous Wessex country of his novels. Here he spent most of his life. As a youth he was apprenticed to a church architect and later studied architecture in London. His real love, however, was poetry, and he composed many poems during these early years. When no publisher would accept them, he devoted the next twenty-five years to the writing of fiction, at first as a means of earning a living. In *Under the Greenwood Tree,* he found the right road for himself as a novelist. With the publication of *The Return of the Native,* fiction writing became not only a profession but also an art to which he brought amazing talents. *Tess of the D'Urbervilles* and *Jude the Obscure* were equally distinguished, but they were so savagely attacked in the press that Hardy abandoned the writing of fiction entirely. He was now free to devote the remaining years of his life to poetry.

His first volumes of poems, *Wessex Poems* and *Poems of Past and Present,* were collections of lyrics he had written before and during his career as a novelist. Other collections of lyrics continued to appear, the last, *Winter Words,* published after his death. The climax of Hardy's public career was *The Dynasts,* a three-part epic of the Napoleonic era which, like his novels, exhibits the "Immanent Will" operating ruthlessly and purposelessly in human affairs. He became perhaps the most important of the English "naturalists," writers who felt that men are the pathetic victims of cruel or indifferent natural forces which they cannot control. Hardy died in 1928. His heart lies buried in his beloved Dorset, his ashes next to those of Dickens in Westminster Abbey.

James Joyce (1882-1941), one of the most influential writers of the twentieth century, had a life-long struggle to secure not only a livelihood but also an understanding and acceptance of his work. After receiving his degree in Ireland at the age of twenty, he went to Paris with the intention of studying medicine and writing. He was unable to attend medical school and lived in poverty for several months until his mother's illness brought him back to Ireland. After her death, he continued to write, and, for a while, taught school, but in 1904 he returned to Paris. About a year later he submitted *Dubliners* to an English publisher. However, because of its alleged improprieties and irreligiousness, it was not published until 1914. During this period he made several trips to Ireland, but after 1912 he never returned. He spent his life on the continent in France, Italy, and Switzerland, supplementing his meager income from writing by teaching.

A Portrait of the Artist as a Young Man, published in 1916, is an autobiographical novel in which Joyce traced the growth of a young, sensitive artist faced with family disputes, with conflicts between religion and aesthetic vision, and with the futility of the political disputes which plagued his native land. *Ulysses* (1922) is a highly complex and symbolic work based on a single day in the lives of the characters and involving elaborate parallels with the mythical story of Odysseus. *Finnegans Wake* (1939), an even more complex work, is notable for its experimental use of language.

D. H. Lawrence (1885-1930) was born in the mining town of Eastwood in Nottinghamshire, England, the son of a refined schoolmistress and a rough, earthy coal miner. The conflict between these two opposite personalities later figured prominently in Lawrence's writing. The harsh life of coal miners which he experienced as a child contributed to his strong dislike of industry. This dislike may explain why, throughout his life, he was indifferent to monetary success, although bitterly disappointed that people did not receive his books sympathetically. Physically weak from childhood, he was to suffer serious attacks of pneumonia, which interrupted his several attempts to become a clerk or school teacher and which finally developed into the tuberculosis which caused his death. The closeness of his childhood relationship with his mother was marred by her growing possessiveness. In later years he suffered from the conflict between the emotional claims of his mother and his loyalty to the girl he loved. One of his best novels, *Sons and Lovers*, is built around a similar conflict.

Lawrence's writing is characterized by a keen intuition about people, and many of his psychological insights are based on Freud's ideas of the unconscious. His literary reputation is chiefly that of a novelist, but he also wrote short stories, essays, travel books, and poetry.

Sir Thomas Malory (? -1471) was the son of the High Sheriff and member of Parliament from Warwickshire. He fought at Calais under the Earl of Warwick and about 1442 became himself a member of Parliament from Warwickshire, thus earning the title of Knight. He was arrested in 1451 for committing hostile acts against the Priory of Monks Kirby, but broke out of custody with his servant, swam a moat, and escaped. Later he was rearrested and charged with several crimes of theft and violence. Pleading not guilty before King Henry VI, he was thereafter released.

In prison in 1468 on charges of sedition for championing the Lancaster cause during the War of the Roses, Malory was specifically refused a pardon by Edward IV. Part or all of *Le Morte d'Arthur* was written in prison at this time. The last lines of the poem date its completion between 1469 and 1470. Malory died in London soon thereafter, and was buried in the Church of St. Francis at Greyfriars. His precious manuscript was entrusted to the printer Caxton, who made many changes before publishing it in 1485.

Katherine Mansfield (1888-1923) was born in New Zealand, attended school in London for several years in her teens, and left New Zealand permanently for England in 1908. Her life in London and on the continent was marred by poor health, despair over an unhappy love affair, financial difficulties, the death of a brother in World War I, and a hasty marriage to a man she soon left. Her life in London was influenced by her association with several important literary persons: the distinguished writers Virginia Woolf and D. H. Lawrence, and the journalist John Middleton Murry. Her last years were spent searching for a favorable climate and for new methods of treatment for incurable tuberculosis.

A number of short story writers have been influenced by her techniques. She most often chose to emphasize the "inner action" or internal and psychological conflicts felt by characters at particular points in their seemingly ordinary lives. During her lifetime she published several volumes of short stories, which later appeared as a single volume. She is known for her use of sensual impressions and sharp, telling details.

W. Somerset Maugham (1874–1965) was born in Paris, where his father was legal attache to the British Embassy. Both of his parents died when he was very young, and he went to live with an uncle, a clergyman in a small English town. Here his life in school was unhappy because he was often the victim of unkind jokes about a speech impediment and about his poor health. The experiences of his adolescence, his year as a medical student in Germany, and his struggle to define his philosophy of life—all are presented in fictionalized form in his novel *Of Human Bondage.* His literary views and an account of his own literary development are presented in *The Summing Up.* His interest in contrasting customs and moral codes gained through wide travel and a keen observation of people are evident in such novels as *The Moon and Sixpence, Cakes and Ale,* and *The Razor's Edge,* and in his dramatic comedies *The Circle* and *The Constant Wife.* Nor should the reader overlook his short stories, in which, as in many of his works, the major theme is the relativity of human morals and standards.

Alan Sillitoe was born in 1928 in Nottingham, in central England, and grew up in the slums of that ancient and now highly industrialized city. He was the son of a laborer in a tannery. As is common to this day in English working-class families, he left school at fourteen to contribute to the family income. He held a variety of menial jobs. The key event in his life, as he himself sees it, was joining the Royal Air Force in 1946. He spent two years as a radio operator in Malaya. He was hospitalized for a year and began to write. Leaving the RAF, he married an American school teacher-poet and began to write in earnest. He became friends with the noted poet and novelist Robert Graves, who encouraged him to continue. His first novel, *Saturday Night and Sunday Morning,* was awarded the Author's Club Prize for the best first novel of 1958. He has written many short stories, of which the best known is probably "The Loneliness of the Long Distance Runner."

Jonathan Swift (1667–1745), born of English parents in Dublin, Ireland, received a classical education at Trinity College, Dublin. During ten years as secretary to an influential aristocrat, he continued his self-education. He then entered the Church with expectations of a good position, but he was exiled to a remote parish in Ireland. Returning to England, he served as a political writer for the Whigs; later, he gladly shifted his allegiance to the Tories and had high hopes of being rewarded with an important post. The Tory ministry collapsed when Queen Anne died, and a disappointed Swift returned to Dublin to spend the remainder of his life as dean of St. Patrick's.

In 1704, Swift published two satirical works: *The Battle of the Books* and *A Tale of a Tub.* His most popular satire, *Gulliver's Travels,* appeared in 1726. Swift's final years were extremely painful, wracked by severe mental illness. The epitaph he wrote for himself was a hopeful prophecy: "He has gone where indignation can lacerate his heart no more."

William Makepeace Thackeray (1811-1863) was born in India, but was sent back to England for his schooling when he was six years old. Beginning life with a sizable fortune, he lost his money through unwise business investments and a taste for extravagant luxuries. Indeed, he was locally famous at Cambridge University for his fashionable and exquisitely-tailored wardrobe. Finding himself without funds, without a college degree, and without a profession, he turned to writing to support his family after he left the university. Though his life was bedevilled by misfortune—his wife went insane, leaving him with two small daughers to rear alone, and his own health remained poor through most of his adult life—he still produced several novels of technical excellence and one unquestioned masterpiece: *Vanity Fair.* His other significant works are *Barry Lyndon, The Newcomes, Henry Esmond, Pendennis,* and *The Virginian.* Before he died he recovered his fortune through prodigious hard work and was able to leave his daughters with considerable inheritances.

Virginia Woolf (1882-1941), novelist, critic, and essayist, was born in London, the frail youngest child of a famous literary scholar, Sir Leslie Stephen. The large but close-knit Stephen family divided its time between a town house in Hyde Park Gate and a summer home on the Cornwall coast, the background setting of *To the Lighthouse.* With her husband, Leonard Woolf, she founded the Hogarth Press in order to publish such obscure young writers as T. S. Eliot, Katherine Mansfield, and E. M. Forster. Influenced by Joyce, Proust, and William James, she became a leading novelist with the publication of *Mrs. Dalloway.* Mrs. Woolf committed suicide, by drowning, at the beginning of World War II.

Glossary of Literary Terms

action: what takes place during the course of a novel, drama, or narrative poem.

action, rising: the series of incidents that grow out of the problem to be solved and that build up to the climax.

action, falling: the action following the climax; also referred to as resolution or denouement.

aesthetics: the science or study of the beautiful.

allegory: a narrative in which objects, persons, or events are equated with meanings outside the narrative itself. For example, in the allegory *The Pilgrim's Progress,* Christian stands for any Christian man, and his adventures for the perils and temptations that beset such a man.

allusion: a reference to some person, place, or event that has literary, historical, or geographical significance.

analogy: a comparison of ideas or objects which are essentially different but which are alike in one significant way; for example, the analogy between the grasshopper and the man who lives only for the moment.

antagonist: the force (usually a person) that opposes the main character (the protagonist) in his attempt to solve a problem and thus resolve the conflict in which he is involved.

antecedent action: the events which occurred prior to the time covered in the work and about which the reader or audience must be informed.

anticlimax: an outcome of a situation or series of events that, by contrast with what was anticipated, is ludicrous or disappointing. The anticlimax can often create a humorous effect.

aphorism: a brief statement of a general truth, such as "The devil finds work for idle hands." In present-day usage an aphorism is synonymous with a maxim or proverb.

archaism: a word or phrase no longer used in actual speech:

"Eftsoons his hand dropt he!"
—Samuel Taylor Coleridge

atmosphere: the general over-all feeling of a literary work conveyed in large part by the setting and the mood.

cadence: the effect created by the rise and fall of the voice and by the emphasis and pause required by the meaning. In other words, the rhythm is not determined by a carefully planned combination of accented and unaccented syllables, as in traditional verse.

character: a person in a poem, play, or work of fiction; sometimes an animal or object.

characterization: in a literary work, the portrayal of an imaginary person by what he says or does, by what others say about him or how they react to him, and by what the author reveals directly or through a narrator.

chronicle: a lengthy record of historical events, presented in chronological order.

classicism: the principles thought characteristic of Greek and Roman literature, such as balance, simplicity, restraint, and dignity. See neoclassic.

cliché: an expression used so often that it has lost its freshness and effectiveness.

climax: the point of highest interest or dramatic intensity. Usually it marks a turning point in the action, since the reader is no longer in doubt about the outcome.

coincidence: the chance occurrence of two events which take place at the same time.

conflict: the struggle between two opposing forces, ideas, or beliefs, which form the basis of the plot. The conflict is resolved when one force—usually the protagonist—succeeds or fails in overcoming the opposing force, or gives up trying.

connotation: the implied or suggested meaning of a word or expression.

contrast: the bringing together of ideas, images, or characters to show how they differ.

denotation: the precise, literal meaning of a word or expression.

denouement: the unraveling of the plot, following the climax, in which the writer explains how and why everything turned out as it did.

dialect: the speech that is characteristic of a particular region or of a class or group of people.

dialogue: the printed conversation between two or more characters in fiction, drama, or poetry.

didactic: morally instructive or intended to be so.

digression: a departure from the main subject of a literary work.

episode: a related group of incidents, or a major event, that comprises all or part of the main plot or, in a long work, is related to the main plot.

epithet: an adjective, noun, or phrase that characterizes a person or thing; for example, "brave-hearted William."

euphemism: a mild, inoffensive word or expression used in place of one that is harsh or unpleasant; for example, "to pass away" is a euphemism for "to die."

exposition: the background information that reveals what occurred prior to the time covered in a story, play, or narrative poem; who the main characters are (sometimes before they appear); and what situation has arisen that will lead to a problem requiring a solution.

fantasy: a tale involving such unreal characters and improbable events that the reader is not expected to believe it. Some fantasies are intended merely to entertain; others have a serious purpose as well; namely, to satirize outmoded customs or the stupidity of certain people or groups of people.

figure of speech: the general term for a number of literary and poetic devices in which words or groups of words are used to create images in the mind or to make comparisons:

"... .she [England] is a fen
Of stagnant waters. . ."
—William Wordsworth

flashback: a device by which a writer interrupts the main action of a story or play to recreate a situation or incident of an earlier time as though it were occurring in the present.

foreshadowing: the dropping of important hints by the author to prepare the reader for what is to come and to help him to anticipate the outcome.

form: a fixed metrical arrangement, such as the ballade, the sonnet.

historic present: the use of the present tense to relate incidents that occurred in the past.

humor: the quality that makes something seem funny, amusing,or comic. Humor can arise from action, situation, physical appearance, verbal statement, or from any combination of these.

hyperbole: a figure of speech employing obvious exaggeration; for example, "His mind was a million miles away."

idiom: the language or manner of speaking that is typical of a particular region or group of people.

idyll: a poem or prose piece describing the simple pleasures of rural life.

illusion: a quality of belief evoked by a narrative or drama.

image: a general term for any representation of a particular thing with its attendant and evocative detail. It may be a metaphor, a simile, or a straightforward description. An image may also have symbolic meaning.

incident: one of the events (usually minor) that make up the total action or plot of a drama or work of fiction.

irony: a mode of expression in which the author says one thing and means the opposite. The term also applies to a situation, or the outcome of an event (or series of events), that is contrary to what is naturally hoped for or expected.

locale: the particular place in which the action in a work of fiction occurs.

melodramatic: the quality of a scene, situation, or dialogue that is sensational, violent, or extravagantly emotional.

metaphor: a figure of speech in which two things are compared without the use of like or as:

> "Life's but a walking shadow, a poor player
> That struts and frets his hour upon the stage
> And then is heard no more."
>
> —William Shakespeare

monologue: a long speech by a character in a play or poem.

mood: the frame of mind or state of feeling created by a piece of writing; for example, a skeptical mood or a sentimental mood.

moral: the lesson taught by a literary work.

motivation: the cause or reason that compels a character to act as he does.

movement: a literary trend or development.

narration: an account or story of an event, or series of events, true or imaginary. Also the act of narrating such an account or story.

narrative poem: a story told in verse form.

paradox: a statement which on the surface seems contradictory, yet if interpreted figuratively, involves an element of truth:

"The child is father of the man."
—William Wordsworth

parallelism: the grouping together of similar ideas by the use of coordinate constructions:

"Some books are to be tasted, others to be
swallowed, and some few to be chewed and
digested. . ."
—Francis Bacon

paraphrase: a restating of the sense of a piece of writing, of approximately the same length as the original but in different words.

parody: a humorous imitation or burlesque of a serious piece of literature or writing.

pathetic fallacy: the ascribing of human traits to nature or to inanimate objects; for example, "a stubborn door."

pathos: that quality in prose or poetry that evokes in the reader a feeling of pity and compassion.

personification: a figure of speech in which places, things, animals, or ideas are endowed with human qualities:

"These shall the fury Passions tear,
The vultures of the mind. . ."
—Thomas Gray

plot: the series of events or episodes that make up the action of a work of fiction.

poetic justice: an outcome of events that rewards the virtuous and punishes the vicious; an ending in which each character gets exactly what he deserves.

point of view: the method used by the short story writer or novelist to tell his story; the position, psychological as well as physical, from which he presents what happens and the characters involved in it.

point of view, first person: the narration of a story by the main character or, possibly, a minor character. As the narrator, he uses the pronoun *I* in referring to himself.

point of view, omniscient: the narration of a story as though by an all-knowing observer, who can be in several places at the same time and can see into the hearts and minds of all the characters.

point of view, omniscient third person: the narration of a story by an all-knowing observer but limited primarily to what one of the characters (usually the main character) could see, know, hear, or experience.

pun: a play on words, either by using words that sound alike but have different meanings or by using a word with two different meanings, both of which apply. For example, this pun on "done" and "Donne":

"When Thou has done, Thou hast not done. . ."
–John Donne

realistic: the faithful portrayal of people, scenes, and events as they are, not as the writer or artist would like them to be.

resolution: the events following the climax of a work of fiction; sometimes called falling action.

rhetorical question: a question that is asked for its dramatic effect and to which no answer is expected.

rogue story: a story presenting the adventures of a rascal of low degree, who makes his living more through his wits than his industry. These stories, which present little more than a series of thrilling incidents, are marked by realistic details drawn from the life of the common people.

romance: a long narrative, either in verse or prose, which deals with chivalric adventures and loves.

romantic: the portrayal of people, scenes, and events as they impress the writer or artist or as he imagines them to be. A romantic work has one or more of the following characteristics: an emphasis on feeling and imagination; a love of nature; a belief in the individual and the common man; an interest in the past, the unusual, the unfamiliar, the bizarre or picturesque; a revolt against authority or tradition.

satire: any piece of writing which criticizes manners, individuals, or political and social institutions by holding them up to ridicule.

scene: (1) an incident or situation which develops out of the preceding action and flows into the action that follows; for example, a scene in which two guests discuss their host while he is momentarily out of the room. (2) One of two or more clearly defined and separate episodes that make up an act.

sentimentality: a superabundance of emotion in a play, poem, or novel.

setting: the time and place in which the events in a narrative (prose or poetry) take place.

simile: a figure of speech in which a comparison is made between two objects essentially unlike but resembling each other in one or more respects. The comparison is indicated by like or as:

"O, my love is like a red, red rose. . ."
—Robert Burns

stereotype: a character who conforms to certain widely accepted ideas of how such a person should look, think, or act.

structure: the organization of elements in a literary work.

style: the distinctive manner in which a writer uses language: his choice and arrangement of words.

subplot: a secondary series of events or episodes that is subordinate to the main plot but, in most cases, contributes to it.

suspense: the reader's or audience's feeling of excitement, curiosity, or expectation about the outcome of a plot.

symbol: an object that stands for, or represents, an idea, belief, superstition, social or political institution. A pair of scales, for example, is often a symbol for justice.

tale: a simple story that recounts a real or imaginary event.

theme: the idea, general truth, or commentary on life or people brought out through a literary work.

tone: the feeling conveyed by the author's attitude toward his subject and the particular way in which he writes about it.

verisimilitude: the appearance or semblance of truth; the use of details in such a way that the reader accepts, at least for the time of reading, the most far-fetched or impossible settings and events.